WICKEN FEN

THE MAKING OF A
WETLAND NATURE RESERVE

WICKEN FEN

THE MAKING OF A
WETLAND NATURE RESERVE

EDITED BY

Laurie Friday

IN ASSOCIATION WITH
WICKEN FEN
A PROPERTY OF THE NATIONAL TRUST

Harley Books (B. H. & A. Harley Ltd)
Martins, Great Horkesley,
Colchester, Essex CO6 4AH, England

Text set in Baskerville by
Saxon Graphics Ltd., Derby
Text printed by St Edmundsbury Press Ltd.,
Bury St Edmunds, Suffolk
Colour reproduced and printed by
Hilo Offset Ltd, Colchester, Essex
Bound by Woolnoughs Bookbinders Ltd
Irthlingborough, Northants

Designed by Geoff Green

Wicken Fen, the making of a wetland nature reserve
published by Harley Books in association with Wicken Fen,
a property of the National Trust. © The National Trust, 1997

British Library Catalogue-in-Publication Data applied for

ISBN 0 946589 33 x (hardback)

ISBN 0 946589 58 5 (paperback)

Contents

(The colour plates are placed between Part Three and Part Four)

AUTHORS

WFLMC = Wicken Fen Local Management Committee (previously the Executive Committee)
WFLAP = Wicken Fen Local Advisory Panel (previously the Local Committee)

SYLVIE M. BALLARD, Education Warden, Wicken Fen 1989–95

TIM J. BENNETT, Head Warden, Wicken Fen 1979–94

PETER M. M. BIRCHAM, Physiological Laboratory, University of Cambridge; WFLAP 1989–

MICHAEL DE L. BROOKE, Department of Zoology, University of Cambridge; WFLMC (Zoological Secretary) 1994–

C. JAMES CADBURY RSPB; WFLAP 1971– ; WFLMC 1986–92

MATTHEW P. CHATFIELD, Property Manager, Wicken Fen, 1995–97

SARAH A. CORBET, Department of Zoology, University of Cambridge; WFLAP 1975– ; WFLMC 1976–95 (Zoological Secretary 1979–1988)

NICHOLAS B. DAVIES, Department of Zoology, University of Cambridge; WFLAP 1979– ; WFLMC 1982–88

JACK P. DEMPSTER, Department of Zoology, University of Cambridge; WFLAP 1973– ; WFLMC 1973–76 & 1996–

ANTHONY B. DRANE, WFLAP (Coleoptera recorder) 1989–

LAURIE E. FRIDAY, Department of Zoology, University of Cambridge; WFLAP 1985– ; WFLMC 1986– (Zoological Secretary 1988–91, Secretary 1991–96, Chairman 1996–)

H. JOHN HARVEY, The National Trust, Cirencester; WFLMC 1966–86 (Secretary 1970–86)

PETER LANGTON, WFLAP (Chironomidae recorder) 1986–

GRANT LOHOAR, Assistant Head Warden, Wicken Fen 1987–94

J. MICHAEL LOCK, Royal Botanic Gardens, Kew; WFLAP 1981– ; WFLMC 1983–91 (Botanical Secretary 1984–86, Secretary 1986–91)

NORMAN W. MOORE, WFLAP 1962– ; WFLMC 1976– (Chairman 1985–96)

IVAN PERRY, WFLAP (Diptera recorder) 1989–

CHRIS D. PRESTON, Institute of Terrestrial Ecology, Monks Wood; WFLAP 1984–

RAY J. REVELL, WFLAP (Lepidoptera recorder) 1989–

TERRY A. ROWELL, Countryside Council for Wales, Bangor; WFLAP 1989–

C. COLIN SMITH[†], St. Catharine's College, Cambridge; WFLAP (Lepidoptera recorder) 1989–97

CHRISTOPHER J. R. THORNE, Department of Biochemistry, University of Cambridge; WF Ringing Group Secretary 1970– ; WFLAP 1972– ; WFLMC 1973–

S. MAX WALTERS, Botanic Garden, University of Cambridge; WFLMC 1949–95 (Botanical Secretary 1949–76 & 1986–90, Chairman 1979–85)

PETER F. YEO, Botanic Garden, University of Cambridge; WFLAP (Hymenoptera recorder) 1976–

[†] Died 16 February 1997

BUCKINGHAM PALACE.

Wetlands throughout the world have come under increasing pressure as a result of the growing demand for productive land. This means that the remaining wetlands are becoming ever more important as refuges for a large number of endangered species.

With so many people apparently believing that the need for the conservation of nature was invented last week, it is sobering to know that the first land at Wicken Fen was acquired nearly a hundred years ago.

The great value of this book is that it traces the whole history of the Fen and explains its significance as an exceptionally rich ecosystem. The experience which the National Trust has gained in its management for so many years should also prove to be most valuable in the development of management plans for temperate wetlands worldwide.

EDITOR'S PREFACE

ICKEN FEN (Plate 1) occupies a rather special place in the Pantheon of
British conservation and ecology.[1]* It was one of the first properties
acquired by the fledgling National Trust, and became one of Britain's first
nature reserves. In the first two decades of this century, the Fen attracted the attention
of some of the pioneers of plant ecology and, as a result, has become one of the best-
studied sites in the country.

Those who are entrusted with the management of Wicken Fen feel very keenly the
weight of responsibility that accompanies this historical background. We are also
extremely fortunate, because research carried out on the Fen itself provides us with
firm guidelines for designing effective management regimes, and the almost iconic
status of the Fen in the British conservation movement secures wide support for our
efforts to protect the reserve against the ravages of the twentieth century.

It is nearly one hundred years since the Fen came under the aegis of The National
Trust, and more than sixty years since the publication of the last comprehensive work
on the Fen, *The Natural History of Wicken Fen*.[2,3] Concluding his introductory chapter,
the editor J. S. Gardiner wrote: 'Scientifically, the more we study Wicken's three fens,
the more we are impressed by their importance ... We want to put on record their conditions now, [to enable] our successors to compare them with what they are 50, 100, or
hundreds of years hence'.[4]

In publishing this book, our aim has been to take up Gardiner's challenge: we trace
the evolution of Wicken Fen National Nature Reserve, looking back over decades of
effort and achievement to compare the Fen of Gardiner's time with the Fen as we
know it today. We in turn wish to set up new bench-marks against which future generations may measure the progress of the Fen.

---

* Superscript numbers refer to the sources listed sequentially at the end of each chapter; the full references may be
found on p.287.

The writers are some of the people responsible for the management of the Fen over the past twenty years, the Fen staff and members of the Local Management Commitee and Advisory Panel. It is a salutary tale – of failure and misunderstanding as well as of discovery and success. There can be little doubt that the quality of the fen habitat declined markedly during the first half of the twentieth century at Wicken. However, as a result of sustained management effort over the past three decades and recent radical measures, Wicken Fen is undergoing a renaissance.

We hope that this account of our experiences will help others entrusted with managing our natural heritage to avoid stumbling into the same pitfalls. This book is also for the 30,000 or so visitors who come to Wicken Fen each year. We are aware that only a few gain any depth of understanding of the demanding and complex task in which the Fen managers and staff are engaged. We hope that this book will go some way to explaining what the Fen's management is all about and why we attempt it.

In the Introduction, Wicken Fen is set in its context as one of four tiny remnants of the Fenland that once extended over vast areas of East Anglia. Wicken Fen has not escaped entirely the vicissitudes occurring in the surrounding countryside. The often-quoted assertion that the Sedge Fen has never been drained[4] is only partly correct[5] and it would be mistaken to hold Wicken aloft as an exemplary fen – the Norfolk Broads are more extensive and ecologically 'intact'.[6] Nevertheless, Wicken Fen remains an invaluable repository of fenland species in an increasingly dry arable landscape.

In Part Two, we describe what the Fen is actually like: the aquatic, reed-bed, sedge, litter, carr and woodland habitats and their characteristic species. Our understanding of these communities, and what happens to them when subjected to different management regimes, is based largely on studies carried out on the reserve. Many of these studies have been published in ecological journals, but others exist only as manuscripts in the Fen archive; here we bring together these various projects to present a record which is as complete and useful as possible.

In Part Three, we examine more closely the three groups of organisms for which Wicken Fen has gained its reputation: the plants, insects and birds. In 1932, J. S. Gardiner wrote that 'Wicken Fen was placed under the control of the National Trust primarily as an entomological and botanical reserve'.[7] This seems a little at odds with the perception of many visitors today, who tend to view the Fen principally as a bird reserve. Is this shift of emphasis real, or does it merely reflect current fashions in the pursuits of natural historians? The long run of botanical and zoological records for Wicken Fen enables us to address this question, by tracing the changing fortunes of some of the fen species, comparing them with trends in the wider countryside, and examining attitudes to the management of different species over the past six decades.

In Part Four, we explore the role of people in simultaneously conserving and exploiting the Fen. The history of Wicken Fen, from mediaeval times into the twentieth century, has been reconstructed by drawing on a wealth of documents in record offices and private collections. Similarly, the story of the National Trust's management of the Fen from the earliest days has been pieced together from the Minutes of the Management Committee, conserved in the Fen archive. We describe the evolution of the management regimes currently practised on the Fen, and examine the mutually beneficial relationship between Wicken Fen and ecological research and environmental education.

In the closing chapter, we look forward to the next century and describe our plans for expanding the nature reserve. The last crops of potatoes, linseed and sugar-beet have now been lifted from the Priory Farm land and the combined forces of men, machinery and sheep are beginning the transformation of arable black peatland back into wetland.

Finally, we present two additional records to complete the story of the making of the reserve: Appendix A contains reference maps of the Fen and Appendix B shows the work programme for a typical year. A further Appendix, listing species of flora and fauna recorded on the reserve since records began up to March 1997, was originally to be published in this volume but has now grown so much that it is being published separately.

ACKNOWLEDGEMENTS

As with all things produced by a committee, this book has taken a long time to come to fruition. I am grateful to all those who responded so promptly to the call for manuscripts, and thank them for their forbearance in agreeing (sometimes more than once) to bring their contributions up to date. My greatest regret is that G. E. Hutchinson, who contributed his early memories of the Fen, C. C. Smith, whose notes on moths appear in Chapter 8, and P. W. Richards, who commented on Chapter 12, did not live to see the book published.

Apart from the authors of the chapters themselves, a number of friends and colleagues have read manuscripts, checked details and unearthed material; I thank Alan Bloom, Philip Broadbent-Yale, Michael Chinery, David Coombe, Jane Croft, Peter Grubb, Angela Hair, Frank Hollick, Gwyneth Howells, Ken Joysey, Kallie Kendall, Martin Lester, Howard Mendel, Duncan Painter, Mike Petty, Paul Richards, Chris Riley, George Salt, Peter Sell, Sue Shaw, Henry Stroyan, Charles Turner, Lorna Walters and Bryan Wheeler. Newnham College has provided small grants towards the production of this book. To any others whom I have inadvertently failed to mention by name, I apologize.

I would also like to acknowledge the contribution made by all the naturalists of previous generations who have written about Wicken Fen; we have made extensive use of direct quotation, because it seems invidious to attempt to improve on the lively eye-witness accounts of the original writers.

Some of the illustrations have been produced especially for this book: the maps are based on artwork by Raymond Turvey, who redrew the Fen map from aerial photographs; many of the photographs were taken by Duncan Painter; and the lively vignettes that grace the beginning of each chapter are the work of Dave Showler.

I owe a special debt of gratitude to two of my fellow contributors, who have provided help and encouragement beyond the call of duty. Terry Rowell played a leading role in getting the book underway, planning and soliciting contributions. Terry has transformed our understanding of Wicken Fen through his historical and ecological research; reference to his thesis and bibliography have undoubtedly saved me from committing a number of embarrassing errors in this book. Max Walters' intimate knowledge of the Fen stems from many years of academic research and membership of the Management Committee. For more than two years, Max has patiently responded to my relentless questioning, sought out records, manuscripts and photographs, and commented on much of the text.

Throughout the project, I have been encouraged by the steady support of my husband, Adrian Friday, and my colleagues on the Wicken Fen Local Management Committee. Sarah Maclure and Jane Reid helped in the preparation of the Index and John Rodford prepared the line diagrams. I am especially grateful to Basil and Annette Harley, whose personal interest and involvement have transformed the business process of publishing the book into something resembling a family affair. I am touched by their unflinching display of faith, repeatedly assuring me that deadlines are merely guidelines, and I thank them for all their hard work in finally bringing this work to press.

This book is published in association with The National Trust without whose sustained support Wicken Fen might have become just another 305 hectares of sugar-beet.

L. E. FRIDAY,
Cambridge, June 1997

References

1 Sheail (1987), pp. 72–79
2 Gardiner & Tansley (1923)
3 Gardiner (1925–32)
4 Gardiner (1928)
5 Rowell (1983a)
6 Fojt (1994)
7 Gardiner (1932b), p. v

PICTURE CREDITS

Text Figures

Chapter 1. (Fig. 1) After R.H. Yapp, 1908, fig. 9; (Fig. 2) Photo: Cambridge University Collection of Air Photographs, no. BSL048.

Chapter 2. (Fig. 3a,b) Photos: P.D. Sell; (Fig. 4) Wicken Fen archive; (Fig. 5) From data in Gilman, 1988, and Wicken Fen Executive Committee (WFEC) Annual Report for 1986; (Fig. 6) After R.H. Yapp, 1908, fig. 11.

Chapter 3. (Fig. 7) Photos: P.M. Jenkin (above), L.E. Friday (below); (Fig. 8) After D.G. Lee, 1988, fig. 2.12; (Fig. 9) After T. Lunel, 1984; (Fig. 10) After A.S.K. Yau, 1994; (Fig. 11) Photo: M.G. Walters.

Chapter 4. (Fig. 12) Drawing by E.A.R. Ennion, 1949, fig. 59, courtesy of H. Ennion; (Fig 13) Wicken Fen Local Management Committee 1992–97 management plan; (Fig. 14) Original drawing; (Fig. 15) D.A. Showler.

Chapter 5. (Fig. 16) After R.H. Yapp, 1909, figs 4,6; (Fig. 17) After R.H. Yapp, 1908, fig. 12; (Fig 18) From V.M. Conway, 1936c, fig. 2; (Fig. 19) Photo: G.E. Briggs, in collection of H. Godwin, Botany School, University of Cambridge; (Fig. 20) After H. Godwin, 1941b, fig. 7; (Fig. 21) After L.E. Friday, P.J. Grubb & D.C. Coombe (in prep.); (Fig. 22) After H.J. Harvey & T.C. Meredith, 1981, fig.; (Fig. 23) After J.P. Dempster, 1995, fig.; (Fig. 24) After J.R. Flowerdew, S.J.G. Hall & J.C. Brown, 1977, fig.4; (Fig. 25) After T.A. Rowell, L. Guarino & H.J. Harvey, 1985, figs 2,4; (Fig. 26) Photo: P.D. Sell.

Chapter 6. (Fig. 27) Photo: M.C.F. Proctor; (Fig. 28) After H. Godwin, D.R. Clowes & B. Huntley, 1974, fig. 2; (Figs 29 & 30) Photos: G.E. Briggs in H. Godwin coll.; (Figs 31 & 32) Photos: D.J. Painter; (Fig. 33) After Rowell, 1983a, fig. 9.7; (Fig. 34) Photo: M.C.F. Proctor.

Chapter 7. (Fig. 35) Stella Ross-Craig, 1954, **vii**, part of pl. 74; (Fig. 36) Photo: D.J. Painter; (Fig. 37) Photo: A. Gagg.

Chapter 8. (Fig. 38) Photos: W.S. Farren (above); anon., in Wicken Fen archive (below).

Chapter 9. (Fig. 39) Photo: J.S.Gardiner, in Wicken Fen archive; (Fig. 40) Photo: anon., in Wicken Fen archive; (Fig. 41) Photo: D.J. Painter; (Figs 42–47) Original maps and diagrams based on data from Wicken Fen Ringing Group; (Figs 48 & 49) Photos: I. Wyllie; (Fig. 50) after N.B. Davies & M. de L. Brooke, 1988; (Fig. 51) Eric Hosking, permission of Frank Lane Picture Agency; (Fig. 52) Frank V. Blackburn.

Chapter 10. (Fig. 53) After H. Godwin, 1941a, fig. 8; (Figs 54–58) After Rowell, 1983a, figs 4.4, 3.1, 3.3, 3.8 and 3.9); (Fig. 59) Photo: anon., from *The Entomologist's Record*, 1966, **78**, pl.IV facing p. 298; (Fig. 60) Photo: anon., in Wicken Fen archive; (Fig. 61) Photo: by permission of the Syndics of Cambridge University Library, ms. 647; (Fig. 62) after T.A. Rowell & H.J. Harvey, 1988, fig. 8.

Chapter 11. (Fig. 63) Photo: G.E. Briggs, in H. Godwin coll.; (Fig. 64) Photo: W.M. Lane, in Wicken Fen archive; (Fig. 65) Photo: D.J. Painter; (Fig. 66) Photo: W.M. Lane, in Wicken Fen archive; (Figs 67 & 68) Photos: D.J. Painter; (Figs 69 & 70) After Wicken Fen Local Management Committee 1992 management plan; (Fig. 71) Photos: anon., in Wicken Fen archive (above), Central Press Photos Ltd (below); (Fig. 72) Maps specially prepared by Messrs Stanford for A. Bloom, 1944, courtesy of A. Bloom; (Figure 73) Photos: A. Bloom; (Figs 74 & 75)

From Wicken Fen Local Management Committee 1992 management plan; (Fig. 76) Photo: D.J. Painter.

Chapter 12. (Fig. 77) Photo: C. Bibby; (Fig. 78) Photo: L.E. Friday; (Fig. 79) After T.A. Rowell, 1983a, fig. 7.2; (Fig. 80) Photo: P.D. Sell.

Chapter 13. (Fig. 81) From 'Draft Terrier' in Wicken Fen archive; (Fig. 82) Photo: D.J. Painter.

We express our gratitude to *The New Phytologist* for Figs 1, 6, 17 and 18; to *Annals of Botany* for Fig. 16; to *Journal of Ecology* for Figs 20, 28 and 62; to John Wiley & Sons for Fig. 22; to Chapman & Hall for Fig. 23; to *Journal of Zoology* for Fig. 24; to *Journal of Applied Ecology* for Fig. 25; to The Royal Society for fig. 53; to *Animal Behaviour* for Fig. 50; to *The Entomologist's Record and Journal of Variation* for Fig. 59; to the estates of P.M. Jenkin, E.A.R. Ennion and G.E. Briggs, and to all individuals whose drawings and photographs, listed above and of which they hold copyright, have so kindly been made available for our use.

The vignettes at the opening of each chapter have been specially drawn for this work by D.A. Showler.

Colour Plates

Photographs have been supplied by the following:

S.G. Ball: Plate 7, fig.3; T.J. Bennett: Plate 3, fig.1; Plate 4, fig.1; Plate 5, fig.8; Plate 12, figs 1,3,4; Plate 13, figs 1–3; Plate 14, fig.1; Plate 15, figs 1,2; Frank V. Blackburn: Plate 9, figs 3,4; M. de L. Brooke: Plate 9, fig.1; Roger Clarke: Plate 9, fig.2; Cambridge University Collection of Air Photographs: Plate 1 – Mosaic of photographs RC8 Kn BO38/RC8 Kn BP66/RC8 Kn BP68; J.P. Dempster: Plate 3, fig.3; Plate 5, figs 2–5; Eaden Lilley Photographers: Plate 11, fig.1; Forestry Commission: Plate 5, fig.6; Plate 7, fig.9; L.E. Friday: Plate 11, fig.2; G. Hewson: Plate 8, figs 4,5; R.S. Key: Plate 6, figs 4–9,12; Plate 7, figs 4,5; N. Larner: Plate 8, figs 2,3; G. Lohoar: Plate 16, figs 1– 4; I.F.G. McLean: Plate 7, fig.7; H. Mendel: Plate 6, fig.11; Roy Miles Gallery/Bridgeman Art Library: Plate 10; J.G. Murrell (Herbarium, Camb. Univ. Coll.): Plate 3, fig.2; National Trust (Wicken Fen Coll.): Plate 6, fig.10; Plate 12, fig.2; D.J. Painter: Plate 2, figs 1–3; Plate 7, figs 1,2,6; Plate 14, fig.2; A. S. Pullin: Plate 5, fig.7; P.D. Sell (Herbarium, Camb. Univ. Coll.): Plate 3, fig.4; Plate 4, figs 2–4; J. Silsby: Plate 7, fig.10; C.J.R. Thorne: Plate 8, fig.1; P. Waring: Plate 6, figs 1–3; M.G. Yates: Plate 5, fig.1; P.F. Yeo: Plate 7, fig.8.

We express our thanks to all the above photographers in whom copyright of their photographs is vested and also the organizations which have loaned pictures. We also thank English Nature for permission to reproduce Plate 9, fig.2, and from whom licences must be obtained for the photography of protected birds under the Wildlife & Countryside Act, 1981.

PART ONE

Introduction

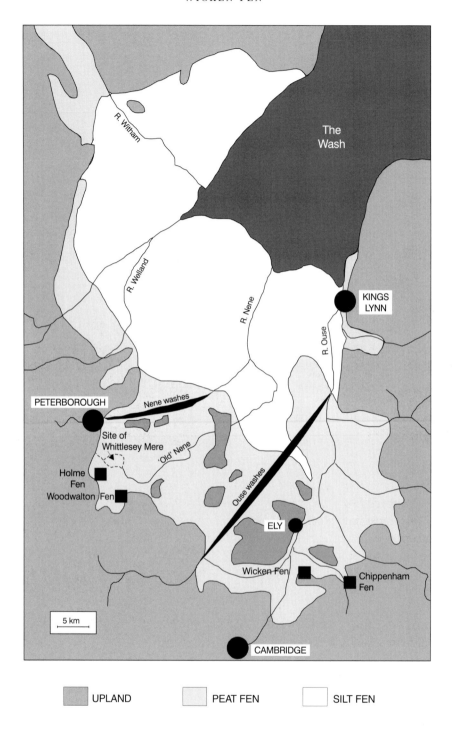

Figure 1 Fenland, showing position of the four Fenland reserves

I

THE FENLAND RESERVES

N. W. MOORE

(after R. Farren, 'Wicken Fen, 1881')

THE NATURE RESERVE at Wicken started as a private hunting ground for Victorian entomologists. Today Wicken Fen is very much more than that; like most nature reserves it has many functions. It conserves habitat and rare species, supports scientific research and education, and enables thousands of visitors to enjoy sights and sounds which would otherwise have ceased to exist.

When far-sighted entomologists so wisely put Wicken Fen into the hands of the newly-formed National Trust they were well aware of the vast changes that had occurred in the Fens. What had once been a vast flood-plain mire of about 3,850 sq.km had largely been transformed into farmland in the preceding centuries. The most fundamental changes had occurred in the last 300 years, and it was obvious that they were conserving something which was in imminent danger of being lost for ever. Today, thanks to a mass of historical and biological information, we can define more exactly what Wicken Fen represents.

Originally a huge area of peatland lay between the uplands of Lincolnshire, Cambridgeshire, Suffolk and Norfolk and the low-lying silts round the edge of The Wash (Fig. 1). It was a topogenous mire, that is it owed its existence to topography, to the low-lying basin in which it lay. Dead vegetation built up in this water-logged area and formed peat. In some areas, *Sphagnum* moss and other bog plants produced raised mires which were ombrogenous, that is they depended on rainfall for their existence. These mires were acidic and poor in nutrients.

This huge complex of topogenous mire (fen) and ombrogenous mire (bog) was subjected to frequent, but irregular, incursions of sea-water and silt from the North Sea, as well as fresh floodwater from the great Fenland rivers, the Ouse, Nene, Welland and Witham. Flooding depended on weather, minor climatic change and coincidence of heavy rainfall in the uplands with the state of the tide in The Wash and North Sea surges. In the areas where flooding was frequent, the flora and fauna must have consisted mainly of very adaptable species, such as reeds and the many species of wildfowl that can feed on a wide range of plant and insect food. The habitats with most species must have been the relatively stable ones round the periphery of the fenland basin, where sudden change was less frequent.

From Roman times until 1630, reclamation of the fertile fenlands was piecemeal. Even after Vermuyden, the Dutch engineer employed by the Adventurers, had completed his task, disastrous floods frequently occurred and ruined many farmers. However, the waters were at least partially tamed. Hundreds of acres were protected from summer flooding and provided rich pastures for sheep and cattle as well as hay which could be fed to stock in winter when the winter floods covered the fens. In those days the Fens resembled the grazing marshes of the Norfolk Broads, the Somerset Levels and Romney Marsh. As soon as winter flooding was controlled, summer pastures were replaced by more intensive arable farming, by wheat, potatoes and other crops. Most of the wildlife retreated to the remaining meres and washlands. With the draining in 1851 of Whittlesey Mere, once one of the largest lakes in England, no large areas of permanent water remained in the Fens (Fig. 2).

Since the catastrophic freshwater floods of 1947 and the great tidal surge of 1953, the Fens have not suffered any great flood of the type which characterized their past. As a result, the vast majority of the area is now turned over to crops. Grazing is virtually confined to those lands which are allowed to flood: the Ouse and Nene Washes (Fig. 1) and some of the flood-plains of the Ouse and Cam. These areas form a crucial part of the flood protection scheme, being allowed to flood in order to keep the arable parts of the Fenland dry. The species that depended on the old marshes and periodic flooding are now largely confined to washlands and nature reserves deliberately set aside to conserve their fen flora and fauna.

Parts of the Ouse and Nene Washes have been made nature reserves and their habitats for birds have been enhanced by the creation of pools and scrapes. Outside the Washes, all the remaining areas of fen of any size have been turned into nature reserves. Wicken Fen (305ha), the pioneer Fenland reserve, was set up in 1899 by the National Trust. Woodwalton Fen was acquired in 1910 by the Hon. N. C. Rothschild as a private nature reserve. Later it was owned and managed by the Society for the Promotion of Nature Reserves. It is now owned by the Royal Society for Nature Conservation and managed by English Nature (formerly the Nature Conservancy

Figure 2   Wicken Fen from the south-west; the drained remnant of Soham Mere is visible in the
middle distance as bright fields of ripening crops.

Council, NCC). In 1952 the Nature Conservancy acquired Holme Fen (260ha) and in
1963 Chippenham Fen (115ha) was established as another National Nature Reserve by
arrangement with the owners. The protection of the remaining fens is an excellent
example of co-operation between private owners, non-governmental conservation
organisations and English Nature, a government body.

The four Fenland reserves share the common characteristic of being mainly on
peat. They all lie on or near the edge of the fen basin and all are subject to successional
changes from open water and open habitats to woodland. This process has been accel-
erated by drainage in the surrounding farmland, which is now noticeably lower than
the reserves and draws water out of the reserves by gravity flow. Originally the four
reserves were more like each other than they are today. For example, peat digging

occurred in all of them. Also, they shared more species; the black bog-rush* (*Schoenus nigricans*) occurred at both Wicken and Chippenham, but is now extinct at Wicken Fen, and the small red damselfly (*Ceriagrion tenellum*), which is now extinct in the Fens, used to occur at both these places too.

Each of the reserves has special features of situation and management history that influence its flora and fauna, but they also share a good deal in common. The ditches at Chippenham Fen are fed by springs and the fen is adjacent to Breckland sands which support typical Breckland species, a situation which is unique to Chippenham. As a consequence, the Fen supports several species which have never been recorded at Wicken Fen (common butterwort (*Pinguicula vulgaris*) and grass-of-Parnassus (*Parnassia palustris*)), or recorded only in the past, on the edge of the reserve (bogbean (*Menyanthes trifoliata*)). However, much of the fen vegetation at Chippenham resembles that of the mixed fen, litter fields and droves of Wicken.

Successional changes have gone further at Holme Fen than at any of the other reserves. Indeed, it is listed as a wood and not as a fen in the NCC's compendium of nature reserves, *A Conservation Review*.[2] It is arguably the finest birch-wood in lowland Britain. Had Wicken and Woodwalton Fens not received the benefit of positive water-level control, it is quite possible that both would now also be dominated by birch.

Holme Fen is on the site of the southern marshy fringe of Whittlesey Mere (see Fig. 1). After the draining of the mere in 1851 the area was cultivated, but later it was abandoned and became a game covert. Despite the changes to woodland, the site still contains elements of the original acidic raised mire including ling (*Calluna vulgaris*), cross-leaved heath (*Erica tetralix*), and species of *Sphagnum* moss. As at Wicken Fen, the great fen-sedge (*Cladium mariscus*), is abundant and bog-myrtle (*Myrica gale*) is also present. Two new meres have been dug in the peat at Holme Fen. One of them has been colonized by the common hawker (*Aeshna juncea*), a dragonfly of acid waters that once occurred at Wicken (Chapter 8).

Woodwalton Fen also has a remnant of acid bog with bog-myrtle, ling and purple moor-grass (*Molinia caerulea*), but otherwise shares many characteristics with Wicken Fen. Much of the reserve is now covered by carr, but unlike Wicken this consists mainly of sallow (*Salix* spp.). As at Wicken, part of the reserve is maintained by cattle grazing. Thanks to arrangements with the Middle Level Commissioners, the banks surrounding the reserves have been strengthened so that water-levels can be controlled. In both cases, part of the reserve can be used as a wash at times of acute flooding. Two meres have been created at Woodwalton; they resemble the mere at Wicken more than those at Holme Fen, which are peaty and surrounded by woodland.

Woodwalton and Wicken both have exceptionally rich flora and fauna and share many species, including notable ones such as fen violet (*Viola persicifolia*), greater spearwort (*Ranunculus lingua*), and greater bladderwort (*Utricularia vulgaris*). The local dragonflies, the hairy dragonfly (*Brachytron pratense*), and the variable damselfly (*Coenagrion pulchellum*), occur at both sites. Bearded tits (*Panurus biarmicus*) can be seen at both

---

* English names of plants follow Stace's New Flora[1]

reserves in winter, but so far this species breeds only at Wicken. Marsh harriers (*Circus aeruginosus*) have bred at both reserves in recent years. The fen woodrush (*Luzula pallescens*) and the large copper butterfly (*Lycaena dispar*) are Woodwalton specialities and do not occur at Wicken.

Wicken Fen has some special features in which it stands apart from the other Fenland reserves. First, it is the largest of the reserves and contains the greatest proportion of open habitat. Secondly, its wild crops of reed and sedge are still harvested as they have been for hundreds of years; this enables bearded tits to breed in the reed-beds and allows marsh pea (*Lathyrus palustris*), milk-parsley (*Peucedanum palustre*) and many other plants to flourish in the sedge and litter fields. Thirdly, the abundance of buckthorn (*Rhamnus cathartica*) and alder buckthorn (*Frangula alnus*) is unique among the four reserves, if not in the whole of Britain. Fourthly, there are numerous species of invertebrates which have been recorded only at Wicken among the Fenland reserves.

All of the Fenland reserves require careful management in order to maintain their mixed fen communities. At Wicken and Woodwalton Fens, in particular, the control of water-levels and of the encroachment of scrub are essential activities. On both reserves, ecological research and accumulated practical experience have been important components in the working out of management strategies. The sharing of experience has also been valuable and has been greatly facilitated by the Management Committees of Woodwalton and Wicken having one or more members in common.

Nature reserves have a two-way relationship with research: they provide the raw material for study and the results of the research usually help the management of the reserve, and hence the survival of its plant and animal species. Wicken Fen provides a notable example of this reciprocal arrangement. Studies on the natural succession of fen vegetation made at Wicken during the first forty years of this century, notably by the late Sir Harry Godwin, were not only pioneer studies in the new science of plant ecology, but they gave the managers of the reserve a basis for their treatment of fen vegetation.

Woodwalton Fen has also been much studied, notably in connection with its plant communities and management but also to determine the habitat requirements of the large copper butterfly and the fen violet; the last is particularly relevant to Wicken Fen. Long-term studies have been made on dragonfly populations at Woodwalton and some work on dragonflies has also been done at Holme Fen. Numerous surveys of particular groups of plants and animals have been done at all four Fenland reserves. This work, and studies on similar habitats in the Norfolk Broads, provides mutual support for the reserve managers.

Small as they are, the four reserves, together with the Ouse and Nene Washes, support a surprisingly large proportion of the habitats and species of the original Fenland. None of them is a substitute for any other; they complement each other. And, for some of the more mobile organisms, particularly birds and dragonflies, they also provide each other with sources of colonists, which may replenish their isolated populations, since none is more than 50km distant from any of the others.

Visitors to the Fenland reserves often have a special quest: they want to see a flower or insect or bird which they have never seen before, or learn about some special feature. For example, they may wish to see the famous pillar at Holme Fen, which shows how greatly the peat has shrunk since the draining of Whittlesey Mere, or to see how sedge is harvested at Wicken Fen. However, many come for much less precise purposes – they just want to experience the Fen, to see, hear and smell its sights, sounds and smells, or, as Dr H. C. Darby, the great chronicler of the Fens has stated, to get 'some idea of the varied peatland landscape as it was on the eve of the "great design" of the seventeenth century.'[3]

What special contributions do the four reserves make to our general awareness of the Fens? Chippenham and Holme Fens support populations of many fen species and both are places of great beauty, but so much of them is now woodland that they no longer feel like fens. Only at Wicken and Woodwalton Fens can you get lost in a flat landscape where the horizon is bounded by tall waving reeds and duck criss-cross the sky. At these two reserves you can see cattle grazing in fenny fields. But only at Wicken Fen is there a feeling of continuity with the past. That is the past where the livelihoods of fenmen unwittingly conserved so many of the plants and animals of the untamed fen: at Wicken Fen the reeds and sedge are still cut.

References

1   Stace (1991)   2   Ratcliffe (1977)   3   Darby (1983), p. 240

PART TWO

Habitats and Communities

2

PATTERNS AND PROCESSES

L. E. FRIDAY AND T. A. ROWELL

THE WICKEN FEN nature trail threads in and out of the fenland habitats for which the reserve is famous. For most of the journey, the impression is of a green, humid world, damp underfoot and deeply enclosed, in which insects labour among colourful herbs beside the path. Near the windpump, the path veers off through bushes, and moss-clad stumps and skeletons of bleached and broken trees, but soon re-emerges amongst reed, through which long expanses of weed-filled ditches can be glimpsed. Occasionally, path-side bushes give way to vistas of open fields of waist-high sedge and grass, waving in the breeze and colourwashed with flowers. It is easy to gain an impression of Wicken Fen as a damp meadow fringed by scrub, a small-scale landscape in which water plays an unusually prominent role.

However, after climbing the ladders inside the Tower Hide and pulling open the shutters, a completely different view of the Sedge Fen suddenly emerges: the path-side bushes merge into ever-larger clumps till they fill the landscape to the north (Fig. 3a). The fields, droves and waterways, so prominent on the ground, divide this bush- and tree-filled landscape into an elaborate patchwork. To the south lies Adventurers' Fen. Here, a large body of open water is revealed, and beyond it golden expanses of reed-

(a)

(b)

Figure 3   Panoramic views from the Tower Hide, 1960: (a) looking north-north-east with the Sedge Fen on the left and Wicken Lode on the right; (b) looking south-south-east across the Mere and Adventurers' Fen towards the Newmarket chalk ridge, with Burwell brickworks in the left distance

beds, the deep green of grazing meadows, and, on the fringe of the reserve, arable fields. Beyond the Fen margin, arable farmland stretches away to the horizon in all directions (Fig. 3b).

These different perspectives tell us a great deal about the nature of Wicken Fen. On the ground, the detail of the distributions of individual plants and animal species and variations in the dampness and evenness of the ground become apparent. Only from a tree-top vantage point are the contrasts between the Fen and the surrounding landscape revealed.

A far deeper understanding of the Fen can be gained from repeated visits, preferably over the course of many decades. The records of the scientists and naturalists who have known the Fen over the past century show that it has changed dramatically during this period; the habitats have shifted, and animal and plant populations have changed. Fortunately, the efforts of these scientists were not limited merely to recording the differences they saw from place to place and from time to time, but extended to investigate the processes giving rise to these patterns.

It has become clear that the forces creating and changing the Fen's habitats are both natural and human. On one hand, the process of natural succession pushes the vegetation towards a climax dominated by woody species. Ranged against this are the activities of many generations of fenland people, cutting, cropping and removing fen produce. The story of this human activity, repeatedly thwarting the natural progression, is told in Part Four. Underlying the habitats that we see is the ubiquitous black peat and, perfusing all, the water that moves into, around and out of the Fen.

FEN PEAT AND FEN WATER

At Wicken Fen, the ground beneath your feet is almost entirely derived from the vegetation, growing and dying over thousands of annual cycles. Swampy wetlands are among the most formidable producers of plant material on earth: *Phragmites* reed may produce up to 3kg of dry organic matter per square metre per year.[1] The reasons for the high productivity of fens like Wicken include the continuous supply of water in all but the severest drought, and nutrients brought in from the surface drainage system.

The annual production of plant material eventually falls to the ground either to be broken down, or stored in the soil. Breaking down the plant remains is the domain of animals and micro-organisms. Where the soil is waterlogged, oxygen is not freely available and the activities of these organisms is inhibited, causing poorly-decomposed remains of plants to accumulate in ever-deepening layers. Thus, on the gault clay wedge that underlies Wicken Fen, peat has been forming for 4,500 years. The peat layer varies in depth from about 4m at the south-western edge of the Fen to less than 1 m at the north-eastern corner.

The peat of Wicken Fen is a sedge peat, formed in a wetland awash with water of neutral to alkaline chemistry; it is therefore quite different from the *Sphagnum* peat formed under acidic bog conditions and found in many mosses elsewhere in Britain. In the stagnant conditions of the fen, seeds, pollen and even whole trees ('bog oaks') have fallen and been preserved, leaving within the peat-layers clues about the flora of the past (see Chapter 10). Interspersed with the layers of peat are deposits of shell marl, derived from the remains of stoneworts (Chapter 7) and the shells of freshwater molluscs laid down in shallow ponds and lakes.

If dead plants are the body of the Fen, then water is its lifeblood. Measurements made in 1929 at Wicken Fen[2] showed that the peat profile to about 80cm depth was less than ten per cent by weight solid matter, the remainder being water. One sample contained only about five per cent solid matter, much less than the solids content of skimmed milk. When you walk on Wicken Fen, you are literally walking on water. The truth of this observation is sometimes brought home, very forcibly, when heavy machinery is used on the Fen.

As long as there is water in the Fen in sufficient quantity, and of the right quality, then plant material will continue to accumulate as peat. If the water stops flowing, if there is simply not enough of it, or if it is enriched with effluent or fertilizer run-off which promote decomposition, then the peatland will die.

To appreciate the delicate balance that keeps the Fen alive, we need to understand where the water that feeds the peat comes from, how it behaves within the Fen, and how the Fen loses it. The word 'balance' is not chosen lightly, because a balance is, indeed, what must be achieved. On average, the Fen must not lose any more water (through evaporation from the vegetation and by seepage into the surroundings) than it gains (through rainfall, flooding, or seepage from watercourses). This balance will, however, only maintain a status quo; if the peat is to grow, then there must be a net gain of water.

Wicken Fen has developed in an area in which agricultural drought occurs, on average, in eight years out of ten. Indeed the rainfall at Wicken is among the lowest in the country at an average of 535mm per annum. Over the summer months, from April to September, the amount of water that can potentially be drawn up by the vegetation and evaporated exceeds the input from rainfall by about 100 mm.[3] While rainfall patterns largely account for year to year variation in the wetness of the peat, the major source of water for the Fen must clearly be sought elsewhere.

The waters feeding Wicken Fen flow in from the calcareous soils derived from the Cambridgeshire chalk uplands. These waters flow in the channel of the New River, along Monks Lode as it passes St Edmund's Fen, then along Wicken Lode past the Fen itself. In the past, waters draining from the Fen following rainfall, or as floods cleared, ran into the Lode and away towards Upware where they joined the Cam. Eventually they would meet the Great Ouse and then, beyond Kings Lynn, the sea (Fig. 4).

As they pass the great peat-body at Wicken, these waters may infiltrate the Fen to become part of its water-table. The Sedge Fen is intersected by a number of ditches of various sizes, and the entire system connects with Wicken Lode. In this way water can enter the Sedge Fen water-table through the peat either directly from the Lode, or after running into the ditch system. Whether this will happen depends on the level of the water-table itself. Adventurers' Fen, on the opposite side of Wicken Lode, is isolated from the Lode by a clay bank and therefore hydrologically distinct from the

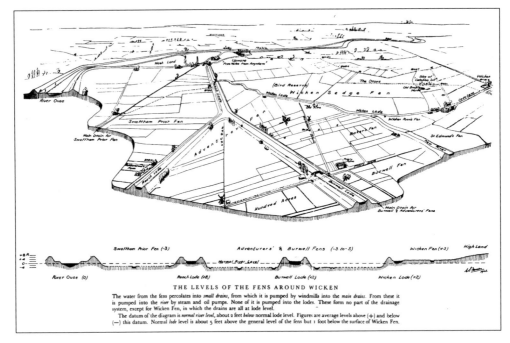

THE LEVELS OF THE FENS AROUND WICKEN

The water from the fens percolates into *small drains*, from which it is pumped by windmills into the *main drains*. From these it is pumped into the *river* by steam and oil pumps. None of it is pumped into the lodes. These form no part of the drainage system, except for Wicken Fen, in which the drains are all at lode level.

The datum of the diagram is *normal river level*, about 2 feet *below* normal lode level. Figures are average levels above (+) and below (−) this datum. Normal *lode* level is about 5 feet above the general level of the fens but 1 foot below the surface of Wicken Fen.

Figure 4   W. S. Farren's panorama⁴ of the drainage system around Wicken Fen in the 1920s, looking from the south-east

Sedge Fen (Chapter 11). From this low-lying area, as for the entire area of the drained fenland, drainage water would have been pumped up into the higher level system of fen ditches. Anyone who experienced the great Fen floods of past decades or has seen archive films[5] of the devastation wrought by tidal surges, will understand the importance of maintaining the integrity of the banks of fen waterways.

We have seen that the Fen formed in a flood-plain situation, but recent changes to the local drainage system have ensured that flooding from the Lode is a very rare event. A flood-plain fen would normally receive regular inputs of nutrient-rich water with a high acid-buffering capacity. Lack of flooding appears to have led to a lowering of the pH of the surface peat, and has also allowed the establishment of calcifuge plants, including *Sphagnum* species (Chapter 6). Although at present these changes are largely the result of human interference with Fenland drainage, they would eventually occur naturally once peat growth had put the surface above the reach of flood waters.

The relationship between land- and water-levels holds the key to the chemical conditions experienced by plants growing in the fen. In a completely waterlogged peat soil, the lack of oxygen will favour bacteria that respire anaerobically. This produces organic acids, ammonium, and a range of potentially toxic ions. Anyone who has strayed into the wettest parts of Wicken Fen will recognize the smell of the noxious gas hydrogen sulphide, released as the swamped Wellington boot is extracted from the ground. Such conditions may kill the roots of some plants, while others, such as reed and true aquatic plants, are able to supply their below-ground parts with oxygen via the leaves and stems, creating a benign micro-environment in which the all-important roots and rhizomes may survive.

Where the water-table lies a few centimetres below the surface, however, soil conditions are far more favourable. Oxygen is available for root respiration and, in fens like Wicken which are fed by calcareous groundwater, the alkalinity of the water mitigates any tendency towards acidification. The surface peat at Wicken is, to the surprise of many visitors, not acidic but neutral or slightly alkaline. However, if water-levels fall below ground level, even by as little as 10cm, the peat surface can become isolated from the groundwater and become acidic through the leaching of nutrients. The top layers of peat will also begin to oxidize and may release nutrients. Thus, any variations of topography (caused by peat extraction or by hummock formation), or changes in drainage, can produce differences in the chemical state of the surface peat, and therefore in the conditions for plant growth.

A more detailed understanding of the movement of water within the peat body is helpful in making management decisions. A basic understanding was reached early in the study of the Sedge Fen, by Godwin and his co-workers in the 1920s.[2] During summer (June to September), rainfall is low and the vegetation is at its most active, pulling water up from the peat and releasing it as vapour to the atmosphere. At times like this, the water-table in the peat is higher close to the ditches than in the areas between them (Fig. 5). The slope in the water-table is a hydraulic gradient down which water from the Lode and ditches runs to replenish the water-table. Such is the power of the vegetation to remove water, that the seepage of water from the ditches is insufficient to maintain a high water-table during the summer. Once the activity of the vegetation lessens in the autumn, and rain becomes more frequent, then the balance shifts and the water-table rises. During the rest of the year (October to May), it is close to the surface and above it in low-lying places. Then, the role of the ditches reverses; the water-table is higher in the middle than it is at the ditch banks, the hydraulic gradient is reversed, and water now runs out of the peat, into the ditches and away to the Lode.

The ditches on Wicken Sedge Fen therefore act as drains during times of high water-table, and as reservoirs from which the water-table is replenished when low. This suggests that, if the Fen is to be restored to the degree of wetness pertaining in undrained fenland, then the ditches should really be filled in. However, they can be used to advantage. If the ends of the ditches are dammed, so that their drainage function is thwarted, then their level can be kept artificially high during the summer, so helping replenish the water-table at a higher than normal rate. It has been suggested that one way to ensure that the Fen is kept as wet as possible is to construct more ditches. With this in mind, some defunct ditches have been cleaned out in recent years. This has had the useful additional effect of providing more freshwater habitat within the reserve (Chapter 3).

A certain amount of stability is afforded to the Fen's hydrological system by the presence of the sluice and pump at Upware (Chapter 10). At the sluice, the level in the Lode is maintained by releasing (or pumping, depending on the level of the river) excess water into the River Cam. So the level in the Lode is kept below a prescribed

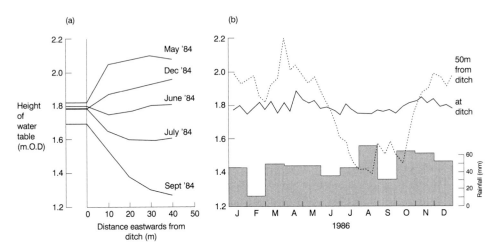

Figure 5 The hydrology of Wicken Fen: (a) changes in water-levels beneath litter fields, measured along a 50m transect running eastwards from Drainers' Dyke during 1984;[6] (b) seasonal changes in water-level during 1986 in two of the dip wells in the same transect, one at the ditch bank and the other 50m away,[6] compared to monthly rainfall

limit which is actually set by the height of the bank on the Burwell side. Unfortunately, nothing can be done to rectify the situation when the level is low, as so often happens in the summer. Until this system was installed in the 1940s, the Fen undoubtedly experienced regular winter flooding by the Lode waters and dry summers; now the seasonal variation in water-levels in Wicken Lode is scarcely noticeable.

Some water also enters the internal ditch system of the Sedge Fen directly at a pumped outfall from the farmland to the north. All water running off arable land is a potential source of pollution, usually containing high levels of nitrates (Table I). Wicken Lode also carries agricultural run-off and may, at some times of the year, be potentially polluting. As long as the Fen is not flooded by this polluted water, it is only the freshwater communities that are affected. Water percolating through the peat appears to be cleansed of the harmful agents.

Studies carried out in the 1970s suggested that the Fen's ability to maintain a balanced water budget had declined since Godwin's studies of the 1920s, at a rate equivalent to the loss of 160 mm of water over the entire Fen per annum. For example, Gowing[9] discovered that water-levels in the dry summers of 1975 and 1976 had fallen 300 mm below the lowest level recorded by Godwin in 1929–31.[10] Annual rainfall had not declined over this period and there was no evidence for increased evapotranspiration. Although grassland had been replaced by scrub over much of the Fen (Chapter 6), this would not necessarily have produced an increase in evapotranspiration (Godwin had shown[10] that the water-table on a hot summer's day was drawn down more under grassy vegetation than under the carr). The most likely cause of the problem was identified as the increasingly rapid loss of water through the northern boundary banks.

Table I. Chemistry of fen waters

Data for Fenland are taken from Perrin (1982)[7] and for bogs from Proctor (1992),[8] except for the pH of rainfall, which was measured at Swaffham Bulbeck, Cambridgeshire
blanks = no data   nd = not detectable   All figures are mg per litre, except for pH

	HCO$_3$	NO$_3$	H$_2$PO$_4$	Mg$_2^+$	Ca$_2^+$	K$^+$	pH
Precipitation (Breckland)	40	0.8		0.47	1.6	1.0	4.5
Wicken Lode Head (range)	157–351	33–57	nd–0.3	3.0–17.0	102–202	3.3–9.9	7.1–8.4
Gardiner's Drove (centre section)	549	0.66	trace	14.0	201	2.6	8.5
Brickpit 76a (range)	276–333	nd–5.9	nd–0.07	6.0–15.0	145–198	6.7–8.5	7.2–7.8
Blanket bog (Plym Head, Devon)		0.0		0.51	0.32	0.47	4.4
Valley bog (Morden, Dorset)				1.74	2.32	1.37	4.2

Great differences exist between the levels of the land and the water-tables in the Sedge Fen and in the farmland to the north and east; water runs out of the Fen, only to be pumped away by the agricultural drainage systems. The hydraulic gradient between the Fen and the farmland will have inevitably increased in modern times as the efficiency of pumping equipment has increased, and the level of the farmland has dropped through peat wastage. The banks between the Fen and the farmland, Howe's Bank and Spinney Bank (see maps in Appendix A), were of no use in preventing water-loss along this gradient, as they had been built merely to retain surface flood water at a time when there would have been little if any difference in level between the Fen and the farmland. The opposing hydrological aims of conservationists and farmers were both confounded by this loss of water from the Fen, the Fen losing its all-important life-blood, and the farmland gaining water that was definitely surplus to requirements. This is no longer the case, as the banks on the northern boundary have recently been waterproofed along their entire lengths (Chapter 11).

FENLAND SUCCESSION

An observer visiting the Fen over many decades might witness subtle changes occurring in one of the ditches or pools. The deep open water of the observer's youth would be full of submerged water-weeds and fringed with *Phragmites* reed. Over the years, as these plants grow and die and their remains build up, the depth of water is gradually reduced until, in summer, pond snails are left gasping in a thin surface film. The reed fringe sends its penetrating shallow rhizome system through the developing deposits, encroaching inexorably towards the centre. As it spreads underground, it sends up shoots, eventually closing in to cover the former open area. After many more annual cycles of growth and death the land surface has risen again in relation to water-levels, and other plants, including perhaps the great fen-sedge (*Cladium mariscus*), invade the winter-wet, summer-dry area. Still later, maybe beyond the life-span of the observer, the drying plot would sprout seedlings of woody species. If the area remained uncropped by animal or human activity, the establishing bushes would grow up to form a shady canopy, discouraging the growth of all but a few herbaceous species below it. Thus a suite of species modifies its own environment, until its growth in those conditions is weakened and it becomes vulnerable to invasion by other species with different requirements, more suited to the new conditions.

The predictable linear progress of succession can be disturbed and even reversed by other changes in the environment that are beyond the control of the plants themselves. The plant-driven succession occurs because land-levels rise, but anything that causes the relative levels of land and water to change will affect the process. If water-levels drop because of increased drainage, succession may progress more rapidly; if water-levels rise when drainage is impeded, or if the level of the land is lowered by, for example, peat extraction, the 'earlier' stages of the succession can re-establish. Entire aquatic communities reassemble themselves very quickly when old, dry and reed-choked ditches are excavated, largely because seeds and spores of earlier plant communities have remained in the sediment and are released from their dormancy by the action of ditching (see Chapter 7).

The other main disruption of the progress of succession at Wicken Fen has been cropping. Unlike most herbaceous communities, the open fields of the Sedge Fen are little affected by grazing; livestock have not traditionally been kept on the Sedge Fen,[11] and rabbits are seldom seen, but hares and deer, especially roe and muntjac, are becoming more frequent. Grazing can be effective in preventing invasion by scrub, as the regular cropping sets back the growth of shrubs more severely than that of the grasses. The crop-taking activities of generations of fenland people have filled this role on Wicken Sedge Fen.

Open herbaceous communities frequently occur on areas of the Fen that are at least as high and dry above the water-table as those occupied by scrub, but which are regularly cropped. The maintenance of herbaceous vegetation out of its normal place in the hydrosere explains why these areas so quickly convert to scrub when the cutting regime lapses. With a well-established programme of cutting or regular disturbance, vegetation can change in a cyclic way, repeatedly progressing only so far in the direction of the hydrosere before being interrupted and set back. Cropping which also involves removal of the cut produce ensures that these cycles truly come back to their starting point; if the crop is left to rot down *in situ*, it contributes to the build-up of the organic soil and slow net progress towards dryness is made.

The vegetational patterns we see at Wicken today are clearly linked to land- and water-levels (Fig. 6). Although they may appear static, they are subject to a range of dynamic forces. Like frames from a film, they provide us with glimpses of different stages in the process of change. In the next four chapters, the Fen's major vegetation types are viewed in 'chronological' order, that is, the order in which the imaginary observer would have witnessed their development in an undisturbed wetland

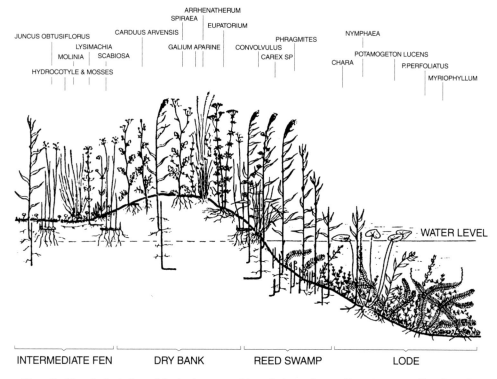

ARRHENATHERUM
SPIRAEA
EUPATORIUM
JUNCUS OBTUSIFLORUS
CARDUUS ARVENSIS
PHRAGMITES
NYMPHAEA
LYSIMACHIA
GALIUM APARINE
CONVOLVULUS
POTAMOGETON LUCENS
MOLINIA   SCABIOSA
CAREX SP
CHARA
P.PERFOLIATUS
HYDROCOTYLE & MOSSES
MYRIOPHYLLUM

WATER LEVEL

INTERMEDIATE FEN   DRY BANK   REED SWAMP   LODE

Figure 6   Yapp's depiction of the hydrosere or 'the relations of some Fen plants to soil moisture'[12]

succession. Research that has been carried out at Wicken Fen over the past 80 years makes it possible for us to examine the individual 'frames' in considerable detail. In some cases, we are also able to run the 'film' forwards, or even backwards, to discover how the vegetation changes in response to changes in hydrology and management.

References

1 Moss (1988)
2 Godwin & Bharucha (1932)
3 Perring *et al.* (1964)
4 Farren (1926b)
5 'Cambridgeshire and the Fens'. East Anglian Film Archive, University of East Anglia
6 Gilman (1988)
7 Perrin (1982)
8 Proctor (1992)
9 Gowing (1977)
10 Godwin (1931)
11 Rowell (1983a)
12 Yapp (1908, fig. 11)

3

AQUATIC HABITATS AND COMMUNITIES

L. E. FRIDAY AND C. D. PRESTON

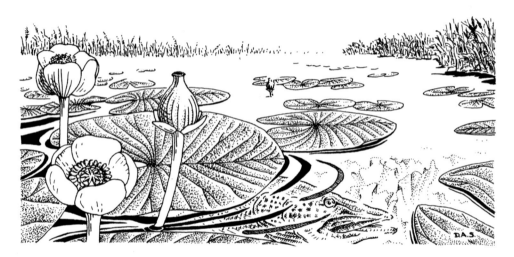

I T IS DIFFICULT for a visitor to Wicken Fen to walk for more than a few minutes without encountering a body of open water of one sort or another. All of these water-bodies are man-made, or at least highly modified, and their diversity of form reflects the range of needs of the people who have worked on and exploited the Fen over the centuries. Some water-bodies continue to serve utilitarian purposes, but all are valued for their natural history interest and contribution to the landscape. Accordingly, the open waters are managed with the dual aims of maintaining their usefulness while retaining and developing their conservation value.

The water-bodies at Wicken represent only a very restricted part of the wide range of freshwater habitats found in Britain. All are very slow-flowing or static; all are shallow, less than 3m deep, and lined with fen peat or clay; all contain highly calcareous, neutral to slightly alkaline water, and, for most of the time, carry in solution low to moderate levels of the essential plant nutrients nitrate and phosphate (Table I, p. 19). There are no stony streams nor, until very recently, any deep lakes. As a result, whole suites of species characteristic of these other types of freshwater habitats are missing from the Fen. However, as Eastham commented in 1932,[1] though the Wicken waters present no physico-chemical features rendering them unique, they still afford a big field for lacustrine research'. This opportunity has been taken up enthusiastically by generations of staff and students of Cambridge University among others.

Wicken Fen's water-bodies are important for two other reasons: first, they represent some of the last tiny fragments of habitat available as refuges for the characteristic species of Fenland waters; and secondly, they are wet 'islands' in an increasingly dry landscape. A range of aquatic species can be conserved within the reserve, from which they may recolonize new habitats that may be created in the wider countryside in the future. Enlightened management depends on ecological research and monitoring (Chapter 12). It has therefore become a priority to build up a solid corpus of data about water chemistry and the aquatic flora and fauna with which future studies may be compared. The results of a number of surveys carried out in recent years are brought together in this chapter in an attempt to provide just such a body of information.

The first section outlines the various origins and general characteristics of the water-bodies; more information may be found in Chapter 10. Variations in water quality and aquatic communities recorded in different parts of the Fen in the past few years are then described and some implications of ditch management techniques are examined. The last section focuses on changes in the aquatic habitats over the past seventy years: to what extent have the flora and flora changed since the publication of *The Natural History of Wicken Fen*?[2,3]

NATURE AND ORIGINS

The different functions of the Wicken water-bodies are reflected in their form and character. We recognize lodes, dykes, drains, ditches, permanent ponds and a miscellany of larger or smaller static waters (see maps in Appendix A).

The lode system comprises artificial water-courses, several metres wide and about a metre deep and so potentially navigable, that drain water away from the surrounding countryside into the rivers and main drainage channels. Monks Lode carries drainage water from the chalk uplands at the margin of the Fens and the surrounding farmland into Wicken Lode and thence into Reach Lode, from which it enters the Cam at Upware (see Fig. 4). Monks Lode and Wicken Lode south of its junction with Monks Lode are perpetually, if sluggishly, flowing, although the flow rate varies considerably at different seasons. Upstream of the confluence, the village end of Wicken Lode is static.

The terms 'dyke', 'drain' and 'ditch' are used in a rather confusing manner to refer to the smaller linear water-bodies of the Fen. The management plan[4] adopts a functional terminology in which 'ditches' are only intermittently wet and rarely flowing, depending on the season, while 'drains' flow for at least some part of the year. The term 'dyke' refers to a water-body without perceptible flow which originally served the purpose of delimiting areas of the Fen. However, the proper names given to individual water-bodies do not necessarily conform to this functional classification: Drainers' Dyke, which dates from the earliest period of the Adventurers' activities in the 17th century (see Chapter 10), performs the function of a dyke throughout most of the year, but after periods of high rainfall or snow melt, it becomes a drain, taking excess water pumped from farmland into the northern end of the channel into Wicken Lode. The internal boundaries of the Fen are marked by ditches, in much the same manner as hedge, bank and wall systems are used elsewhere. This boundary system, which probably dates from the 18th century, suffered periods of neglect during the late 19th century. The main internal ditches were restored in 1925–26, but narrower ditches were allowed to decay; many of these were recut in the 1960s, 1980s and 1990s (Chapter 10).[5]

The ponds on the Fen have diverse origins. The group at the far north-east corner of the Fen occupy former brick-clay pits. The pits were abandoned by the beginning of this century[6] (Chapter 10) and began to fill with water. The ponds so formed and their species assemblages would, therefore, have been no more than 30 years old when *The Natural History of Wicken Fen* was being compiled. These ponds (numbers 78a,b,c,e,f and 76a,b,c), together with the four small ponds (77a,b,c,d) by the windpump, are collectively known as 'the Brickpits', although the origins of the latter four ponds are obscure. The brickpits proper are all steep-sided and up to three metres deep (Fig. 7), while the windpump ponds are little more than one metre deep and more gently shelving.

On Adventurers' Fen are other ponds resulting from clay extraction. Several small ponds which lie in marshy ground alongside the Lode (the 'Old Kilns' brickpits) are now shallow and overgrown, with little open water. By contrast, the 'Sappers' Pond' on the Charles Raven Reserve was enormously enlarged during 1989 to provide clay for reinforcement of the lode banks as part of a catchment flood relief scheme (see Chapter 11).

The Sedge Fen contains a number of shallow, intermittently wet ponds resulting from peat extraction. In the case of the now almost extinct Barnes' Mere, the peat crop was incidental to the main aim of creating open water (see Chapter 9.1). Further small 'experimental' peat-diggings of the 1950s and 1970s resulted in ephemeral waterbodies, some of which developed an interesting flora including the rare charophyte *Nitella tenuissima* (Chapter 7).

Other ponds on the Fen have been made with conservation, research or visitors in mind. A small pond which is still known as 'the Experimental Pond' was excavated alongside, and in communication with, the north end of Drainers' Dyke in the 1920s. Some notes on the early flora and fauna of this pond are provided by Griffiths[8] and Harris,[9] but few later records exist of its use for 'experimental' purposes. The largest expanse of static water, the Mere, was created for wildfowl; its development and success are described in Chapter 9. In 1985 and 1991, ponds were dug in the Education Area on the edge of the Poor's Fen to provide further facilities for the growing numbers of school parties visiting Wicken for environmental education (Chapter 12). Other much smaller ponds were produced using explosives in 1988, to provide a focal point for the new hide on the boardwalk in the carr to the west of the Brickpits. In the winter of 1991–92, a new pond appeared at the junction of Drainers' Dyke and Cross Dyke as a result of a bizarre accident, when a piece of heavy equipment sank under its own weight in the wet peat.

Figure 7 The Main Brickpit photographed in the 1920s[7] (above), and 1980s (below). The windpump in the background of the older photograph stood alongside Sedge Fen Drove and was associated with the brickworkings. (See Chapter 10)

A myriad of smaller water-bodies comes into being on the Fen at various times of the year. These include water-filled ruts, holes in the trunks of the older trees in the carr and woodland areas, and water-traps in the axils of some herbaceous plants. While some of these are vital for the life-histories of a number of the Fen's characteristic species, such as the mosquitoes that breed in tree-holes (Chapter 8), these ephemeral water-bodies are not considered further here.

CHEMISTRY, MIXING AND STRATIFICATION

Some of the Fen's water-bodies are connected to other waters for most or all of the year, while others are isolated, except when the water-table is extremely high. The sources of water for these two categories are very different: the lodes and drains receive, either directly or indirectly, water from outside the Fen, while the isolated ponds and ditches are fed by rainwater and by water moving laterally through peat. This has important consequences for the quality of water and for the flora and fauna of these water-bodies.

There are three points at which water from surrounding areas may enter the Fen: via the New River (which runs through farmland throughout its course) and Monks Lode; by pumping into the north end of Drainers' Dyke during the winter; and from the direction of Spinney Abbey farm at the extreme north-east corner of the Fen. All of these inputs are potential sources of enrichment by agricultural fertilizer or pollution by pesticides.

In 1985–86, the nitrate and phosphate contents of various waters of the Fen were monitored throughout the year.[10] Nitrate and phosphate are normally present at low concentrations in Wicken water, and, if added in large quantities, encourage greatly increased algal growth which may be detrimental to submerged plants and indirectly alter the animal community. The maps of nitrate concentrations show enormous differences both between sites and within some waters at different times of the year (Fig. 8). The isolated brickpits (78a and 76b) maintained low concentrations of less than 5mg nitrate per litre throughout the year, while the adjacent pond 78e, which is connected to a potential source of 'non-fen' water, varied between vanishingly low levels in the summer and autumn of 1985 to 65mg per litre in the winter. Spinney Bank ditch, which leads into 78e from the north, contained 91.6mg per litre in winter; this is nearly twice the maximum nitrate concentration permissible in drinking-water supplies as laid down by the EEC directive of 1980. This enriched water apparently did not enter Gardiner's Ditch, which is isolated from the dykes at either end except in times of prolonged drought. In such circumstances, water may be let in from Drainers' Dyke or pumped in from the windpump ditch, but only if the quality of the water is sufficiently high.

Other studies carried out by staff and students of the University of Cambridge in 1976 and 1981 found seasonally elevated nitrate concentrations in Wicken and Monks Lodes and Drainers' Dyke ranging between 1 and 92mg per litre. By comparison, levels of nitrate in the brickpits did not exceed 6mg per litre. (The mean concentration

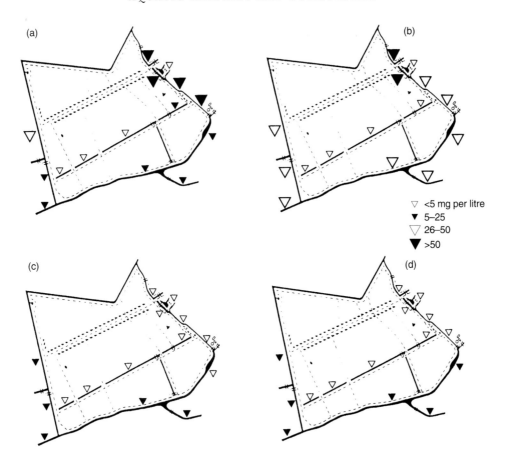

Figure 8   The concentration of nitrate nitrogen in the waters of the Sedge Fen in 1985–86:[10] (a) January;
(b) April; (c) July; (d) October

in rainfall as measured on the Breckland between January and April 1981 was 0.8mg per litre, and water in the peat of the 'Godwin Triangle' at the junction of Drainers' Dyke and Wicken Lode contained less than 6mg per litre; see Table I).

Phosphate has also found its way into the Fen waters from the surrounding farmland. In July 1984, a dense algal mat developed on brickpit 78e, suggesting that enrichment might have occurred. Extremely high levels of phosphate in the ditch running from Spinney Abbey Farm towards Spinney Bank were discovered.[11] It seems that the boundary earthbank was not watertight and enriched water seeped into the Fen. This produced phosphate concentrations in the ditch along Spinney Bank exceeding 90µg per litre; this is a level associated with moderate enrichment in lakes such as the Norfolk Broads.[12] The concentration in the main brickpit at this time was rather less than 30µg per litre; for most of the time, it is barely detectable. The water-proofing of the boundary bank should ensure that such incidents do not happen again.

This episode illustrates the vulnerability of the Fen's waters to occurrences beyond its control. This has been reinforced several times in recent years when raw sewage has found its way into the southern end of the windpump ditch (78d) after pumps have failed in Lode Lane. The effects of any such spillage are likely to be greatest in those water-bodies in which there is little or no flow, and especially when water-levels are low. Nutrients or organic matter entering the Lodes would be relatively quickly flushed through, while the same discharge entering one of the intermittently flowing or static ditches would persist and affect the flora and fauna for much longer. It is therefore worth looking in more detail at the enrichment of 78e in 1984 to assess the possible dangers posed by such accidents to the ecology of the Fen's waters.

The flora and fauna of 78e have changed dramatically in recent years and Lunel's findings[11] suggest a causative link with the enrichment episode. Prior to 1984, the pond was noted for its clear water and extensive beds of *Ceratophyllum demersum* (rigid horn-wort) with a rich and distinctive invertebrate fauna.[13] These submerged weeds then entirely disappeared, shaded out in summer by a mat of alga so dense that, in 1990, it supported a floating canopy of *Berula erecta* (lesser water-parsnip). The subsequent decomposition of this dense algal mat caused the daytime dissolved oxygen level to fluctuate widely and to fall to around seven per cent saturation.[11]

An algal bloom has reappeared on the brickpit each summer for at least a decade, suggesting that the nutrients originally responsible have remained within the pond. The movement of water through these ponds is extremely slow. Phosphate is likely to have been absorbed into the bottom sediment whence it can be recycled into the water-column each year. The problem of persistent enrichment by phosphate, years after the source has been removed, is well known in the sewage-polluted Norfolk Broads. Removal of the bottom sediment has proved to be one (rather costly) solution to the problem in the Broads;[12] this might profitably be tried on the much smaller scale of brickpit 78e, if the nutrient-rich spoil could be disposed of away from the Fen.

The temperature of the surface water changes over 24 hours in all the water-bodies, but the diurnal range of temperatures experienced varies enormously between lodes, ditches and ponds. During the summer, when daily range is greatest, the surface waters of Wicken Lode typically vary by only a few degrees centigrade through the day and night.[11] The effects of irradiance of the surface are evidently counteracted by mixing and diluted by the large volume of water. In the small brickpit 76b, however, the daily range of surface temperature may be as much as $10°C$ in July, with the minimum around dawn and the maximum late in the afternoon when the pond emerges from the shade of its own reed fringe.

More far-reaching in its effect on the aquatic environment, however, is the variation of water temperature with depth. Heating of the water at the surface causes it to expand and decrease in density, so that it will tend to float on the cooler water below. At noon on a hot day, the surface temperature of the flowing parts of the Lode will rarely be more than $2°C$ higher than that of the water at 1 m depth on the bottom, and the water remains well mixed[11] (Fig. 9). The water temperature gradient between the top and bottom of the Main Brickpit (76a) might be little more, about $4°C$ over 3 m, but the effect here is quite different: the difference in density, together with minimal wind disturbance, creates a stable stratification in which the surface waters do not mix with those at depth. Studies of the Main Brickpit and other ponds by P. M. Jenkin and J. T. Saunders in the 1930s[14] showed that stratification began in the first two weeks of May, when the surface waters warmed above a critical temperature of 10°C, and broke down in the autumn as the surface waters cooled and mixing by the wind could occur. In most winters, a second period without mixing occurs under ice-cover, so that the Wicken ponds typically have an annual cycle of prolonged summer and shorter winter stratification, with mixing to depth occurring only in spring and autumn.

Stratification caused by vertical temperature gradients has a strong influence on the chemistry of a water-body, with profound consequences for the flora and fauna. In summer, nutrients become depleted in the sunlit surface waters as they are taken up by rapidly multiplying algal cells (the phytoplankton). Nutrients are ultimately transported to the bottom in a rain of dead cells and the faeces of grazing microscopic crustaceans (the zooplankton) and are not replenished on a large scale in the upper waters until the autumn mixing.

A study by a student class, on the concentration of nutrients at different depths and at different times during a summer's day and night in the Main Brickpit, has shown that subtle changes in nutrient levels in the surface waters are possibly linked with vertical migration of the zooplankton.[15] Transient increases in ammonium, oxidized nitrogen and phosphate in the surface waters between midnight and dawn were associated with the migration of copepods, cladocerans and rotifers from the bottom up to the surface. This pattern might be explicable in terms of the excretory activities of these minute animals, followed by rapid uptake of the nutrients by algal cells as daylight returns. This study has been most informative in revealing the complexity of small-scale chemical and biological patterns which can arise in a sheltered, enclosed water-body. The observed patterns of nutrient concentrations and species distributions in the water-column may best be likened to a kaleidoscope, continuously changing in all three spatial dimensions as well as in time.

Where vertical mixing does not occur, there may be serious consequences for the availability of dissolved oxygen at different depths. The water in the lodes is almost always well oxygenated and the level of oxygenation varies by no more than about 20 per cent with depth, even in August.[11] By contrast, oxygen levels in the Main Brickpit rarely exceeded 70 per cent in the sheltered surface waters and dropped rapidly with increasing depth to zero at two metres (Fig. 9).

Throughout the summer period of stratification, decomposition of organic matter on the bottom of the pond depletes the oxygen contained in the lower waters. The oxygen used by the decomposer organisms cannot be replenished because there is no mixing with the surface waters and, in this particular case, the bottom lies too deep for photosynthesis to occur. However, even the shallow ponds near the windpump may suffer deoxygenation from mid-May to August (as they did in 1931[14] and 1995), reflecting the extreme degree to which they are sheltered from the wind by the reed fringe. This creates a patchwork of small ponds with quite different chemical ecology: in the

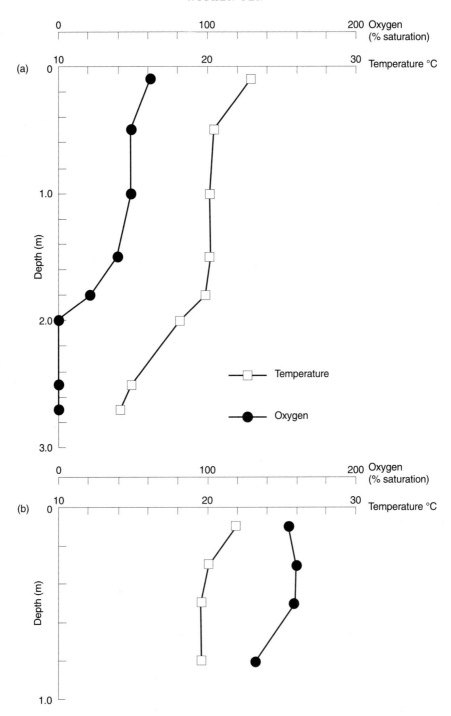

Figure 9   Changes in water temperature and oxygen concentrations with depth during August:
(a) the Main Brickpit; (b) Wicken Lode[11]

surface waters of the deeper ponds, nitrogen is present in the form of nitrate, whereas, in the shallower ponds, ammonium is the dominant ion. This apparently subtle difference may have important consequences for floating aquatic plants that derive nutrient ions from the water.

Deoxygenation also creates respiratory problems for the organisms living on the bottom and severely affects the functioning of the community. The fauna of the deeper parts of the brickpits is likely to be restricted to those species tolerant of low oxygen concentrations. Studies of the breakdown of *Phragmites* (reed) litter in the Main Brickpit showed that the number of different types of detritus-feeding invertebrate colonizing litter at different depths corresponded to the availability of oxygen: between 16 and 22 different types were found in the top metre, where oxygen was freely available, but fewer than ten in the low oxygen conditions at two metres depth or more.[16] The deep-water fauna consisted mainly of oligochaete worms and chironomid midge larvae (particularly those species that have haemoglobin pigments to act as an oxygen store) and lacked the caddis-flies, snails and mayfly larvae found in the shallower areas. The rate of decomposition of *Phragmites* was considerably slower in the depths than in the shallows. This was probably because of reductions in the activity of the microbial and fungal decomposers and also in the numbers, diversity and activity of the invertebrates that process the larger pieces of litter into smaller, more easily decomposed particles.

Some organisms thrive in anoxic pondwater. In July 1980, a red coloration appeared in the water of brickpit 78e, caused by a dense aggregation of the purple sulphur bacterium *Chromatium*.[17] These bacteria use hydrogen sulphide to reduce carbon dioxide in the production of carbohydrates; growth is therefore favoured by the deoxygenated conditions in which hydrogen sulphide is produced. The bacteria were concentrated in the water at precisely the level at which dissolved oxygen concentration dropped to zero, between 60 and 90cm depth.

Daily changes in the chemistry of the Fen's waters occur as a result of the metabolic activities of the submerged vegetation. The plants produce oxygen while using up carbon dioxide in photosynthesis during daylight hours, and take up oxygen while releasing carbon dioxide as they respire throughout the day and night. The effects of diurnal cycles of plant metabolism are most marked in small, well-vegetated, static waters, such as the smaller ditches and brickpits, where the pH may rise to 8.4 at the peak of photosynthetic activity.[18] If the water is more alkaline than this, many freshwater organisms are not able to survive.

THE FEN'S AQUATIC FLORA AND FAUNA

Because the lodes, ditches and ponds differ in their physical and chemical characteristics, it is reasonable to expect that their flora and fauna might differ accordingly. All the evidence available in *The Natural History of Wicken Fen* and the results of the surveys described below confirm that this is so. It is rarely possible, however, to pinpoint exactly which physical or chemical variables might be responsible for the occurrence of any given species in one habitat but not in another, simply from observations of their distributions. Indeed, there is a whole range of additional factors at work, shaping aquatic communities by influencing the distributions of individual species. These include the method and frequency of management; the presence of particular other species; and geographical proximity to other waters. In addition, there are almost indiscernible subtleties of character that create an impression of chance differences in the communities of adjacent, apparently similar habitats.

PATTERNS OF DISTRIBUTION

Most of the studies of the Fen's aquatic plants of the past decade have concentrated on the lodes, ditches and ponds of the Sedge Fen. The flora of different water-bodies fall into distinct groups that share species in common, and these are clearly related to the type of habitat: the lodes and Drainers' Dyke; three sections of Gardiner's Ditch and other large ditches; and smaller ditches and ponds (Table II, pp. 34–35). The 'lode' group is rich in species, including flowing-water species, such as *Oenanthe fluviatilis* (river water-dropwort); *Potamogeton perfoliatus* (perfoliate pondweed), a species which does not produce floating leaves and tends not to occur in shallow water; *Sagittaria sagittifolia* (arrowhead); *Nuphar lutea* (yellow water-lily); and some species, such as *Hottonia palustris* (water-violet) (Plate 3, Fig. 1) and several other *Potamogeton* species, that are equally likely to occur in small ditch habitats.

The floral lists of the ditches and ponds vary enormously between sites. However, some species tend to occur only in small water-bodies: for example the liverwort *Ricciocarpos natans* and *Utricularia vulgaris* (greater bladderwort). The most similar ditch and pond flora tend to be those of geographical nearest neighbours, for example the sections of Gardiner's Drove and the ponds 77a/b and 77c/d.

The Natural History of Wicken Fen contains many references to the patterns of distribution of invertebrate species among different types of aquatic habitat. Some authors, such as Hutchinson (writing about water bugs),[19] Balfour-Browne, Omer Cooper and Tottenham (water beetles),[20,21] and Lewis (mosquitoes),[22] drew attention to the influence of the abundance of aquatic vegetation, in both its living and decaying state, on the distribution of species and even families of insects. Others, such as Wood,[23] writing on the caddis-fly larvae in the flowing and static stretches of Wicken Lode, suggested that flow (and presumably the consequent physical and chemical characteristics outlined above) was an important factor.

Recent work supports the distinction between the major types of water-body, but also draws out some subtle, and some very striking, variations between different ponds and ditches. A systematic survey concentrating on the invertebrates that live on the bottom sediment and will crawl or swim into traps was carried out by David Lee in 1985–88.[10] One of the most obvious patterns to emerge is the existence of a 'lode' type of bottom community, defined partly by the presence of the amphipod shrimp *Gammarus pulex* in the lodes and Drainers' Dyke and its absence from ditches and ponds. Two other crustaceans, the introduced amphipod *Crangonyx pseudogracilis* and the isopod *Asellus aquaticus*, occur in all the sites. These two species are known to be tolerant of fairly low oxygen concentrations, while the *Gammarus* is not, so that this pattern may reflect the effects of flow and mixing on dissolved oxygen concentrations.

A survey of the weed-dwelling invertebrates of sixteen ponds and ditches in July and August 1989 produced 108 species.[24] The degree of similarity between sites was generally very low, with some common species occurring in all sites and many other species being discovered in only one or two sites. For example, *Asellus aquaticus* was found everywhere, while the very similar *A. meridianus* was found only in brickpit 76b. In 1990, some of the ponds (76a, 78e, and 77b) were surveyed as part of the National Pond Survey project, using techniques designed to give standard samples from ponds of all types and sizes throughout Great Britain. The results from the Wicken ponds could then be compared with a large data set and the ponds classified according to the major types to be found in the country. Not surprisingly, the Wicken ponds fall within the 'lowland, base-rich' national pond grouping for both their flora and fauna; indeed, the data gleaned from these ponds now form part of the 'definition' of this type of pond community in Britain.[25]

A comprehensive study of the Fen's ditch fauna began in 1992. Duncan Painter has surveyed the invertebrates of five ditches in different stages of hydroseral development: North Dyke, newly recut along the dry former ditch line; Malcarse Dyke, previously shallow and overgrown and newly re-excavated; Cross Dyke, previously cleared out in 1984 and partly re-excavated in 1991–2 in alternate 50m stretches; Gardiner's Ditch, cut in five separate sections thirteen years previously; and Sedge Fen Drove ditch, untouched for many decades and hardly more than a shallow depression drying out in most summers. The results reveal the very distinctive nature of the fauna of the very oldest ditches.[26] Sedge Fen Drove ditch contains a number of rare species, including the nationally scarce caddis-fly *Phacopteryx brevipennis*. It would also appear to be a primary source of the Fen's mosquitoes.

The fauna of the newer ditches show marked differences between ditches and between older and recently-cleared sections. Painter followed up his general survey by studying changes in the fauna of Gardiner's Ditch following the re-excavation of six 50m-stretches in the spring of 1993. He found that the only species of dragonfly to lay eggs in the densely reeded sections of the ditch was the large red damselfly (*Pyrrhosoma nymphula*). The only large dragonfly found flying within the *Phragmites* was the hairy dragonfly (*Brachytron pratense*). The behaviour of the adult dragonflies is clearly reflected in the subsequent distribution of larvae: only *Pyrrhosoma* larvae were recorded in large numbers in the densely reeded sections, while larvae of the families Aeshnidae and Libellulidae were confined to the newer sections.[27]

The new ditch sections have proved to be numerically richer in adult water beetles, but the older sections contained more species of conservation interest, such as the *Red Data Book* fen species *Hydraena palustris* and *Dryops anglicanus*[28] (see Chapter 8). The densely reeded sections supported a greater number of species of mollusc than the newer sections, and of the 22 species recorded from the ditch seven were found only in the older areas. However, the rare bivalve *Pisidium pseudosphaerium* was recorded only from the newer sections.[29]

Table II. Macrophyte distributions in 19 sites at Wicken Fen, surveyed in 1988–90 by C. D. Preston, S. M. Walters & L. E. Friday. Charophyte identifications were confirmed by N. F. Stewart

	Wicken Lode			ML	DD	Gardiner's Ditch				CD	TD	SP	BP	77	77	77	77	78	76
	1	2	3			1	2	3	4					a	b	c	d	d	a
'Lode' Species																			
Alisma																			
lanceolatum	×	×	×																
Apium																			
nodiflorum	×				×														
Butomus																			
umbellatus			×	×	×														
Carex riparia			×																
Eleocharis																			
acicularis	×	×	×																
Equisetum																			
fluviatile			×																
Glyceria																			
fluitans	×																		
Myosotis																			
scorpioides		×																	
Nitella																			
flexilis		×																	
Oenanthe																			
fluviatilis	×	×	×	×	×														
Potamogeton																			
friesii		×																	
perfoliatus	×	×	×	×															
pusillus		×																	
Sagittaria																			
sagittifolia	×	×	×	×	×														
Schoenoplectus																			
lacustris	×	×	×																
Veronica cf. *catenata*	×	×			×														
'Lode & Ditch' Species																			
Alisma plantago																			
-aquatica	×	×	×				×	×		×		×							
Callitriche sp.	×									×									
Chara hispida																			
var. major	×	×		×	×		×	×		×	×	×	×						
vulgaris	×	×	×	×	×					×									
Glyceria maxima	×	×	×									×							
Hippuris																			
vulgaris	×	×			×					×									
Hottonia																			
palustris	×	×	×	×	×					×	×								
Iris pseudacorus						×	×	×											
Myosotis laxa		×								×									
Myriophyllum																			
verticillatum	×	×			×					×		×							
Nuphar lutea	×	×	×	×	×														
Persicaria																			
amphibia		×							×										
Phalaris																			
arundinacea	×		×							×									
Potamogeton																			
crispus	×	×	×	×	×							×							
lucens	×	×	×	×	×	×	×												

KEY TO HEADINGS

ML = Monks Lode

DD = Drainers' Dyke

CD = Commissioners' Drain

TD = Thomson's Ditch

SP = Spinney Bank

BP = Borrow Pit

Table II. (cont.)

	Wicken Lode			ML	DD	Gardiner's Ditch				CD	TD	SP	BP	77 a	77 b	77 c	77 d	78 d	76 a
	1	2	3			1	2	3	4										
Potamogeton pectinatus	×	×	×	×	×								×						
Ranunculus circinatus	×	×	×	×	×							×							
Rorippa nasturtium-aquaticum				×					×										
Sparganium emersum	×	×	×	×	×				×										
Zannichellia palustris		×								×	×	×							
'General' Species																			
Berula erecta	×		×	×			×	×							×			×	
Ceratophyllum demersum	×													×	×				×
Elodea nuttallii	×		×	×								×						×	
canadensis	×	×	×	×	×			×	×									×	
Lemna minor	×	×	×		×		×	×	×			×	×		×			×	
trisulca	×						×	×	×	×	×			×	×			×	
Nymphaea alba	×	×	×	×	×	×				×									×
Phragmites australis	×	×	×	×	×	×	×	×	×	×	×	×		×	×	×	×	×	×
Rumex hydrolapathum		×																×	
Sparganium erectum	×		×	×		×	×	×		×		×						×	
Typha latifolia	×		×					×										×	
'Ditch and Pond' Species																			
Callitriche platycarpa												×							
obtusangula										×									
Chara globularis var. virgata							×	×			×								
pedunculata							×												
Epilobium hirsutum																		×	
Hydrocotyle vulgaris				×			×	×											
Juncus subnodulosus				×		×	×	×											
Lemna minuta											×								
Mentha aquatica				×		×	×	×											
Myriophyllum spicatum												×							
Potamogeton berchtoldii										×									
coloratus				×		×	×	×			×			×					
natans					×		×	×				×	×						
Ranunculus lingua							×												
trichophyllus									×	×									
Ricciocarpos natans							×	×											
Samolus valerandi						×	×	×											
Utricularia vulgaris							×	×	×	×	×			×	×	×	×		×

Painter's study has also demonstrated the distinctiveness of the invertebrate fauna of the ditches on the Sedge Fen as compared with those on Adventurers' Fen. Rather unexpectedly, the ditches on Adventurers' Fen (which have been either neglected, as around the Mere, or perform important drainage functions) are equally rich in species and possibly even more valuable as habitats for fenland beetles and molluscs than the more lovingly conserved Sedge Fen ditches.[27]

The maintenance simultaneously of ditches in all stages of hydroseral succession on the Fen should lead to the highest overall diversity of species and conservation of those species characteristic of old fen habitats. This study appears to vindicate the recent changes in the management plan for the Fen's ditch system, to keep some old ditches inviolate, to allow some new ditches to revert to dryness, and to clear others on long cycles, cutting only short stretches at a time (Chapter 11).

The fish of the Mere and Wicken Lode have been surveyed periodically by Anglian Water, the former National Rivers Authority (NRA), now the Environment Agency, and the Institute of Freshwater Ecology. The Mere fish community is dominated by common and silver bream (*Abramis brama* and *Blicca bjoerkna*) with an apparently high incidence of hybrids, including a putative silver bream/rudd cross.[30] One of the most abundant fish species in Wicken Lode is the bitterling (*Rhodeus sericeus*), an introduced species whose life-cycle is dependent on its milt and eggs passing through the respiratory current of the freshwater mussels, *Anodonta* and *Unio*. The fertilized eggs develop and hatch within the mussel's mantle cavity and the young fish leave through the respiratory siphon. Needless to say, the mussels are a conspicuous element of the bottom fauna in the Lode. Studies by David Aldridge of the ecology of bitterling and mussels in Wicken Lode began in 1993. These have demonstrated a distinct preference for *Unio tumidus* as a host for bitterling and revealed a curious twist in the story. Mussels disperse as parasitic glochidia larvae on the fins and gills of fish; of all the fish species investigated as hosts for glochidia, bitterling had by far the lowest infestation rates, with the parasites dropping off within a few days of attachment.[31]

Other species of fish found in the lodes are roach (*Rutilus rutilus*), common bream, rudd (*Scardinius erythrophthalmus*), perch (*Perca fluvatilis*), pike (*Esox lucius*), eel (*Anguilla anguilla*), ruffe (*Gymnocephalus cernua*), tench (*Tinca tinca*) and gudgeon (*Gobio gobio*). Some of the smaller water-bodies also contain fish, notably the brickpits (76a, 76b, 76c), where rudd are present in considerable numbers and to quite large size, the Windpump Ditch and ponds 78e and 78f. Pike, eel and ten-spined stickleback (*Pungitius pungitius*) have been found in some stretches of Gardiner's Ditch. Some other ditches, such as the newly-cleared North Dyke, which is blocked off at both ends, and ponds 77a–d, appear to have no fish. The absence of fish is, however, far harder to establish than their presence, and eels seem to find their way into almost every suitable water-body.

Frogs (*Rana temporaria*) and toads (*Bufo bufo*) are common on the Fen, and smooth newts (*Triturus vulgaris*) are frequently encountered in the education area ponds, to the visible and audible delight of young visitors. Great-crested newts (*Triturus cristatus*) have also recently colonized the pond-dipping ponds. Grass snakes (*Natrix natrix*) are not uncommon, and may often be seen swimming across the lodes, ponds and ditches, sometimes, somewhat disconcertingly, below the surface.

VARIATIONS ON A THEME: THE SPECIES OF 'ISOLATED' WATER-BODIES

Even the most casual glance at the ponds in the brickpit area will suggest that their species assemblages are rather varied: the visible differences result from the dominant species of water-weeds, but beneath the surface, the animal communities may be equally distinctive. Yet these ponds all lie within an area 100m by 300m, share a similar substratum, are about the same depth and are all about 80–90 years old. Although ponds 78c, e and f have suffered eutrophication in recent years, not all the biological difference between the groups can be explained in terms of chemistry. What other factors might be responsible for shaping the species assemblages of these water-bodies?

From the point of view of an aquatic organism, a pond may be an isolated patch of suitable habitat completely surrounded by hostile dryness that must be traversed to reach another suitable patch. Exactly which aquatic species colonize successfully depends partly on the dispersal ability of the organisms: flying insects generally have better chances of arriving than flightless insects, flatworms and snails; plants that can regenerate from tiny fragments are more likely to travel and establish more readily than those that cannot; some plants and animals, or their desiccation-resistant seeds and eggs, may hitch a lift on the feathers and feet of birds; other species might be transposed by the deliberate or unwitting action of human beings.

However, none of the aquatic habitats on Wicken Fen is totally isolated from other waters. Even in a moderately wet winter, the Fen is wet enough to support many semi-aquatic species in its surface irregularities. Indeed, some of the richest habitats at Wicken for hydrophilid water beetles are the damp ruts and old peat-diggings in the sedge- and litter-fields. For species such as these, the fen ponds are only seasonally isolated habitats. In times of exceptionally high winter rainfall, the ditches and ponds may overflow, and it is possible that the brickpits might originally have received at least some elements of their aquatic flora and fauna in this manner.

In the colonization of patchy habitats, there is always an element of chance as to whether a dispersing organism actually arrives at another suitable patch or not and, if it does, whether or not it can establish itself there. Establishment will depend on water chemistry, and on the assemblage of species already in residence, which is in itself partly moulded by chance events. It should not be surprising, then, that different species lists are obtained for adjacent, apparently similar habitats.

Peter Langton's field notes of the distribution of larval populations of chironomid midges at Wicken illustrate the degree to which the fauna of adjacent ponds can differ, even in respect to organisms well able to disperse between them. In the 1970s, he found that pond 78e had 16 species of chironomid larvae that did not occur in the Main Brickpit (76a) a few metres away, while 76a had 13 species not found in 78e, and the two ponds shared 23 species in common.[13] Some of these differences may be attributable to the very much more extensive *Ceratophyllum/ Utricularia/ Fontinalis* weed-beds in 78e. Since the pollution incidents of the 1980s, the weed-beds, and the chironomid fauna, of 78e have been drastically altered.

The macrophytes undoubtedly form an important part of the habitat for aquatic invertebrates, and the main plant species may vary dramatically between neighbouring ponds. This is well illustrated by the flora and fauna of the windpump ponds, surveyed in the summer of 1989.[24] Pond 77a was dominated by *Potamogeton coloratus* (fen pondweed), *Utricularia vulgaris* and *Ceratophyllum demersum*, and 77b by the two latter species, but 77c and 77d were entirely covered by a dense growth of charophytes. While the invertebrate fauna of 77a and 77b were broadly similar, that of 77c was very different. At least some of the differences noted may be attributable to the peculiar characteristics of the alga *Chara*; its odd smell is due to the presence of allyl compounds, which are known to elicit behavioural responses in some invertebrates.

The presence of fish can also affect invertebrate communities through their predatory activities. The effect is often most clearly seen in the zooplankton, on which most cyprinid species feed at some time in their lives. Fish hunt by sight and will generally take the larger or more heavily pigmented members of the zooplankton. Large cladocerans tend to be scarce in ponds containing fish, unless there are beds of water-weed to afford cover where they can feed while hidden from their predators. The zooplankton communities of Wicken Lode and of the Main Brickpit (both of which contain fish) are dominated by species of small body size. However, the weed-beds of the Main Brickpit harbour larger cladocerans, such as *Simocephalus vetulus* and *Sida crystallina*, and the predatory species *Polyphemus pediculus*;[7] although *Polyphemus* has a small body-size, its exceptionally large eye presumably makes it as visible to fish as the larger species. Studies of the Fen's pond communities, carried out by Cambridge University student classes over several years, show that the zooplankton assemblages in adjacent ponds can be startlingly different. One of the most important factors shaping these communities seems to be selection of certain body sizes: in general, ponds containing fish have smaller species of copepods and cladocerans than do ponds which are thought to be fish-free (Fig 10).

While visual predators select the larger items, predators with other methods of capturing their prey may select the smaller organisms. Larvae of the phantom midges *Chaoborus* are constrained to catch zooplankton that are neither too large nor too spiny to be handled by the mouthparts. These curious larvae, almost invisible save for the pairs of air-filled sacs which are used to adjust the buoyancy of the animal, are abundant in the fish-free waters at Wicken, as they themselves are vulnerable to predation by fish.

But perhaps the main predator of microscopic crustaceans is not an animal at all. In the height of summer, the ditches and ponds of Wicken Fen are dotted with the butter yellow flowers of *Utricularia vulgaris*. There is more to this beautiful plant than meets the eye; it is one of Britain's few carnivorous plants. The underwater shoots are covered with tiny suction traps, which capture freshwater crustaceans, insect larvae and worms small enough to be drawn through the 1 mm-diameter trap door.

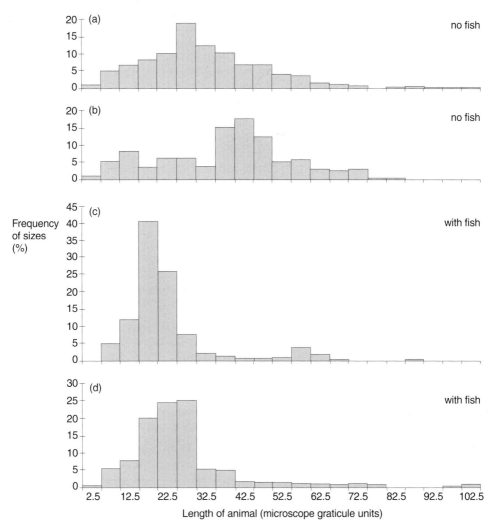

Figure 10 Size-frequency distributions of zooplankton (all species) in samples collected during October 1984[32]: (a) pond 77a; (b) pond 77d; (c) Main Brickpit 76a; (d) Wicken Lode

Research carried out in the brickpits at Wicken has revealed that each bladderwort stem produces 12–20 new leaves per week from April to September and each leaf carries 30–100 traps.[33] At any one time, more than a thousand traps, ranging in size from 1–5mm long, will be set and ready to catch prey on any one plant. Each trap retains the indigestible remains of all its prey throughout its lifetime, so it is possible to determine the rate of prey capture. In the relatively unproductive environment of the Wicken brickpits, a trap may catch, on average, one prey every three days, and the total caught in a trap's lifetime averages about six animals. Multiplying by the rate of trap production suggests that, each year, each plant would catch about a quarter of a million of the tiny animals that creep over its surface, grazing on its algal coating.

CHANGES IN AQUATIC HABITATS AND SPECIES SINCE 1930

The extensive species lists published in *The Natural History of Wicken Fen* afford the opportunity to identify some ways in which the Fen's aquatic habitats and communities have changed over the past seventy years. Although the older records are often imprecise as to which water-body is involved, it is possible to detect some clear trends, additions and extinctions. Some of the changes that emerge are evidently connected with the dispersal or introduction into the Fen of species expanding their range within Britain; some reflect national trends of changing species abundance; and others appear to be related to changes in the Fen's aquatic habitats, whether due to disturbance (such as pollution, navigation and various forms of management) or neglect.

The aquatic crustacean fauna provides examples of quite dramatic changes in species incidence and abundance that suggest a variety of different causes. Most, if not all, of the Wicken water-bodies have been invaded by the North American amphipod *Crangonyx pseudogracilis*. This species was first recorded in Britain in the 1930s and has spread extremely rapidly. We have no record of its first appearance at Wicken, but it is now one of the most abundant aquatic animals on the Fen. The native amphipod *Gammarus pulex* was recorded as 'present in small numbers in the lodes' by J. Omer Cooper in 1925,[34] and this is still the case in the 1990s. *Gammarus pulex* seems neither to have been displaced by the invading species nor to have spread with it into the static, less well-oxygenated water-bodies (see above). A crustacean that has disappeared from the Fen, probably because of habitat change, is the native crayfish, *Austropotamobius pallipes*. The single population at Wicken was known to be declining in the 1920s[34] in common with other contemporary populations throughout the country.

The two common species of water-hoglouse, *Asellus aquaticus* and *A. meridianus*, present something of a mystery. In the 1920s, *A. meridianus* was found in enormous numbers, 'in some waters of the Fen being the most abundant aquatic animal',[34] while *A. aquaticus* was not nearly so numerous. This was still the case in the Main Brickpit from 1975 to 1978.[35] However, the thousands of *Asellus* recorded in the surveys of the 1980s and '90s were all *A. aquaticus*, with the exception of a single male of *A. meridianus*, found in brickpit 76b in 1989[24] and the population discovered in 1992 in Sedge Fen Drove.[26] The apparent replacement of *A. meridianus* by *A. aquaticus* is a well-known phenomenon in British water-bodies, but the explanation is far from clear. It is unlikely that the two species compete for food because their shared resources (decaying vegetation and its microflora) are always exceedingly abundant, but subtle differences in their tolerance of water chemical conditions, temperature, predation or changes in aquatic habitats may be involved.

Some other animal invasions of the Fen have occurred since 1932. Bitterling, now one of the most abundant fish in Wicken Lode, was not recorded on the Fen in 1932,[36] and is presumably a deliberate introduction to the Cambridgeshire lode system. The

North American flatworm *Dugesia tigrina* is now abundant at the village end of Wicken Lode, but apparently has not penetrated further into the Fen. This species was probably introduced into Britain in aquarists' weed and the first certain records in Britain date from 1956.

Fish, plants and invertebrates might possibly invade and spread around the Fen as a result of inadvertent transport by people, whether anglers, wardening staff or freshwater biologists. It seems likely that the distribution at Wicken Fen of the rare cladoceran *Daphnia rosea* in widely-scattered isolated water-bodies may simply reflect the progress of the recorder's pond net around the Fen.[37]

The snail *Potamopyrgus antipodarum* (= *P. jenkinsi*) is likely to have arrived at Wicken by its own considerable powers of dispersal. This species has recently been recognized as a native of New Zealand. In Britain, it was known only from brackish waters until towards the end of the last century, with the first inland record being made in 1893. It has since spread rapidly through freshwaters, especially along the canal network. Although notable for its absence from Wicken Fen prior to 1926, *P. antipodarum* (as *P. jenkinsi*) was found at Wisbech in 1909 and its invasion 'of the whole of Fenland' was thought to be only a matter of time.[38] In 1989, *P. antipodarum* was found in the westernmost section of Gardiner's Ditch[24] and has since appeared in some other sites. One other introduced mollusc that has proved very invasive elsewhere in Britain, the zebra mussel (*Dreissena polymorpha*), was recorded in the River Cam at Upware as early as the turn of the century;[39] it has not yet been recorded from Wicken Fen, although dead shells may be found in material dredged from Burwell and Reach Lodes.

One notable animal species that has disappeared from Wicken and from most other parts of East Anglia largely because of detrimental habitat changes is the otter (*Lutra lutra*). In 1923, Evans noted that the drainage of the Fens had apparently had little effect on the otter ('it is still numerous'[40]), but there was clearly some concern about its status at Wicken because J. S. Gardiner felt moved to declare in 1928 that 'the story that we have killed it or allowed it to be killed is a fabrication'.[41] The absence, at Wicken Fen, of stumps, tree roots and broken bank 'such as they find and love on ordinary river sides'[40] made their breeding on the Fen unlikely. Riparian management undoubtedly reduces habitat for otters, but it is unlikely to be the sole cause of their demise as there is strong evidence that otters are now reappearing in the clinically tidy lode system in the 1990s. The American mink (*Mustela vison*) has been extending its range in Britain since the 1950s and is now well established at Wicken Fen. There is no evidence that the arrival of mink at Wicken is responsible for the loss of otters, but the decline in water voles (*Arvicola terrestris*) noted at Wicken Fen (and elsewhere) during the 1980s might possibly be linked to the predatory activities of mink, as might fluctuations in the breeding success of wildfowl. The changing fortunes of various wildfowl species on the Fen are described in Chapter 9.4.

The aquatic flora of the Fen has also undergone substantial change over the past sixty years and shows parallels to changes in the aquatic fauna. There have been a number of additions to the species list, some native and some alien. Three alien waterweeds, all of North American origin, have become established at Wicken in recent years; their presence provides one more indication that no nature reserve is immune from changes occurring in the surrounding countryside. In 1984, *Elodea nuttallii* (Nuttall's waterweed) was recorded in the ditch near the William Thorpe Building, some 18 years after its first British record, and 10 years after its first appearance in Cambridgeshire. In some places on the Fen it grows alongside *E. canadensis* (Canadian waterweed), itself an introduction which escaped from a ditch alongside the Cambridge Botanic Garden in 1848 and spread rapidly, becoming well established at Wicken by 1923.[42] The tiny *Lemna minuta* (least duckweed) was first discovered in Britain in Cambridge in 1977[43] and appeared at Wicken in 1989. *Azolla filiculoides* (water fern) was noted as present in Wicken Lode in 1921, but was not seen subsequently till 1967.[44] It seems to have disappeared again, but it has a reputation for being sporadic in its occurrence, so we may expect to see it on the Fen in the future.

Several aquatic plants have been lost from the Fen. These include *Hydrocharis morsus-ranae* (frogbit), *Stratiotes aloides* (water-soldier) and *Utricularia minor* (lesser bladderwort). *Hydrocharis* has suffered a dramatic decline throughout the region, and indeed in many parts of England, where agricultural enrichment of water-bodies seems to have been the reason.[45] Eutrophication may have caused it to decline in Wicken Lode, but this cannot be responsible for its loss from the isolated Fen ditch system. The demise of *Stratiotes* may also be part of a general decline caused by deterioration in water quality. *U. minor* has probably disappeared with the loss of the mildly-acidic habitats associated with peat-diggings on the Fen. It is hoped that one or more of these species might reappear from buried seed as some ditches are reopened and small-scale peat-digging is resumed (Chapter 11).

The neglect of the internal ditches during the first half of this century and the reopening of some of them also seem to have been responsible for changes in the abundance of some aquatic plants. Evans recorded in 1923 that certain 'lesser channels which can be traced in the main Sedge Fen have dried up completely, and so reduced the stock of such genera as *Potamogeton* (Pond-weed), with the loss of several species in quite recent years'.[46] On the other hand, the opening up of some of the Fen drains had led to the 'intrusion of some [species] which are not sedge fen plants at all'. These included charophytes, *Hottonia*, *Sagittaria*, *Nymphaea*, *Nuphar*, *Lemna minor* and *L. trisulca* (ivy-leaved duckweed), all of which are relatively tolerant of periodic disturbance and which we now take for granted as part of the 'fen' flora.

The flora of Wicken Lode has been comparatively well-documented over the years and it has been possible to relate some observed changes with the use and management of the waterway. Perhaps the most striking difference between the situation in the 1920s and in 1989 is the loss of the 'thick growth of *Chara* under the banks'[47] which had evidently been a favourite hunting ground for mollusc enthusiasts. The loss of *Chara* beds has been noted in many other water-bodies, where eutrophication and disturbance have been implicated.

A survey of the Lode in 1976 by Max Walters established that the number of species had not declined appreciably since his earlier survey in 1951, but the abundance of some submerged species seemed much reduced.[48] *Baldellia ranunculoides* (lesser waterplaintain), *Hydrocharis*, *Hippuris vulgaris* (mare's-tail) and *Elodea canadensis* had all disappeared from or became rare in the Lode, and *Eleocharis acicularis* (needle spike-rush), which had formed a more-or-less continuous sward on the bottom of the Lode in the early 1950s, was scarce in 1976. Conversely, *Ceratophyllum demersum* and *Sparganium emersum* (unbranched bur-reed), which were not recorded in 1951, had become very abundant by 1976. These changes he suggested might be attributed to nutrient enrichment, although it is possible that changes in use of the Lode by boat traffic might also be invoked.

Very few boats used the Lode between 1900 and 1960, but then the volume of recreational traffic increased sharply, with large, propellor-driven craft making their way right up to the village end of the Lode. The churning of the shallow water-column and surface sediment created turbidity as well as mechanical damage to the plants. In 1976, a visual comparison of Monks Lode, which was not part of the navigation system, with Wicken Lode was informative: the former was half-choked with floating and emergent vegetation (Fig. 11), while the latter was kept 'open' by the traffic with a broad swathe cut through the water-weeds down the middle of the channel.

Since 1983, boat traffic has been forbidden in Wicken Lode upstream of the junction with Monks Lode. The aquatic vegetation in this stretch is now particularly lush and is cut at least once a year. Submerged vegetation, dominated by *Oenanthe fluviatilis* and *Sparganium emersum*, and floating-leaved species, such as *Nuphar lutea*, now cover the entire width of this part of the Lode. *Hippuris vulgaris*, *Potamogeton praelongus* (long-stalked pondweed) and *Elodea canadensis* have reappeared, and *Eleocharis acicularis* is now present in extensive swards. The part of the Lode that remains navigable tends to be more turbid than the upstream stretch, but this has a seasonal aspect, which suggests that it may be associated as much with suspended sediment washed in from Monks Lode in times of high rainfall as with boat traffic.

POSTSCRIPT

In 1926, Frank Balfour-Browne gave a gloomy prognosis for the future of the Fen:

> 'Various efforts have been, and are being, made to preserve the fauna and flora in the small area of Wicken Fen, efforts which, I venture to think, will prolong the existence of the remnant, at most, for a few years. In spite of the steps which are being taken, the natural conditions are changing rapidly and with these, the [water beetle] fauna is also changing'.[49]

With the unfolding of the new management programme over the next few decades, we hope that the habitats of all types of aquatic organisms, from the 'fen' species to the 'opportunistic' species, will be maintained, and with them the organisms themselves.

Figure 11 Arrowhead (*Sagittaria sagittifolia*) in Monks Lode, 20 August 1977

References

1 Eastham (1932), pp. 634–635
2 Gardiner & Tansley (1923)
3 Gardiner (1925–32)
4 Wicken Fen Local Management Committee (1992)
5 Rowell (1986a)
6 Rowell (1982a)
7 Jenkin (1928)
8 Griffiths (1925)
9 Harris (1926)
10 Lee (1988)
11 Lunel (1984)
12 Moss (1983)
13 Langton (March 1989, report in Fen archive)
14 Jenkin (1982)
15 Corbet *et al.* (1980)
16 Polunin (1982)
17 McGarry (1982)

18 Saunders (1925)
19 Hutchinson (1926)
20 Balfour-Browne (1926)
21 Omer Cooper & Tottenham (1932)
22 Lewis (1932)
23 Wood (1929)
24 Friday (unpublished)
25 Pond Action (1991, unpublished)
26 Painter & Friday (1994)
27 Painter (1995)
28 Shirt (1987)
29 Painter (1994)
30 Johnson (1985)
31 Aldridge (thesis in preparation)
32 Yau (1994)
33 Friday (1988)

34 Omer Cooper (1925)
35 Polunin (1979)
36 Gardiner (1932a)
37 Hearn (unpublished)
38 Oldham (1926), p. 200
39 Brindley (1904), p. 115
40 Evans (1923a), p. 28
41 Gardiner (1928), p. 376
42 Evans (1923b)
43 Preston (1991a)
44 Perring (1968)
45 Preston & Croft (1997)
46 Evans (1923a), p. 44
47 Brindley (1925), p. 155
48 Walters (1976, unpublished report in archive)
49 Balfour-Browne (1926), p. 212

4

REED-BEDS

T. J. BENNETT AND L. E. FRIDAY

THE COMMON OR Norfolk reed (*Phragmites australis*) is one of the most abundant and widespread higher plants to be found at Wicken Fen. It is probably impossible to be anywhere on the reserve and not find it. Reed-beds appeal powerfully to the senses: at any time of the year, it is an extraordinary experience to be enclosed by their physical presence, and their sounds and colours change dramatically through the seasons. The rattling and crackling of the dead stems on a warm winter's day can be surprisingly loud. Where reeds are cut, they provide an unusual but traditional winter scene, as the marshmen harvest them for thatching. The rapid green regrowth in the spring all too soon gives way to the swishing of tall stems with their long lance-like leaves, to be followed in high summer with the contrasting deep purple inflorescences. The changes during the latter part of the year are more subtle as the seeds ripen, the leaves fall and the mature straw-coloured stems are revealed again. Aesthetic considerations alone would justify the conservation of Wicken's reed-beds.

Phragmites australis is the tallest of Britain's native grasses, attaining a height of up to three metres. Impressive though the reeds themselves may be, there is more of the plant below ground than there is above. Strong horizontal rhizomes ramify the soil, sending up forests of vertical shoots that give rise to the aerial parts. The above-ground parts die each year, although the dead stems and leaf bases may remain standing for several years. The rhizome system, however, is perennial and potentially immortal, producing new growth and shoots year after year, perhaps for centuries. In this way, an extensive bed of reed might arise from one rhizome system, descended from a single original seedling or fragment of rhizome. These underground parts are the key to the exceptional powers of reed to regenerate after cutting, fire or frost. Like many truly aquatic plants, *Phragmites* maintains a supply of oxygen to its rhizomes: air spaces connect the bases of the stems to all parts of the rhizome system and ensure that gaseous exchange can occur, even when the water-table is well above ground level. Much of what we know about the ecology of *Phragmites* in East Anglia has been established by the research of Sylvia Haslam, working in the Botany Department of the University of Cambridge.[1]

Reed tends to occur at Wicken wherever the water regime is suitable. Since the management plan for the Fen emphasizes the conservation of the diversity of traditional fen habitats, the management strategy adopted in different parts of the reserve inevitably varies. Reed is therefore subjected to a variety of different treatments, depending on where, and with which other species, it occurs. The National Vegetation Classification scheme (NVC) identifies four community types dominated by *Phragmites*; all of these are represented at Wicken and each has a distinctive distribution around the Fen (see Table V, Chapter 5). To the north of Wicken Lode the *Phragmites australis–Peucedanum palustre* (milk-parsley) and *Phragmites australis–Eupatorium cannabinum* (hemp-agrimony) fen communities form large expanses of open 'litter' fields. Some areas probably also fall within the *Phragmites australis–Urtica dioica* (common nettle) community. In all these areas the presence of reed is largely incidental, although in managing them there is a clear bias towards suppressing its dominance through the cutting regime. Among the vast tracts of fen carr, where since the dieback of *Frangula alnus* (alder buckthorn) (Chapter 6) the ground flora has again become far more diverse, *Phragmites* has not fared particularly well. Most of the carr area is left undisturbed, but some areas are being cleared to recreate more open conditions. Reed performs very much better where the carr is actively being suppressed; in these areas, early and frequent cutting of the sward will probably need to be sustained if a diverse herbaceous community is to be established.

Pure *Phragmites* swamps and reed-beds occur in those areas where the water-level is above ground for several months of the year, but where standing water is less than about 1.5 m deep. In drier areas, reed is joined by other herbs of marshy ground, and shrubs eventually take over; where the water is deeper, aquatic plants prevail. However, in intermediate conditions, and especially where water-levels fluctuate about ground level, reed has a competitive edge. On the Sedge Fen, reed-beds are confined to the fringes of the redundant brickpits. Here, the rather transient nature of the shallow-water community is all too obvious: in recent years, the ponds nearest to the windpump in particular have become so rapidly colonized by reed and filled with its accumulated litter, that it has been necessary to dredge them out. The main brickpits, however, are deeper and steep-sided, so that the reed fringe has failed to overwhelm the ponds, even after almost a century of growth (see Fig. 7, p. 25).

However, on Adventurers' Fen, which lies to the south of Wicken Lode, the extent of the reed-swamp community is far greater. In the interval between the two World Wars, much of Adventurers' Fen was probably more attractive to wildlife than it is now. In his book *Adventurers Fen*, Eric Ennion recounts the history of that part of the Fen lying to the south of Burwell Lode, just outside the present reserve boundary. The undrained fen, with its traditional ways of life, was drained and cultivated throughout the Great War, but was subsequently reclaimed by nature during nearly two decades of neglect. By the mid-1930s, the area had almost entirely been taken over by reed-beds. Ennion provides a glimpse of 'what real fen was like' in his vivid descriptions of a water-filled wilderness:

> 'One evening at the end of May 1939 I took the punt into one of the larger pools, wedged it among the reedmace and sat down. Fourteen black terns, a mob of swifts and three or four of the big water bats who lived in the pollard willows were wheeling overhead. They were all too intent on the evening meal – moths and sedgeflies hatching and rising from the rushes and sedges – to worry about me.'[2] (Fig. 12)

Figure 12 'Black Terns, Swifts and Water Bat' from Eric Ennion's drawings of South Adventurers' Fen[2]

In the preface to the first edition of his book,[3] Ennion describes the destruction of this paradise during the early years of the Second World War, first by drainage, then by fire and finally the plough. The southern part of Adventurers' Fen remains under agriculture to this day. A similar fate befell the area north of Burwell Lode,[4] some of which lay within the National Trust reserve and included extensive reed-beds (Chapter 11). Since its decommission from war service in 1952, the National Trust land on Adventurers' Fen has been 'reclaimed' in an attempt to regain its ornithological richness (Chapter 9.1). The long-term plans drawn up at the time for a 'marshland reserve' are still being actively pursued today (Chapter 13).

The re-creation of a reed-filled reserve on Adventurers' Fen has not been without its problems. Almost at the outset, tension emerged between two possible aims: managing the area for wildlife on one hand or for the cultivation of a saleable crop on the other. It was soon apparent that some sort of compromise accommodating both of these activities within the nature reserve would be desirable, and the Management Committee has been exercised as to how to achieve a balance ever since. Only very recently has it been possible to reach a satisfactory solution to the problem, the result of fundamental changes in the way the commercial crop is harvested and of a sound appreciation of the needs of the organisms associated with reed-beds.

REED HARVESTING AT WICKEN FEN

Reed has been harvested for centuries for thatching the roofs of buildings. Although it has almost certainly been used in this way at Wicken, as throughout the Fens, for centuries, there is little documentary evidence to support this. Early accounts of the Management Committee show that, from the earliest days of the nature reserve, reed harvesting was a routine activity, but on a rather piecemeal basis. The staff at the time had a programme of regular dyke maintenance using scythes, but clearly took the opportunity to tie up bundles of reed for sale. The Annual Report for 1930/31 states 'the cutting is necessary for the maintenance of the fauna and flora of the Fen; the sales sometimes pay the wages of additional labour, but never more'.[5] It is unclear from these early accounts how frequently a particular dyke was cleared in such a way, but it is unlikely to have been on a strict annual basis.

This fortuitous by-product of ditching was nevertheless seen in a commercial way and concern was expressed following an apparent drop in demand in the late 1930s. This stimulated an investigation into the suitability of reed and sedge as raw material in the making of paper, a common use for these products in parts of eastern Europe today. In 1951 the desire to establish larger areas away from the dykes led to the setting up of an experiment on Sedge Fen Drove to try and establish short strips of pure reed.

Following the excavation of the Mere in 1952 (Chapter 9.1), it was anticipated that reed-swamp would establish quickly in and around it. Subsequent reports document the speed with which this happened, as reeds previously confined to the drainage dykes while the land was under cultivation were allowed to spread across the now wetter open-field system. By 1958, reeds were already being cut in this area, and the following year it seemed to be with disappointment that the inability to cut any on the Mere was reported. It was possible to do this in 1960 but it was done principally to encourage birds.

Concern about the lack of funds available to guarantee the long-term future of the reserve continued to influence the Committee's thinking, especially as it now had grand ideas for the development of the area as a marshland reserve. The Committee's Annual Reports prominently recorded the number of reed bundles sold and even the income gained from this, along with comments about whether this was better or worse than expected. In 1963 the Fen's recently appointed Warden-Naturalist, Charles Mitchell, realizing that the reed crop had considerable commercial potential, suggested that the Committee should regard West Adventurers' Fen as a productive reed-bed, while the area across Harrison's Drove around the Mere should be managed for ornithology and science (see maps, Appendix A). This policy was accepted and largely remains to the present day.

Although it was envisaged that the reed harvest should be no more than a modest contributor to funds (and a means of keeping the staff gainfully employed throughout the year), ways of speeding up the cleaning and tying of cut bundles were actively investigated. A 'Mayfield' cutter was purchased and fitted with a special box attachment to catch the reeds as they were cut. All these efforts were to no avail: yields, and the income generated by the sale of the crop, fluctuated unpredictably. However, an upward trend began to be discernible over the next few years. As Wicken reed became more widely known, demand increased, with the result that prices went up. By the late 1970s the sale of reed was the single largest source of income to the Fen and represented nearly 20 per cent of the total receipts (Fig. 13).

Some of the concerns of twenty years ago were similar to those of today, one of the most important being the control of water-levels on the commercial beds. In unmanaged reed-beds, water-levels follow the natural hydrological cycle, flooding in winter and falling in summer. However, if, as at Wicken Fen, access for men and machines is required during the January–March harvesting period, it is necessary to draw down water-levels in winter and flood the fields in summer. Exposing the ground in winter may improve the quality of the crop provided frosts do not occur late in the spring. Although a proportion of the emerging shoots may be killed, these are replaced by a larger number of new shoots, thus producing a denser and more uniform crop.

Summer flooding creates ideal conditions for rapid growth. In midsummer, a stand of *Phragmites* transpires a prodigious amount of water, equivalent to 1.0–1.5 m of rainfall.[1] Since the total annual rainfall at Wicken rarely exceeds 0.55 m, it is clear that groundwater or standing water must supply the deficit. Summer flooding also prevents the establishment of most other herbs and shrubs, whose roots are less tolerant of water-logging. Flooding of the main reed-beds has so far been achieved by allowing winter water-levels to build up on the Mere side of Harrison's Drove and then allowing water to spill across to the reed-beds immediately after the harvest (Chapter 11).

The sequence of drought years that began in 1987 has demonstrated just how vital water supply is to the production of a good quality reed crop. After only two dry sum-

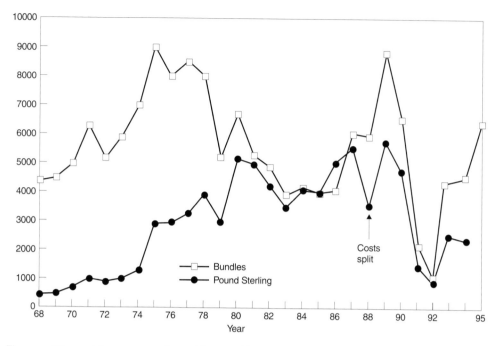

Figure 13   The reed harvest: quantity and income. From 1988 onwards, labour and costs have been split
with a thatcher.

mers and winters, it proved impossible to run water on to the reed-beds after the harvest
and this left the crop of new shoots vulnerable to late frosts. Nettles and willowherb
(*Epilobium* spp.), however, thrived under the drier conditions and effectively suppressed
the regrowth of reed. The resulting crop was poor, thin and full of weeds, and much
of it was of no commercial value. This problem may in future be resolved by running
water directly on to the reed-beds from Wicken Lode in late winter and storing some
of this winter water for release later in the growing season (Chapter 11).

A number of innovations in the cultivation of the reed-beds and the harvesting of
the crop have been introduced at Wicken during the past decade; the practices currently employed are described in Chapter 11. With regard to the reed-bed habitat and
its characteristic species, the most significant changes have resulted from a shift in
emphasis in the Management Committee's policy towards the harvest. As more and
more people visit Wicken, and the income they generate rises, so the sale of crops has
become of lesser importance in the Fen's budget (see Fig. 75). Indeed, commercial
cropping is now scarcely cost-effective, but some continued cropping is likely, if only to
perpetuate this fenland activity. Rather, it is now possible to concentrate on the conservation potential of Adventurers' Fen, and to pursue the aim of creating a wetland
reserve.

CONSERVING THE REED-BED COMMUNITIES

Over the past few years, the Fen staff and Management Committee have been able to evaluate the different techniques of reed-bed management from two apparently opposing viewpoints: commerce and conservation. In its deliberations on the issue, the Trust consulted widely with a number of other individuals and bodies, such as the British Reed Growers Association, the Nature Conservancy Council (now English Nature)[6], the Royal Society for the Protection of Birds (RSPB) and County Wildlife Trusts, all of whom have similar concerns.

The RSPB stands at one end of the spectrum, being in the particularly fortunate position of usually having the freedom to concentrate entirely on nature conservation at its reed-bed sites. On its own reserves, it is often able to raise the water-levels readily to combat succession without incurring prohibitive costs or affecting neighbouring landowners. It may even be feasible to scrape off the ground surface, to bring it down to the water-table. The RSPB has carried out a great deal of research into management techniques,[7] as well as having thoroughly surveyed all British reed-beds larger than two hectares.[8] Some 45 per cent or more of the reed-beds considered in the survey are cut commercially and many of these hold populations of such specialized birds as bitterns (*Botaurus stellaris*), marsh harriers (*Circus aeruginosus*), bearded tits (*Panurus biarmicus*), and Cetti's and reed warblers (*Cettia cetti* and *Acrocephalus scirpaceus*) (see Chapter 9.4). Although it can be argued that reed cutting may adversely affect populations of such birds, it must be acknowledged that many of these sites might, were it not for their commercial value, have been neglected, progressed to scrub and lost their ornithological interest long ago.

The *Phragmites australis* swamp and reed-bed community is rather poor in terms of botanical diversity (which may account in part for the enthusiasm shown for it by ornithologists), while some of Britain's rare and spectacular bird species are reed-bed specialists. It is, therefore, not surprising that the aims of reed-bed management tend to be dominated by ornithological interests. In such circumstances, the general aim would be to perpetuate this otherwise transient phase of fen succession by a programme of cutting and/or burning to prevent succession to scrub, and the close monitoring and manipulation of the water-table.

Two other aspects of commercial harvesting are of particular concern to ornithologists. The first involves its timing: at virtually all sites where reed harvesting takes place, including those where nature conservation is not the primary objective, it is normal to cease cutting by the middle of March. This eliminates disturbance to the birds, all of which breed, or at least establish territories, early in the spring. The recent changes in practice at Wicken Fen (Chapter 11) have created sufficient time and flexibility in the work schedule to ensure that an early finish can be achieved, even if the beginning of the harvest is delayed by bad weather.

The second arises from the artificial lowering of the water-level at a time when it would normally be high; this is likely to be detrimental to bitterns, which are known to favour a constantly high level. This problem has largely been overcome at Wicken by creating areas of permanent open water within the commercial reed-beds. Before the fields were flooded following the harvest in 1989, the entire network of old field-boundaries within the reed-beds was mechanically excavated and a number of completely new spurs dug out into the middle of the field. There is now a longer, deeper and wider network of interconnecting water-bodies within the area of the commercial reed-beds than ever before (Fig. 14). In addition, the resulting spoil now supports bands of reed 3–4m wide on either side of the water that are impossible to cut. These narrow bands, which act rather like hedges, also provide new, more permanent feeding and breeding habitat for bearded tits and reed warblers, as well as breaking up the large fields into smaller units.

The invertebrate communities of reed-beds have until recently tended to be over-looked in management schemes. As with the birds, there are several specialist species which rely on the presence of large stands of *Phragmites*. A suite of flies and hymenopterans, together with their parasites and lodgers, uses the sheltered living space provided by the leaf-base galls of the chloropid fly *Lipara lucens*[9] (Fig. 15). The

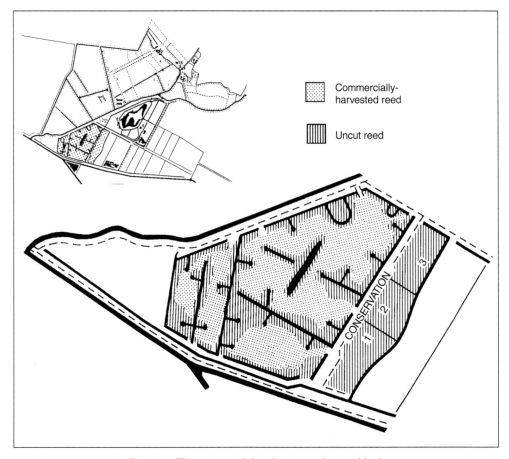

Figure 14 The commercial and conservation reed-beds

Figure 15   The invertebrate community of common reed (*Phragmites australis*)

ON LEAVES
Philudoria potatoria (drinker) L
Mythimna obsoleta (obscure wainscot) L*
M. straminea (southern wainscot) L&P
Senta flammea (flame wainscot) RDB3 L*
Simyra albovenosa (reed dagger) L
Hyalopterus pruni (an aphid)

BLOTCH MINES ON LEAVES
Elachista cerusella (a 'micro') L&P
Cosmopterix drurella (a 'micro') L*
C. lienigiella (a 'micro') L&P*

WITHIN STEMS
Senta flammea P*
Donacaula mucronellus (a 'micro') L&P
Brachmia inornatella (a 'micro') L*&P
Mythimna obsoleta P
Archanara geminipunctata (twin-spotted wainscot) L&P*
A. dissoluta (brown-veined wainscot) L&P*
Arenostola phragmitidis (fen wainscot, 'reed bug') L*
Chilodes maritimus (silky wainscot, feeds on *Arenostola*) L*
Phragmataecia castaneae (reed leopard) RDB2 L&P*
Lasioptera flexuosa (a cecidomyid)
Pimpla sp. (ichneumonid parasite of *Lasioptera*)*

IN BASE OF STEMS
Schoenobius gigantella (a 'micro') L&P
Donacaula mucronellus L&P
Rhizedra lutosa (large wainscot) L*
Chilo phragmitella (a 'micro') L&P*

IN ROLLED SHOOTS
Schoenobius forficella (a 'micro') L&P

IN LITTER/ON THE GROUND
Mythimna pudorina (striped wainscot) L&P
M. straminea P
Rhizedra lutosa P*
Arenostola phragmitidis P*
Simyra albovenosa P
Cosmopterix drurella P*

IN RHIZOME
Rhizedra lutosa L*

IN ROOTSTOCK
Chilo phragmitella L*

IN LITTER UNDERWATER
No invertebrates are known to be specific to reed litter, but more than 30 spp. have been identified as being involved in the breakdown of reed litter at Wicken Fen.[10]

gall of *Lipara lucens*

IN *LIPARA* GALLS
Lipara lucens (a chloropid fly)*
L. rufitarsis (a chloropid)
L. similis (a chloropid) RDB2*
Polemochartus liparae (braconid parasite of *Lipara*)*
Stenomalina liparae (chalcid parasite of *Lipara*)*
Scambus phragmitidis (ichneumonid parasite of *Lipara*)*
Cryptonevra consimilis (chloropid in gall of *L. similis*) RDB2*
Cecidomyid flies
Hylaeus pectoralis (a solitary bee)
Passaloecus clypealis (aphid-hunting solitary wasp)
Chrysis spp. (ruby-tailed wasps)

* found only on *Phragmites*: L, as larvae; P, as pupa

larvae and pupae of several species of wainscot moths live entirely on or within the stems, leaves and rhizomes of reed. The larvae of the rare reed leopard (*Phragmataecia castaneae*) (Plate 6, Fig. 2) overwinter twice within their feeding galleries in hollow reed-stems, before emerging in their third year. The adults of these moth species often do not fly far from their place of emergence.

All these insects, whether feeding on live plant material or among the accumulation of dead and decaying stems, provide a rich food source for the birds. On the other hand, some of the stem-borers, if they reach very large numbers, can be serious pests of commercial reed-beds[10]. The Fen wainscot (*Arenostola phragmitidis*) has been suffi-ciently troublesome in some reed-growing areas to earn itself the disparaging epithet of 'reed bug'. It seems that Wicken has an especially rich diversity of reed-dwellers.[11]

In determining the management strategy of a particular reed-bed the insect popu-lations within it certainly need to be taken into account. Some recent data from Hickling Broad in Norfolk show that ground-living and reed-dwelling invertebrate communities are certainly affected by removal of reed by either cropping or burning, although little difference was found in the assemblages surviving the two treatments.[12] However, for some species that lay their eggs very low down on reed stems, cutting is likely to be less detrimental than burning. Flooding will not harm those species that pass their whole life-cycle on the reed stems and leaves, but those pupating in the soil are likely to be adversely affected by inundation at the critical time of year.

Clearly, if the whole of a site containing one or other of these specialized organisms were to be cut it would be disastrous. In practice it is unlikely that more than half of a site would produce reeds suitable for thatching. At Wicken Fen, approximately 7.5ha of reed out of a total area on Adventurers' Fen of 34ha are cut commercially as 'single wale', that is, on an annual basis. This limited harvesting has a number of ecological benefits: first, it checks the rate of natural succession to scrub; secondly, it adds diver-sity and age structure to the stands of reed; and thirdly, it provides suitable breeding habitat for certain birds such as snipe and redshank. To these should be added the per-petuation of a traditional rural industry: Wicken Fen is the only site in Cambridgeshire where reeds are harvested and the only National Trust site in the country where the property staff are themselves involved in the operation. The role that Wicken Fen can play in conserving and illuminating the social history of Fenland is gradually emerg-ing and has been greatly strengthened by the restoration of the 'Fen cottage' (See Plate 16) which is thatched with Wicken reed (Chapter 12).

With regard to the ecological system of which *Phragmites* is a part, the regular har-vesting of reed stems can represent a considerable loss of nutrients. Sylvia Haslam[1] gives figures for the annual loss of plant nutrients in single wale harvesting of one hectare as including 16–42 kg nitrogen, 0.8–3.0 kg phosphate and 4–15 kg potassium. This is in spite of the fact that reed efficiently reclaims nutrients from the dying stand-ing crop and diverts them into the rhizomes at the onset of winter. At Wicken Fen, as at most sites, this annual loss is probably made up by inputs from drainage water and from commuting wildfowl. From an entirely different viewpoint, however, this export of nutrients from the Fen to the roofs of village homes throughout the county may be beneficial in offsetting the steady input of agricultural nutrients to the Fen's major water-bodies (Chapter 3). Indeed, the nutrient-absorbing capacity of *Phragmites* has become a subject of considerable interest in the water-treatment industry in recent years: reed-beds may in future play a role in cleansing the effluent from sewage works in rural areas of Britain, as they already do in parts of Europe.

In order to increase the area of reed-bed habitat for birds, and to provide areas that were not subject to commercial harvesting, a 'conservation reed-bed' (Fig. 14) was established in 1971 adjacent to the main cropping site. Uncut reed-beds afford a quite different habitat from annually cut beds, because of the mixed ages of the standing stems and the accumulation of litter on the ground.[13] The litter layer, of fallen culms and decomposing leaves, provides a valuable resource for nesting birds and an important habitat for invertebrates. Decomposing leaves are a primary source of food in both the terrestrial and aquatic food webs of reed-beds, and many of the moths associated with reed pupate on the ground (Fig. 15). The litter creates a pocket of still air close to the ground in which temperature fluctuations are smaller than on bare ground and which protects invertebrates (as well as emerging reed shoots) from frost.

Uncut reed-beds are, however, vulnerable to bush encroachment. If *Salix* seedlings are able to establish themselves, the saplings prove quite resistant to summer flooding. Limited bush growth is tolerated in some areas of Wicken's commercial reed-bed, but it is controlled by occasional cutting and by (rather infrequent) burning. Although a very quick and effective way of clearing a field of weeds, burning removes the litter layer and destroys invertebrate populations. For this reason, only small areas are treated at a time, and on a long cycle. The conservation reed-bed has been divided into three roughly equal blocks and, every other year, one of these has been burned in turn (Fig. 14). That is, each block is subject to a six-year burning cycle. This programme would allow even the reed leopard, with its three-year life-cycle, to raise a new generation every year on most of the conservation area. After twenty-five years, however, this regime is to be reassessed because of the very poor quality of reed on the site. More frequent burning, together with increased water supply, should help to restore a more uniform *Phragmites* swamp.

Fire is an indispensible part of reed-bed management at Wicken Fen, so it is fortunate that this type of limited, controlled burning for conservation purposes has not been prevented by legislation, which came into force in 1993, to control the disposal of arable residues by burning.

AN EXPANDING HABITAT

In the near future, it is hoped that the reed-beds of Adventurers' Fen can be extended eastwards across the southern boundary of the reserve (Chapter 13). It is therefore appropriate to ask how decades of changes in practice and policy on the reed-beds have affected the resident species, and whether current management appears to be successful. This question is probably best addressed by looking at the effects on key species. It would be difficult to do this for the insects because there are few quantitative data covering the period of change with which to compare any new figures. More, however, is known about the birds.

It would appear that, prior to the wartime drainage of Adventurers' Fen as a whole, bitterns (*Botaurus stellaris*) regularly nested in what must have been an ideal habitat for them. Because of their specific requirements, habitat changes, possibly coupled with the effects of pesticides, have left them at very low numbers in Britain today (Chapter 9.4). The winter visitors that are recorded nearly annually in the Wicken reed-beds are almost certainly continental birds escaping the harsher conditions of the mainland winter, as they invariably depart again during February. It is hoped that enlarged reed-beds, higher water-levels and the new stretches of water hidden within the fields will prove beneficial to them.

Marsh harriers (*Circus aeruginosus*) have bred successfully on several occasions on the Fen in recent years. There is evidently no shortage of food: four chicks were fledged in both 1981 and 1985 and six in 1995, and the surrounding farmland supports several hen harriers (*Circus cyaneus*) in most winters. Generally wetter conditions and more broken-up fields should add extra security that might induce nesting on a regular basis in the near future. Disturbance from people walking on the exposed public footpaths is more likely to prove a limiting factor. Marsh harriers are doing well in Britain at present (Chapter 9.4), so the recent establishment of at least one pair has not been unexpected.

Bearded tits (*Panurus biarmicus*) have wintered regularly at Wicken Fen since 1959. They almost certainly bred in 1980, when a pair summered, and certainly did so in 1983. Numbers have fluctuated but have increased to a maximum of five pairs, suggesting that the species has now established itself as a true resident. The network of new linear waterways within the reed-beds should prove increasingly attractive as several seasons of growth die back and accumulate as a permanent litter layer. The dividing-up of the large commercial fields and the provision of a number of safe havens should also be beneficial. It is possible that bearded tits are able to survive here only because of the reed-harvest. The birds are largely dependent on a diet of reed seeds during the winter. From casual observations it is obvious how many more inflorescences there are in areas that were cut the previous winter compared with the uncut areas. If cutting were to cease, this food resource might cease to be sufficient to support a large wintering population or to provide enough energy to bring birds into breeding condition.

Reed warblers (*Acrocephalus scirpaceus*) are already the commonest breeding bird on the reserve (Chapter 9.2) and many pairs have long had to resort to breeding in apparently less favourable areas. They have already colonized the new excavations of the reed fields and now breed along the new 'hedges' right in the heart of the reed-beds. Wicken Fen is also eminently suitable for Cetti's warblers (*Cettia cetti*), as successful colonization and breeding in the early 1980s has shown. However, the species is on the edge of its range in this country and the severity of future winters is likely to be more important than habitat quality in determining the success or otherwise of any future attempt permanently to establish itself here.

This account has concentrated almost entirely on Adventurers' Fen, but there are growing areas of reed on the Sedge Fen. At the far end of that part known as Verrall's Fen recent changes in the water-table have completely altered the vegetation. Only ten years ago, it was an almost impenetrable tangle of windblown scrub. As a result of the waterproofing of Howe's Bank (Chapter 11) and the creation of open water at a constant level on all sides, the area is being transformed into 14ha of quaking swamp. *Phragmites* is reasserting itself, and showing signs of dominating the area, just as it did at the turn of the century.[14] Hidden among the reed and drowned bushes are numerous small permanent pools of water already frequented by grebes and ducks and alight with the flowers of aquatic plants. The scene is powerfully reminiscent of those on Adventurers' Fen as it reverted to swamp after the First World War:

'bushes were dying out and the reeds slowly strangling all lower growth.... The water-weeds spread from the ditches as fast as the reeds. In a few seasons sheets of water were covered yellow and white...'[15]

References

1 Haslam (1972)
2 Ennion (1949), p. 95
3 Ennion (1942, fig. 59)
4 Bloom (1944)
5 Wicken Fen Executive Committee Minute Book in archive
6 Rowell (1988a)
7 Burgess & Evans (1988)
8 Bibby & Lunn (1982)
9 Salt (1947)
10 Polunin (1979)
11 D. Clements, thesis in preparation
12 Ditlhogo *et al.* (1992)
13 Cowie *et al.* (1992)
14 Wallis (1904)
15 Ennion (1949), p. 68

5

SEDGE, LITTER AND DROVES

L. E. FRIDAY AND H. J. HARVEY

IN WINTER, the herbaceous vegetation of the Sedge Fen appears rather uniform, with only the tall pale ranks of reed and the short green swards of the
droves to dissect the rough dull brown grassland. From April to September,
however, the fen fields become a kaleidoscope of different colours and textures, as
grasses, sedges and dicotyledons go through their flowering cycles. Such patchy diversity presents a challenge to the tidy minds of ecologists who might wish to classify the
various types of fen herbaceous vegetation.

Perhaps the first attempt to provide an ecological classification of the Fen's vegetation was made by Wallis in the *The Flora of the Cambridge District* of 1904.[1] Wallis lists
some of the more important species found respectively in the dry and damp parts of
the Fen (Table III).

R. H. Yapp, writing in 1908, realized that this polarization of species into 'dry' or
'damp' did not take into account the spectrum of plant distributions that he had
observed in fenland. He noted that 'all kinds of plants intermediate between' wet and
dry occur, and attempted to produce a list (Table IV) placing 'some of the commoner

Table III. Wallis' table of plant species found in 'dry' and 'damp' conditions.[1]
Current synonyms are given in square brackets

Dry	Damp
Cladium	*Phragmites*
Molinia	*Thalictrum flavum*
Rhamnus catharticus [cathartica]	*Lathyrus palustris*
Frangula alnus	*Convolvulus [Calystegia] sepium*
Salix sp.	*Caltha palustris*
Cnicus pratensis [Cirsium dissectum]	*Lastrea thelypteris [Thelypteris palustris]*
Peucedanum	
Calamagrostis epigejos	
Potentilla sylvestris [P. erecta]	

Table IV. Part of Yapp's table[2]

Wet marsh plants
- *Phragmites communis [australis]*
- *Juncus obtusiflorus [subnodulosus]*
- 'many of the carices'; *[Dactylorchis] incarnata*; *Caltha palustris*; *Menyanthes trifoliata*.

Intermediate forms
- *'Lastrea thelypteris'*; *Iris pseudacorus*; *Thalictrum flavum*; *Lathyrus palustris*; *Lythrum salicaria*; *Oenanthe lachenalii*; *Hydrocotyle vulgaris*; *Lysimachia vulgaris*; *Mentha aquatica*; *Galium palustre*; etc.
- *Ophioglossum vulgatum*; *Calamagrostris epigejos*; *Agrostis canina [?stolonifera]*; *Potentilla sylvestris*; *Angelica sylvestris*; *Valeriana dioica*; *V. officinalis*; *Scabiosa succisa [Succisa pratensis]*; *Carduus pratensis [Cirsium dissectum]*; etc.

Dry marsh forms
- *Molinia caerulea*; *Aira [Deschampsia] caespitosa*; *Peucedamum palustre*; *Convolvulus sepium*
- *Spiraea [Filipendula] ulmaria*; *Symphytum officinale*; *Eupatorium cannabinum*.

marsh plants approximately in order, with respect to the degree of soil moisture which would seem to be the optimum'.[2]

He also pointed out the many irregularities in the surface of the Fen that produce local differences in the relative heights of soil and water: towards the end of July, the elevated patches of the Fen, including the raised margins of the ditches, were easily recognizable from a distance by the masses of flowering meadowsweet (*Filipendula ulmaria*). Later in the year, these 'islands' were marked by flowers of hemp-agrimony (*Eupatorium cannabinum*).

Yapp demonstrated, by a series of field observations and experiments, that the amount of soil moisture available exerts 'a profound influence on the distribution of the Fen plants'. Marsh plants generally have creeping subterranean stolons and rhizomes that form a tangled mass just below the surface of the fen soil. Yapp noted that the underground parts of 'wet-marsh' species adjust their position according to the state of the soil: in wet areas, the rhizomes are near the surface, in dry areas, they may lie at some depth. He suggested that 'wet' plants can invade dry areas by 'undermining' them, but that 'dry' plants are less able to cope with the conditions found in wetter areas. Thus the wet parts of the Fen are occupied by 'wet plants', the dry areas chiefly, but not exclusively, by 'dry plants' and the 'intermediate' areas by a complex mixture of species.

He was also struck by the stratification of the aerial parts of different species, creating dense stands of vegetation with flower-spikes of reed and sedge projecting above a canopy of leaves and inflorescences of diverse species, a middle layer of grasses and the leaves of taller species, a dwarf herb layer and finally ground-dwelling species such as mosses.[3] Using extremely simple but innovative instrumentation, he measured the temperature and the rate of evaporation of free water (such as would occur from the leaves of plants receiving an abundant supply of water) at different heights above the ground in two different types of herbaceous vegetation (Fig. 16).

Yapp was able to show that plants growing in different strata are subject to quite different physical conditions: a tall plant, such as reed, in the 'canopy' experiences far greater ranges of temperature and air movement and may lose about 40 times more water than a ground-hugging species, such as marsh pennywort (*Hydrocotyle vulgaris*). Both species are rooted in the same ground, with the same relationship between land- and water-level, yet they sustain quite different water demands. Clearly, the water relations of two species grouped together in Yapp's original classification of 'wet' and 'dry'

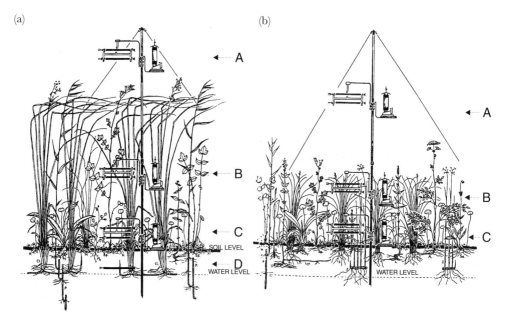

Figure 16 Yapp's measurement of temperature and evaporation rates at different heights in (a) 'mixed sedge' and (b) 'litter'.[3] The sampling heights (**A–D**) are approximately 140, 65, 13 and –15cm in (a) and 105, 50 and 15cm in (b).

marsh plants may be quite different. The explanation lies partly in the depth at which their roots develop: Yapp's diagram shows the stratification of roots below stands of mixed herbaceous vegetation, with the roots of the taller species spreading along the line of the water table, and the shorter species rooting near the soil surface. So there may be wide variation in the rooting environment, as well as the aerial microclimate, of species on the same plot. This, together with the hydrological characteristics of the Fen, helps to explain why no healthy plant on the Fen is seen to wilt, even at the height of summer.

Yapp adopted the local terms 'sedge' and 'litter' to describe the major types of herbaceous vegetation on the Fen, although he noted that 'a definite mapping of the different plant associations represented here would be a difficult, if not an impossible, task'. He applied the term 'sedge' to vegetation dominated by great fen-sedge, or 'saw sedge', (*Cladium mariscus*) and cropped once every four years, and the term 'litter' to a more diverse vegetation cut about once in two years.

In the 1920s, Godwin further refined the classification of the Fen's vegetation.[4] He distinguished two communities of 'sedge': 'pure sedge' (rather scarce at Wicken Fen), a virtually impenetrable stand with few species other than *Cladium*, and 'mixed sedge', containing a range of other species (Fig. 16). 'Litter' was defined by Godwin by three criteria: the presence of large amounts of purple moor-grass (*Molinia caerulea*), the presence of a large number of dicotyledonous species and the absence, or virtual absence, of *Cladium*. He also recognized the vegetation of the tracks and paths as a distinct 'drove' community. Godwin's vegetation types are clearly defined, but, as he conceded, 'the confusion with which [they] are intermingled can hardly be appreciated by anyone unfamiliar with the Fen'.[5]

For the past thirty or forty years, descriptions of the vegetation of the Fen have recognized three major herbaceous plant communities: 'sedge', 'litter' and 'droves' (Plate 2, Figs 1–3). The distinction made by Godwin between 'pure sedge' and 'mixed sedge' tends to have been ignored and the term 'litter' used in a much wider sense than by Godwin. All tall grass-dominated areas now tend to be known as 'litter', although only a small proportion is now dominated by purple moor-grass; in the remainder, purple small-reed (*Calamagrostis canescens*), wood small-reed (*C. epigejos*) or reed canary-grass (*Phalaris arundinacea*) are the principal grass species.

Such nomenclatural difficulties are very likely to arise in spatially complex habitats, but, at Wicken Fen, the situation is further complicated by the management of the vegetation. 'Sedge' and 'litter' are distinct traditional crops at Wicken (see Chapter 10), and the vegetation of the areas from which they have been (and are) taken may reasonably be referred to by these same functional terms, regardless of the fine details of their species composition. Similarly, the floristically distinct 'drove' communities are defined by the particular management technique of mowing access routes through the Fen, and, as such, their geographical location tends to be maintained more precisely and more independently of local conditions than those of the other herbaceous communities.

Is there a ready solution to this problem of classification? In the past few years, it has become possible to compare the vegetation variants seen at Wicken Fen with those in other parts of the country. The National Vegetation Classification (NVC) scheme[6,7,8,9] provides a framework into which we can attempt to fit the Fen's vegetation types, objectively define our terminology, and see how (and why) Wicken Fen differs from other sites (Table V). The Fen's herbaceous vegetation falls within the broad category of 'Swamps and Tall Herb Fens',[9] but precise allocation to NVC sub-communities is hampered by a lack of recent quantitative data from Wicken Fen.

SEDGE

Cladium mariscus is one of the largest and most conspicuous members of the sedge family. Its pleated leaves with their murderously serrated margins and the dense panicle of brown flowers on stems up to 2m tall are easily identified amongst the taller-growing vegetation on the Fen. The species has been a mainstay of the local thatching industry over many centuries (Chapter 10) and has long been a traditional crop at Wicken. It gained another particular association with the Fen during the 1930s when Verona Conway carried out detailed studies on the ecology of *Cladium* at Wicken. The results are published in a series of articles in the *New Phytologist* between 1936 and 1938.[10,11,12,13,14]

The plant is aquatic in the sense that it flourishes best where its roots are below the level of the water-table. Like other emergent plant species, such as reed, its tissues show a very high proportion of air spaces: Conway[12] showed that *Cladium* rhizomes are 38 per cent by volume air space, and the roots 60 per cent. Because these air spaces are confluent with spaces in the shoots, oxygen can diffuse down from the atmosphere into the submerged parts and the plant is therefore virtually independent of the low-oxygen conditions that can arise in wet soils.

Godwin & Bharucha[15] show *Cladium* occupying the wetter positions in the stages of succession. There is every reason to suppose that, due to falling water-levels, succession and other changes, pure sedge is even less abundant now than in the 1920s. However, there are some fairly extensive areas approximating to pure sedge on the Fen, and it seems even to have increased in certain situations. The largest blocks are in Wicken Poor's Fen, lying between Monks Lode and Wicken Lode, and Common Fen, lying between Sedge Fen Drove and Gardiner's Drove towards the eastern end of the Fen (see map, Appendix A). Both of these areas were probably amongst the last on the Fen dug for peat. In the 1920s, Godwin[4] noted the Common Fen was one of the best litter areas on the Fen, but the purple moor-grass has now been replaced by sedge, a reversal of the expected successional trend and perhaps linked to changes in the cropping regime (see below).

Sedge may also have increased on Adventurers' Fen where it occurs around the old brick pits at the junction of Harrison's Drove and Wicken Lode. Evans[16] knew of no *Cladium* on Adventurers' Fen in the 1920s, although in 1939 he reported finding two clumps there at an earlier, but unspecified, date. Small isolated patches of pure sedge survived amongst dense scrub on Verrall's Fen in the late 1970s and are likely still to be

Table V. Possible equivalents between Wicken communities and National Vegetation Classification (NVC) communities[6,7,8,9]

Wicken community	Possible NVC equivalent
Floating-leaved aquatics	*Lemna minor* floating mats (A2):
	L. trisulca–Riccia–Ricciocarpos sub-communities
Submerged aquatics	*Nuphar lutea* community:
	(species-poor sub-community A8a)
	Ceratophyllum demersum pools (A5)
	?*Potamogeton pectinatus–Myriophyllum spicatum* community (A11)
Emergent aquatics	*Typha latifolia* (S12) and *T. angustifolia* (S13) swamp
Reed swamp	*Phragmites australis* swamp (S4)
Pure sedge	*Cladium mariscus* sedge swamp (S2)
Mixed sedge	*Phragmites australis–Peucedanum palustre* fen (S24):
	Symphytum officinale sub-community
Grass dominated communities (Litter)	
Calamagrostis dominant	*Phragmites australis–Peucedanum palustre* fen (S24):
	Symphytum officinale sub-community
Mixed sedge to litter transition	*Molinia caerulea–Cirsium dissectum* fen meadow (M24):
	Eupatorium cannabinum sub-community
Molinia dominant	*Molinia caerulea–Cirsium dissectum* fen meadow:
	Typical sub-community
Droves	*Juncus subnodulosus–Cirsium palustre* fen meadow (M22):
	Typical sub-community
	Briza media–Trifolium species sub-community
Fen Carr	*Salix cinerea–Betula pubescens–Phragmites australis* woodland (W2):
	Alnus glutinosa–Filipendula ulmaria sub-community
	?*Sphagnum* sub-community
Hawthorn scrub	*Crataegus monogyna–Hedera helix* scrub

present. One characteristic common to all the areas described above is that they have not been cut for many years. This situation favours dominance by sedge and seems to result in only slow colonization by woody species.

The maintenance of *Cladium* as the principal component of the vegetation relies on informed management, because the effects of cutting at different seasons and with different frequencies depend crucially on the growth characteristics of the dominant plant. *Cladium* grows from two zones of cell division: the root tips and the bases of the shoots. The region that produces the aerial parts lies several centimetres below the ground (Fig. 17), which effectively protects it from frost. Conway showed that this growing point is frost-sensitive, but that the temperature in the peat at the level of the rhizome rarely, if ever, falls below freezing[11] (Fig. 18).

However, the young aerial shoots remain frost-sensitive until about 15cm tall,[14] so cutting late in the year makes the regrowth vulnerable to frost. Cutting also severs the air channels leading down into the underground parts, which can then 'drown' if the plant is overtaken by prolonged winter flooding. *Cladium* leaves are perennial, remaining green for two or three years, so that annual cutting severely weakens the plant. These observations have guided present management policies for sedge at Wicken (Chapter 11).

Cladium is a slow-growing species that, under the right conditions, can form very dense growths, often to the exclusion of other species. One square metre of mixed sedge may yield 1.4 kg of dry dead material in comparison with 1.2 kg dry mass of living material; the amount of dead matter lying in pure sedge would be even greater.[5] This dead-leaf mattress can present a considerable fire risk, providing kindling for the green sedge and small bushes. The devastating effect of such a fire was felt when, on 15 August 1929, fire tore through the area between Wicken Lode and Sedge Fen Drove[17] (Fig. 19). An earlier conflagration, started accidentally by his own admission by the entomologist David Sharp, led Gardiner[18] to declare the careless smoker to be the greatest threat to the Fen.

The mattress formed by sedge may exert a considerable influence in suppressing other species, so that *Cladium* may achieve dominance 'by means rather of the dead than the living parts' of the plant.[19] Godwin[4] predicted that periodic cutting would open up a sedge-dominated community to create a greater admixture of more rapidly-growing species. Curiously, some of the fields cut intensively as litter over the

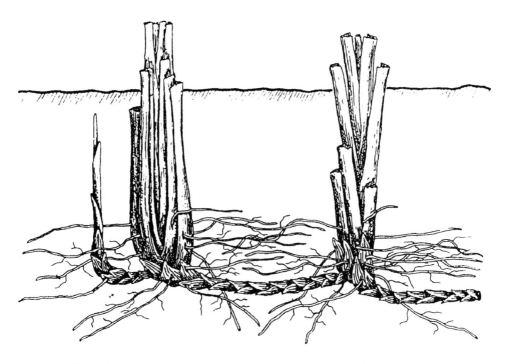

Figure 17   Yapp's figure of great fen-sedge (*Cladium mariscus*) 'in moderately damp soil (September)'[2]

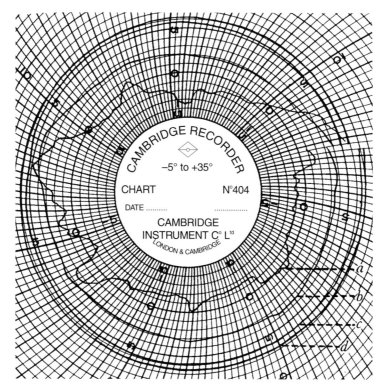

Figure 18 Conway's temperature measurements for 7–14 January 1935:[11]
(a) 5 cm above soil surface; (b) in the soil surface; (c) 15 cm below; and
(d) 30 cm below soil surface

past two decades have shown a considerable increase in abundance of *Cladium*;
whether this is linked to the cutting regime is doubtful. Rather, the recent increase in
wetness may be responsible (see below).

MIXED SEDGE – 'EXPERIMENTS IN CROP-TAKING'

'Mixed sedge' is probably the most extensive herbaceous community to be found on
the Fen. This tall-growing community is the 'sedge' described by Yapp in his study of
plant/water relations.[3] It is usually dominated by monocotyledons, with common reed
(*Phragmites australis*) and purple small-reed (*Calamagrostis canescens*) as well as sedge. It is
also rich in tall dicotyledons, such as yellow loosestrife (*Lysimachia vulgaris*), purple
loosestrife (*Lythrum salicaria*), hemp-agrimony (*Eupatorium cannabinum*), meadowsweet
(*Filipendula ulmaria*) and, in some places, milk-parsley (*Peucedanum palustre*). Sedges and
rushes, such as blunt-flowered rush (*Juncus subnodulosus*) generally form a conspicuous
understorey, in which purple moor-grass, marsh pennywort (*Hydrocotyle vulgaris*) and
marsh fern (*Thelypteris palustris*) may also be abundant.

Figure 19 The aftermath of the Fen fire, 25 August 1929

A particular type of 'mixed sedge' community, with abundant common comfrey (*Symphytum officinale*), seems to be characteristic of the Fenland basin (see Table V). This vegetation is found at both Wicken and Woodwalton Fens, but Wicken is distinguished by the abundance of fen bedstraw (*Galium uliginosum*). The Cambridgeshire vegetation type also differs from the 'typical' *Symphytum officinale* sub-community, found extensively under similar management on peat soils in the Norfolk Broads, in having common meadow-rue (*Thalictrum flavum*), but lacking several species such as cowbane (*Cicuta virosa*). Comfrey (Plate 3, Fig. 2) is one of a number of the 'mixed sedge' dicotyledons that prove irresistible to insects, providing a rich supply of nectar and pollen over the summer months (Chapter 8).

Yapp's work[3] contains the germ of a suggestion that cutting might be a factor capable of converting sedge into litter. It was clearly evident that cutting frequency influenced both the species composition of the vegetation and the entomological interest it produced: 'two and three year sedge' could confidently be recommended as the best hunting ground for 'micromoths'.[20] Godwin saw crop-taking as a powerful influence that might 'deflect' the normal hydroseral succession towards alternative vegetation end-points.[4] He investigated this idea in research projects on the Fen that began in the summer of 1927, with the fencing off of two strips, one parallel with the north end of

Drainers' Dyke in a uniform area of 'mixed sedge' and the other south of Sedge Fen Drove in rather less uniform 'litter'.

Each strip was divided into five plots, each 20m square and subject to different cutting regimes: one was cut every year, another every second, another every third, another every fourth year, and one left uncut. The cutting was carried out in October (in line with the practice at the time on the Fen), and the cuttings removed. Changes in the species composition of the vegetation of permanent quadrats in each plot were monitored at the time of each cutting over a period of 12 years.

The results from the first twelve years of monitoring the 'Godwin Plots' demonstrated a clear transition from the *Cladium* and *Molinia* 'mixed sedge' to a *Molinia*-dominated, herb-rich 'litter' under an annual cropping regime, with severe suppression of *Cladium* within a few years[21] (Fig. 20). Other tall-growing species typical of 'mixed sedge', such as hemp-agrimony and milk-parsley, also declined under frequent cutting, being replaced by lower-growing 'litter' species. The plots of mixed sedge cut at two- and three-year intervals seemed to be 'transitional' in their composition, with elements of both ends of the spectrum. The plots in 'litter' showed relatively little change under the different cutting cycles: the species list of the annually-cut was slightly longer than for the 2- and 3-year plots, but there was no obvious sign of *Cladium* becoming established under the 4-year regime. The area left uncut over the twelve years demonstrated a further loss of species, and *Cladium* became abundant,

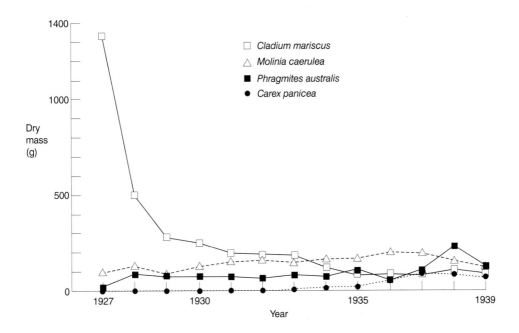

Figure 20 Changes in the composition of the vegetation in the annually-cut 'mixed sedge' plot as revealed by the dry mass of the four dominant monocotyledonous species harvested each year 1927–1939[21]

although there was some indication that these clumps might have arisen from plants already present in the plot in 1927 and had not necessarily become established after cropping ceased.

The slowness of *Cladium* in reinvading and establishing itself when the mowing regime is relaxed is very striking. By a series of experiments in which he sowed *Cladium* seeds and transplanted seedlings into stands of mixed sedge of different ages, Rowell[22] was able to show that long cropping-cycles apparently produce conditions which are inimical to the seeds and seedlings of the dominant species: no seedlings, whether from sown seed or transplanted, survived in four-year-old 'sedge', while 18.8 per cent of seedlings from sown seeds and 80 per cent of transplanted seedlings survived in one-year-old 'sedge'.

Godwin's observations ended in 1940 and the plots were left uncut. However, in 1955, the experiment was revived by D. E. Coombe, using only the 'mixed sedge' plots, as part of a field study for final-year Botany students in the University of Cambridge. The 'uncut' plot was left untouched but the four 'mown' plots were cleared of the alder buckthorn (*Frangula alnus*) that had thoroughly invaded the site and the cutting cycles of 1, 2, 3 or 4 years were reinstated. From 1955 to 1982, the five plots were surveyed by successive cohorts of students, producing a fascinating set of data relating vegetation changes to mowing regime (Fig. 21).

The fifteen years of neglect had caused the vegetation of the five plots to converge as woody and herbaceous invaders established themselves, although the legacy of the previous treatments could still be discerned in the presence of 'litter' species, such as devil's-bit scabious (*Succisa pratensis*), and the scarcity of *Cladium*, in the annual plot.

From 1940 onwards, the uncut plot had become increasingly dominated by *Frangula*, in step with other areas of the Fen subjected to increasing groundwater deficit (Chapter 2). The *Frangula* developed into a dense thicket, but during the 1960s the individual trees became overmature and the canopy became more open. A wide range of woody species, such as bittersweet (*Solanum dulcamara*), downy birch (*Betula pubescens*) and brambles (*Rubus* spp.) became established, together with an understorey dominated by grasses (*Calamagrostis canescens* and *Phalaris arundinacea*) and common nettle (*Urtica dioica*). The two species of small-reed, *Calamagrostis canescens* and *C. epigejos*, show striking changes in abundance: neither species was represented in any of Godwin's 1940 plots, but both had invaded most plots by 1955, mirroring a general pattern over the Fen as a whole (Chapter 7). The two species show, however, completely different responses to the resumption of mowing: *C. canescens* flourished in the uncut plot and decreased in abundance with frequency of mowing, while *C. epigejos* was scarce in the scrub and abundant in the mown plots.

Over the 27 years of observation since 1955, the vegetation of the five experimental plots diverged widely. The decline of *Cladium* in the frequently-mown plots is very striking, as is the development of a distinctive assemblage of species in these plots. The reconstituted 'litter' vegetation is characterized by abundant meadowsweet, marsh thistle (*Cirsium palustre*) and yellow loosestrife and includes some species virtually confined to the annual and biennial plots, such as devil's-bit scabious, early marsh-orchid

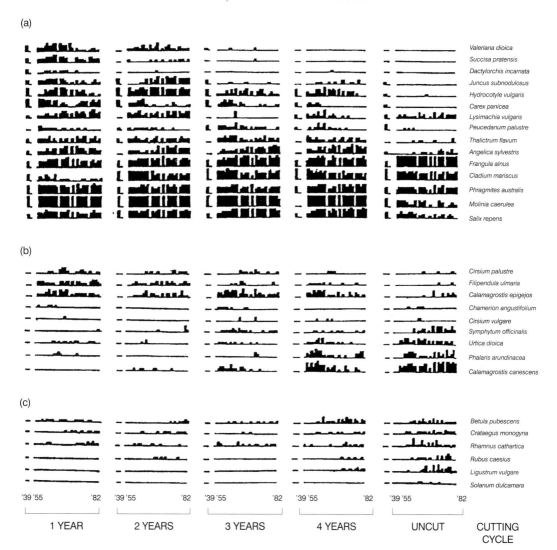

(a)

Valeriana dioica
Succisa pratensis
Dactylorchis incarnata
Juncus subnodulosus
Hydrocotyle vulgaris
Carex panicea
Lysimachia vulgaris
Peucedanum palustre
Thalictrum flavum
Angelica sylvestris
Frangula alnus
Cladium mariscus
Phragmites australis
Molinia caerulea
Salix repens

(b)

Cirsium palustre
Filipendula ulmaria
Calamagrostis epigejos
Chamerion angustifolium
Cirsium vulgare
Symphytum officinalis
Urtica dioica
Phalaris arundinacea
Calamagrostis canescens

(c)

Betula pubescens
Crataegus monogyna
Rhamnus cathartica
Rubus caesius
Ligustrum vulgare
Solanum dulcamara

| '39 '55 '82 | '39 '55 '82 | '39 '55 '82 | '39 '55 '82 | '39 '55 '82 | |
| 1 YEAR | 2 YEARS | 3 YEARS | 4 YEARS | UNCUT | CUTTING CYCLE |

Figure 21 Changes in the vegetation of the Godwin plots 1955–1982[23]

(a) species present in at least one of the plots in 1939 and showing response to cutting regime;
(b) herbaceous species invading since 1939; (c) woody species invading since 1939
The relative abundance in each year of the thirty most abundant species is scored on a scale of 5 (corresponding to 'dominant' in the DAFOR scale†) to 1 ('rare'). The short bar preceding the main axes denotes the year 1939 (data from Godwin).[21] The frequency of cutting the plots decreases from the left to the right.

† Dominant, Abundant, Frequent, Occasional, Rare

(*Dactylorchis incarnata*) and marsh valerian (*Valeriana dioica*). The litter of 1955–82 is, however, substantially different from the original vegetation of the 'litter' plots of 1929:[21] the consequences of 15 years of neglect are still apparent in the persistence of abundant *Frangula* and occasional specimens of other woody species, such as hawthorn (*Crataegus monogyna*) and purging buckthorn (*Rhamnus cathartica*).

In addition to the trends clearly associated with mowing frequency there is another, more subtle, pattern in the data: all five plots underwent a period of relatively rapid change in the composition of the vegetation from about 1962, but then settled into a new assemblage from about 1968. Some individual species declined through the late 1950s to recover during the 1960s and 1970s (such as blunt-flowered rush (*Juncus subnodulosus*)) while other species (marsh pennywort and marsh valerian) exhibited the opposite behaviour. On the plots cut every third and fourth years, these trends were accompanied by a rise in species richness in the early 1960s followed by a gradual decline throughout the 1970s. The annual and biennial plots, by contrast, showed a steady slight increase in numbers of species from 1955 to 1982. In every case, the composition of the vegetation was quite different in 1982 from that seen in 1955, or even in 1940.[23]

Do the patterns of diversity and of abundance of individual species seen in the new experiment simply reflect the evolution of the sward under the renewed mowing regimes, or should other factors be invoked? Two other ecological changes that occurred in the vicinity of the plots during the 1960s might be implicated. First, the water-table in the plots, which had, according to the Warden, Charles Mitchell, dropped from about one foot below ground level in 1940 to six or seven feet below by 1961, was restored to something like its old level when Drainers' Dyke was recut in 1962. There are no hydrological data to illuminate the vegetation study, but the stabilizing effect of open water on the water-table in the surrounding peat is well established (Chapter 2) and it is almost certain that the water regime in the plots since 1962 has been quite different from that experienced in the previous two decades. Secondly, the area around the perimeter of the mown plots was cleared of *Frangula* in 1959–60. This led to an irruption of 'weeds' close to the experiment, which is reflected in a brief flush of seedlings of species such as rosebay willowherb (*Chamerion angustifolium*) and spear thistle (*Cirsium vulgare*) in the marginal areas of the plots.

The mowing of the Godwin Plots is still maintained, but these are now the only areas of mixed sedge on the Fen to be cut in October according to Godwin's original regime. Rowell[22] has assembled historical and biological records from the mid-17th century onwards that show the traditional time for sedge-cutting to have been from May, through June and possibly as late as August (Chapter 10). Somehow, winter cropping became the norm when the Fen became a nature reserve. As a result of complaints from the Entomological Society of London during the 1930s that the winter-cut areas were declining in interest and floral diversity, experiments were tried to test the effects of summer cutting[22] (see Chapter 11). Apparently, *Cladium* did not show any appreciable decline when cut annually in June or July, even after five years. Godwin's conclusions about the effect of cutting frequency on *Cladium* must therefore be viewed with caution, because he was mistaken about the right time of year for

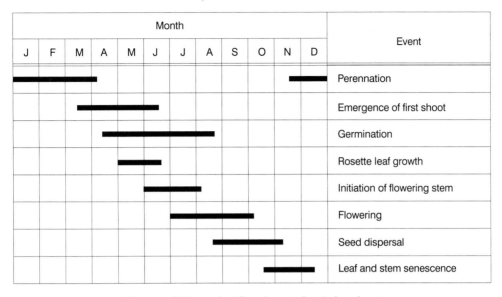

Month												Event
J	F	M	A	M	J	J	A	S	O	N	D	
████										██		Perennation
		████										Emergence of first shoot
			████									Germination
			██									Rosette leaf growth
				██								Initiation of flowering stem
					███							Flowering
						███						Seed dispersal
								██				Leaf and stem senescence

Figure 22   Milk-parsley (*Peucedanum palustre*) phenology[25]

cropping. The current practice at Wicken Fen is cutting in early summer every third or fourth year (Chapter 11).

The time of year at which the sedge crop is taken is not only vital to the well-being of the dominant species, but it is also important in determining the vigour of other components of the vegetation. The 1930s' experiments in summer cutting produced a spectacular result after only one summer cut: on one of the plots, some dicotyledons (notably milk-parsley and hemp-agrimony) flowered more profusely than the investigators had 'ever seen in the Fen before'.[24]

Milk-parsley (Plate 3, Fig. 3), the larval food plant of the swallowtail butterfly (Chapter 8) has declined catastrophically at Wicken Fen over the course of this century; could this decline be linked to the cropping regime? Milk-parsley behaves at Wicken Fen as a herbaceous perennial, with the overwintering root producing new leaves and stems each spring (Fig. 22). In the managed sedge-fields, each plant produced a single flower-head with six to eight umbels, but in the unmanaged sedge, the older plants were capable of producing two or three flowering stems and many more umbels.

A number of factors seem to be responsible for the decline of milk-parsley on the Fen. Meredith[26] showed that cutting mixed sedge in the late summer caused increased mortality in established seedlings and prevented seed production; the cutting time for areas rich in milk-parsley has accordingly been brought forward to late spring. Cutting the sedge-fields on a three-year cycle produced mortality in established plants (and so reduced flowering performance), but had the beneficial effects of promoting germination and discouraging seed predators, so increasing the establishment of new plants. Perhaps the most detrimental factor, however, had been the progressive drying of the

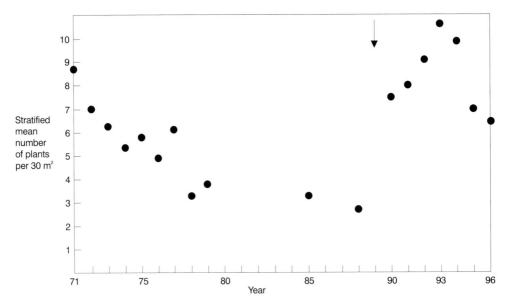

Figure 23   Changes in the density of plants of milk-parsley (*Peucedanum palustre*) in compartment 15 since 1971.[28] The arrow indicates the date of waterproofing the Fen's northern boundary.

Fen since the 19th century and the invasion of scrub in uncut areas (Chapter 6). Meredith was able to show that at Wicken Fen regeneration of *Peucedanum* from seed was reduced in uncut, shady areas and suggested that this might be linked to the greater numbers of seed predators such as small mammals in this type of habitat. He also discovered that most seeds from a single seed-head tend to land within five metres of the parent plant, so that the plant would be slow in reinvading areas from which it has previously gone extinct. The seeds are well adapted for floating[27] and dispersal might therefore have been thwarted by the lack of surface flooding on the Fen. In recent years, this dispersal problem has been overcome by scattering seed into rehabilitated sedge-fields.

The abundance and condition of milk-parsley has been monitored closely since 1971 with a view to reintroducing the swallowtail butterfly (see Chapter 8). Numbers declined steadily up till 1988, but, from 1990 to 1994, there was a remarkable recovery[28] (Fig. 23) which coincided with the completion of water-proofing of the Fen's northern margin. However, severe drought in the summer of 1995 produced a set-back in *Peucedanum* growth. In the absence of definitive experiments, it is impossible to be sure whether the changing fortunes of *Peucedanum* are truly the results of hydrological changes, because sedge-cutting practices have also changed during the past decade. Indeed, there are no quantitative hydrological data to demonstrate a change in the water-table as a result of the water-proofing project, but it is acknowledged that the Sedge Fen is generally wetter than before, although a prolonged drought can still cause

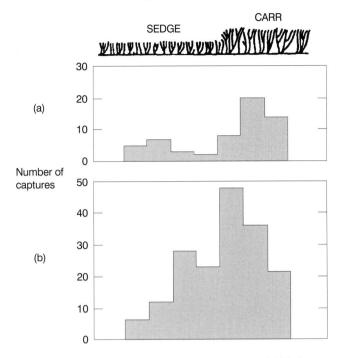

Figure 24 Distribution of bank voles (*Clethrionomys glareolus*) captured (a) in January, when the sedge fields were flooded, and (b) in February and May, when they were not[29]

the centre of the Fen to dry out. Increased wetness during late winter and spring may improve the growth of *Peucedanum*, although experiments carried out by Meredith suggested that flooding during the summer might be detrimental to the plant. A further possibility is that a high water-table would discourage the activity of small mammals that feed on the seeds.

The commonest species of small rodent at Wicken Fen appears to be the bank vole (*Clethrionomys glareolus*). In a study carried out in the 1970s,[29] bank voles were found to occur at high densities in unmanaged sedge, but in managed sedge- and litter-fields they tended to prefer the field edges adjacent to uncut carr (Fig. 24). The markedly three-dimensional nature of the vegetation in unmanaged areas appears to afford an excellent habitat for small mammals, with dense ground cover provided by a natural thatch of slowly-decaying *Cladium* leaves. The short-tailed or field vole (*Microtus agrestis*), on the other hand, showed a marked preference for grassy patches in sedge-fields and for litter- rather than sedge-fields. They were most often associated with purple small-reed, which is likely to form a major part of their diet at Wicken Fen.

Flooding of the Fen surface can be a critical event for small ground-dwelling animals. Bank voles and shrews evidently take refuge in dense sedge and sedge/carr transition habitats, and can be caught in traps placed up to a metre above the ground.[29] Prolonged flooding may result in a decline in bank vole numbers and the elimination over the flooded area of field voles. Similarly, Dawson[30] records that ground beetles at

Wicken Fen migrate into tussocks in winter; they tend to do this even in very dry conditions, but, in a wet year, the structural diversity of the vegetation would afford a means of escaping the rising water-table. Whilst drowning is an obvious peril for fenland beetles, the 'growth of dense choking sedge and litter' may, 'by excluding sunlight, warmth and air circulation', be just as influential in determining their distribution on the Fen.[31] The entomologists of the 1920s complained that neglect had ruined the best beetle-hunting areas on Adventurers' Fen and called for a resumption of regular vegetation cropping.

LITTER

'Litter' is mixed vegetation of medium height, dominated by grasses, and which, at Wicken Fen, has traditionally been harvested for animal bedding (Chapter 10). The term refers to two distinct types of vegetation, one dominated by *Molinia caerulea* and the other by species of *Calamagrostis*. It appears that litter may be a relatively late addition to the vegetation of the Fen: neither *Molinia* nor *Calamagrostis* appear on Babington's 1860 list of plants 'that most abound' at Wicken,[32] and the crop did not assume any importance until the slump in sedge prices at the turn of the century (Chapter 10).

The litter communities are of particular interest at Wicken because they are the most botanically diverse of all the vegetation types on the Fen, and they support a rich and important invertebrate fauna. The classic 'litter' of Wicken Fen, as described by Godwin,[4] may be equated with the typical sub-community of the NVC *Molinia caerulea–Cirsium dissectum* fen meadow community (Table V). Although dominated by purple moor-grass, other tall species such as common reed, purple loosestrife, yellow loosestrife, marsh thistle and creeping willow (*Salix repens*) and low-growing species such as carnation sedge (*Carex panicea*), devil's-bit scabious and large bird's-foot trefoil (*Lotus uliginosus*) are also abundant. This type of fen meadow occurs widely, but sparsely, across southern and eastern England. It can be found not only on peat soils, as at Wicken, but also on mineral or peaty mineral soils that tend to be base rich and neutral to alkaline in pH. It is more generally found in damp rather than dry or wet situations.

Molinia-dominated 'litter' is now of quite restricted distribution on the Fen, surviving only in areas which have never been invaded by scrub or where occupation by scrub was brief. It may be that the community was never very widespread on the Fen, for Godwin[4] lists only ten 'plots' on which good examples of 'litter' could be found. Godwin's records suggest that, in the 1920s, the best areas of 'litter' were then found at the western end of the Sedge Fen, close to Drainers' Dyke; indeed it was in this area that he located his experimental plots on which he investigated the effect of cutting on 'litter' (see above). Recent surveys confirm that *Molinia* is still more abundant at the western end of the Sedge Fen than elsewhere, both in the 'sedge' and 'litter' fields and on droves.

Calamagrostis-dominated litter is now by far the commoner type at Wicken, yet neither *C. canescens* nor *C. epigejos* was recorded as a component of 'litter' by Godwin. His only reference to these species[5] names them as occurring in areas from which scrub had been cleared. Only a decade later, in 1939, Evans[33] considered both species 'too common' at Wicken and a conspicuous component of the vegetation (see Chapter 7). The two species of *Calamagrostis* seem to take advantage of disturbed habitats, such as those cleared of scrub over the past thirty years.

'Litter' was traditionally maintained at Wicken by summer cutting, which had the satisfactory effect of stimulating germination and flowering of the various constituent species, so providing excellent forage for insects. This pattern changed in the early years of this century to winter and then to August/September. Over the past few

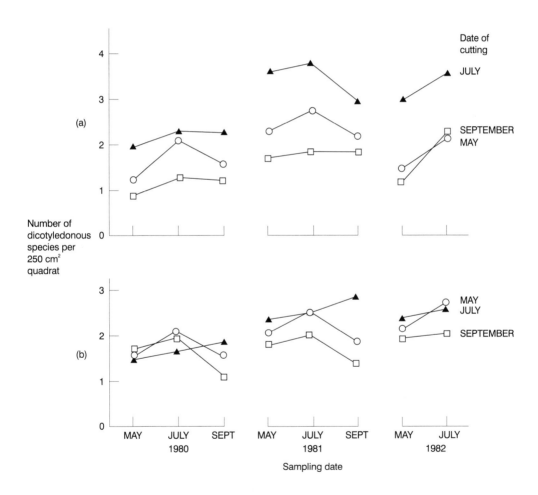

Figure 25 Changes in dicotyledonous species richness under three different seasonal cutting regimes[34] (a) in purple moor-grass (*Molinia caerulea*) and (b) in small-reed (*Calamagrostis* spp.) litter

decades, it has been the general impression that the abundance of dicotyledonous plants in litter has declined and the proportion of monocotyledons increased. In 1979 a series of plots were set up in two areas of litter dominated by *Molinia* and *Calamagrostis* species respectively to investigate the effect of cutting date on the composition of the vegetation.[34] In each area, the plots were cut annually, some early in the growing season (at the end of May), others late in the growing season (at the end of July), and others at the end of September. In each case, the cuttings were removed and not allowed to form a 'mattress' of dead material (which may attain a thickness of 10–20cm, outweighing the living material and excluding all but a few vigorous species).[5] Over the two years of the experiment, the abundance of dicotyledonous species in the *Molinia* litter increased under all treatments, with the greatest change in the July-cut plots. Only yellow rattle (*Rhinanthus minor*) declined. An increase in the number of species of dicotyledons in the sward was also achieved, along with a general increase in *Molinia* itself (Fig. 25a). In the *Calamagrostis* litter plots, species diversity increased under the earlier cutting regimes, but not in the September-cut plot (Fig. 25b). This was accompanied by a marked increase in the abundance of *C. epigejos* and bedstraws (*Galium* spp.).

Cutting in July also improved the flowering performance of some species, confirming the observations made in the 1930s' summer-harvesting experiment. Particularly dramatic differences were noted in the performance of *Calamagrostis epigejos*, which flowered abundantly in the July-cut plots but hardly at all in the September-cut plots.[35] Rowell speculated that cutting late in the year might kill those stems that would normally produce flowers in the following year.

In this experiment, it proved difficult to separate the results of the seasonality of cutting from the effects of applying an annual cutting regime on areas that had been cut less frequently in the immediate past. Annual cutting is likely to reverse the loss of species often noted in grasslands and fens when regular management is abandoned. In these cases, dead organic matter builds up and the grasses become increasingly dominant. However, it seems likely that cutting at different times of the year will favour different species according to their annual patterns of growth and reproduction. Apart from the obvious effect of cutting at different times on the successful setting and dispersal of seeds of various species, there is probably also a difference in the subsequent conditions for germination and seedling growth: a sward cut in autumn will create in the following spring a more open vegetation, with a more favourable light climate near the ground, than a sward cut early in the year and allowed to regrow during the summer. The effect of these changes will, of course, extend to the organisms for which the litter-fields provide food, cover and other resources.

It is partly with this in mind that the present management policy at Wicken Fen is to divide litter-fields into smaller areas and cut some in spring, some in summer and some in autumn, and to assign some to annual cycles, some to biennial cycles and some to cutting in two years in every three (Chapter 11). It is also to be hoped that this complex pattern of management will go some way towards restoring the small-scale mosaic of diversity originally created by the division of the Fen into many small strips of land in

Figure 26   Sedge Fen Drove, 8 August 1991

the 17th century. These plots were owned and worked by a large number of different local people, engendering a patchwork which was lost when the strips were amalgamated into the nature reserve from the turn of the century (Chapter 10).

DROVES

Sedge Fen Drove is at least 300 years old, dating from the subdivision of the Fen in 1666 (Chapter 10) and the path along Wicken Lode is probably also very old. Other access paths almost certainly existed when the Fen was regularly cropped, and these paths may have formed the basis of the present grid of droves, which dates from the period 1926–34. Today, a typical Wicken drove is 5–10m wide with a central strip mown to allow access for visitors and Fen staff (Fig. 26). In good growing conditions, this may mean fortnightly mowing on the main routes. On either side of this strip is a wide border which is cut in the autumn to maintain a short, species-rich sward. Here ragged-robin (*Lychnis flos-cuculi*), water mint (*Mentha aquatica*), yellow-rattle and various orchids (Chapter 7) flower in colourful succession, providing feeding, meeting and breeding places for a bewildering diversity of insect life.

The central strip takes the full brunt of trampling and, in wet conditions, the turf surface can be badly churned up. Breaks in the turf allow the entry of 'weed' species such as greater plantain (*Plantago major*). This familiar plant was not recorded at Wicken Fen till 1966; although this may reflect to some extent the tendency of botanical recorders to overlook the most commonplace (Chapter 7), the plant has certainly increased its hold on the Fen. It can now be found growing along all the well-used

79

tracks, and shows a clear zonation, with most plants concentrated in heavily disturbed parts of the central strip and declining towards the borders.

In the very wettest parts of Sedge Fen Drove (such as the hollows that probably arise from traffic damage),[22] the trampled sites tend to hold water throughout most of the year. These semi-permanent water-bodies become covered with floating and plicate sweet-grasses (*Glyceria fluitans* and *G. notata*), which sprout early in the year and provide a source of food for moorhen. The trampled muddy patches are also excellent places for observing Diptera (Chapter 8).

The relatively inconspicuous plants of Wicken's droves deserve careful monitoring. Sedge Fen Drove supports three species of *Eleocharis* (Chapter 7), small plants which are unlikely to survive in tall vegetation, and it is possible that their survival there is linked to constant disturbance. Few-flowered spike-rush (*Eleocharis quinqueflora*), which is not known from any other Cambridgeshire locality, has shown signs of spreading to some of the cross droves where the cut central strip is of relatively recent origin. Marsh arrowgrass (*Triglochin palustris*) appears to be most abundant on the older droves (Sedge Fen and Gardiner's Droves and droves alongside Wicken Lode and Drainers' Dyke) and to be scarce on other droves. The distribution of jointed rush and blunt-flowered rush (*Juncus articulatus* and *J. subnodulosus*) on Sedge Fen Drove suggests a basic ecological difference between the species: the former occurs on the cut and trampled central strip, and the latter in the mown side strips.

The vegetation on most of the Fen droves can be referred to one of the two sub-communities of the NVC *Juncus subnodulosus–Cirsium palustre* fen-meadow community (Table V). This type of vegetation is widespread on moist, base-rich and near-neutral soils in the lowlands of southern England, but is particularly common in East Anglia. Mowing seems to be important in both creating and maintaining the community and this is well demonstrated at Wicken Fen where the relaxation of the normal mowing regime can lead to increases in species such as common reed and meadowsweet.

References

1 Wallis (1904)
2 Yapp (1908)
3 Yapp (1909)
4 Godwin (1929)
5 Godwin & Tansley (1929)
6 Rodwell (1991a)
7 Rodwell (1991b)
8 Rodwell (1992)
9 Rodwell (1995)
10 Conway (1936b)
11 Conway (1936c)
12 Conway (1937)
13 Conway (1938a)
14 Conway (1938b)
15 Godwin & Bharucha (1932)

16 Evans (1925)
17 Godwin (1932)
18 Gardiner (1928), p. 382
19 Godwin & Tansley (1929), p. 440
20 Farren (1926a), p. 180
21 Godwin (1941b)
22 Rowell (1983a)
23 Friday *et al.* (in preparation)
24 Wicken Executive Committee Minute Book (23 June 1954)
25 Harvey & Meredith (1981)
26 Meredith (1978)
27 Meredith & Grubb (1993)
28 Dempster (1994)
29 Flowerdew *et al.* (1977, fig. 4)

30 Dawson (1965)
31 Omer Cooper *et al.* (1928), p. 268
32 Babington (1860)
33 Evans (1939)
34 Rowell *et al.* (1985)
35 Rowell (1983a), fig. 11.6

6

CARR AND WOODLAND

L. E. FRIDAY, S. M. WALTERS AND J. M. LOCK

T HE MAJORITY of the Fen is covered by woody vegetation. Most of this is scrub, known as 'carr', while woodland (in the generally accepted sense of tall-growing trees) is quite limited in its distribution. All of this shrubby vegetation is relatively recent, dating back no further than the late 19th century. How and why did Wicken Fen acquire this covering of dense thicket? Fortunately, we have a series of excellent eye-witness accounts of the development of carr.

When Wallis described the Fen in 1904, the vegetation was quite different from what we see today:

> 'The fen itself appears during most seasons of the year as a brown waste dotted with bushes which are apparently increasing in number; in some places, especially along the northern edge of the fen, they form dense masses of cover, excluding all other vegetation. Elsewhere, when not entirely absent, they are scattered and usually smaller in size'.[1]

The 'dense masses' consisted primarily of alder buckthorn (*Frangula alnus*) (Fig. 27). Babington's *Flora of Cambridgeshire* of 1860[2] does not include this species in the Wicken list, but he apparently recorded it there in 1861, just too late for publication. Once

Figure 27   Alder buckthorn (*Frangula alnus*)

established at Wicken, *Frangula* spread very rapidly: by 1881, H. Dixon was describing it as 'common' at Wicken,[3] and by 1898 W. West said it was 'abundant'.[4]

A. H. Evans' personal experience of the Fen went back to 1875. Writing in 1925, he described fifty years of change in which vegetational decline had accompanied the social changes of the times (see Chapter 10):

'the Fen shews many differences from 1875 ... [it was] then at its worst; most owners cared little for their plots ... sedge-cutting, once a regular occupation, was becoming more and more confined to the most accessible parts near the Lodes ... birds had a very bad time and the insects hardly a better. Neglected areas became covered with seedling trees and bushes.'[5]

Clearly, the invasion of scrub was having far-reaching effects on the rest of the Fen's flora and fauna even in the late 19th century. By 1908, the *Frangula* was rampant:

'Between the centre of the Fen and Wicken Lode village this species alone forms many extensive thickets; so dense that practically all other vegetation is excluded. The great number of seedlings and young plants of various ages which are found not only bordering these thickets, but elsewhere on the Fen, bears witness to the rapid rate at which this species is increasing. Its fleshy fruits are readily eaten by birds, and seeds frequently found in bird-droppings afford evidence that this is a common means of dispersal.'[6]

Willows were also on the increase:

> 'young bushes are cut with the sedge so long as they offer no great resistance to the cut-
> ters. Many are perhaps killed in this way, while others form coppiced growths. When,
> however, a bush is large enough to interfere with the cutting, it is left alone, and so may
> attain maturity.'[7]

The effect on the existing flora was profound. By 1929, Godwin noted that:

> 'In all parts of the fen the sedge and litter may be seen in various stages of colonisation
> by bushes, and as the density of these increases the *Cladium* and *Molinia* are killed out, so
> that in the final 'fen-carr', which is a densely canopied thicket some 5 metres high, a
> characteristic shade flora occurs.'[8]

Yapp realized that both the hydrology of the Fen and the patterns of crop-taking
played a major role in controlling the establishment of woody saplings. In spite of the
obvious immediate decline in the floristic interest of the Fen, he was apt to take a more
pragmatic view of the fen vegetation in its evolutionary context:

> 'There can be little doubt that Wicken Fen is becoming drier, and that the number of 'dry
> plants' is increasing. The bushes are also certainly becoming more numerous, apparently
> with considerably rapidity…It therefore seems probable that Wicken is on the verge of
> another forest period, and that sooner or later it will become practically a huge marsh
> thicket. Then finally, if the Fen is not in the meantime appropriated by man for other pur-
> poses, the Rhamni and Salices of the thickets may once again be replaced by stately forest
> trees, growing above the spot where their predecessors still lie buried in the peat.'[7]

Godwin rose to the challenge of investigating the dynamics of the sedge/carr transition, just as he had studied the relationship between sedge and litter. He foresaw that
the issue was not straightforward:

> 'numerous and varied problems surrounded the processes of bush establishment and of
> the development of scrub (fen carr) subsequently'.[9]

Godwin and his student F. R. Bharucha had noted that an aerial photograph of 1926
showed a very conspicuous pattern of bushes in long parallel rows, and that, when visited on the ground, these rows corresponded with the ridges 'the result probably of
former peat cutting' while the empty rows in-between corresponded to furrows.[10]
Their study of the relationships between the distribution of vegetation types and
hydrology led to the hypothesis that the 'control of bush growth by the water table is a
phenomenon of winter flooding'.[11] Before the installation of the sluice at Upware in
the 1940s (Chapters 2 & 10) winter flooding was an important feature of the Fen's ecology and would have its greatest effect in any low points in the peat surface.

The cessation of cropping was obviously also a major cause of scrub development.
In 1923, Godwin fenced off two areas of the Fen and set up two permanent transects,
to be left uncut and surveyed over a number of years to map the progress of vegetational change. The transect at the northern end of Drainers' Dyke was established in
typical mixed sedge which had been cut regularly at intervals of less than three years
until 1918 and then left uncut. The changes over 12 years were dramatic: saplings of

alder buckthorn, hawthorn and grey willow (*Salix cinerea*), which had become established since the last sedge crop was taken, grew up to overtop the sedge, and guelder-rose (*Viburnum opulus*) became well established. The bush crowns rapidly expanded and coalesced into larger masses to form a closed canopy.[12] Godwin opportunistically took advantage of the fact that a similar area of *Frangula* carr was being cleared at the time to create Gardiner's Drove. His analysis of the bushes from this clearance revealed a density of about 1.4 living bushes per square metre, with each bush having about four major trunks, and a vegetation height of 2–3m. He also noted that all the bushes were less than 24 years old, yet very many of the stems were dead or dying.

By mapping the fenced triangular area at the junction of Drainers' Dyke and Wicken Lode (called by Godwin 'Reserve A', but now known as the 'Godwin Triangle'; see map in Appendix A) over fifty years, Godwin demonstrated the comprehensive colonization of sedge by both alder buckthorn and purging buckthorn (*Rhamnus cathartica*). At the start, there was already a large central clump of old *Rhamnus* bushes with some *Salix cinerea*, a scattered fringe of mature bushes of various species, and a central field of mixed sedge, which had been uncut for several years and contained seedling bushes.

The most striking development over the first ten years was the astonishing rate of growth and consolidation of the bushes in the northern half of the plot (Fig. 28).[12] By 1972, when the plot was resurveyed,[13] *Rhamnus* carr had almost completely taken over the southern half, overwhelming the *Salix cinerea*, while *Frangula* had formed an almost continuous cover of the northern part. The dominant species of the mixed sedge ground flora (*Cladium* and *Molinia*) had been virtually extinguished (Fig. 29), leaving a shade flora dominated by nettle and brambles (*Rubus* spp.), marsh fern (*Thelypteris palustris*) and meadowsweet (*Filipendula ulmaria*). Guelder-rose, which had appeared to be rapidly expanding in 1934, had almost disappeared, probably as a result of defoliation by the chrysomelid beetle *Galerucella viburni*, a species which first appeared in the Fen in the 1930s (Fig. 30).

The two buckthorn species evidently spread by both seed dispersal and expansion of established plants. Yapp had already noted the frequency of *Frangula* seeds in bird

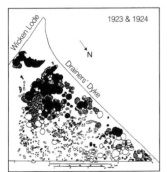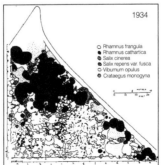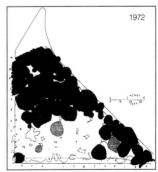

Figure 28 The development of carr on the 'Godwin Triangle' in 1923/24, 1934, and 1972[12,13]

Figure 29   Buckthorn (*Rhamnus cathartica*) stool with remains of great fen-sedge (*Cladium mariscus*)

Figure 30   Defoliation of guelder rose (*Viburnum opulus*) by the leaf beetle *Galerucella viburni*, 24 August 1948

droppings and Godwin[12] discovered that *Frangula* fruits were avidly taken from the bushes in 'Reserve A' as they ripened in September by large flocks of migratory field-fares (*Turdus pilaris*). Fruits of *Rhamnus* (and of guelder-rose) were less readily taken and tended to remain on the bushes into the winter. However, a larger proportion of *Rhamnus* seeds appeared to be transported some distance away from the parent plant. Indeed, much of the *Frangula* fruit appeared simply to drop to the ground below the seed parent. When Godwin discovered that one of his water-level recorders had been requisitioned by a field mouse (*Apodemus sylvaticus*) for a nest (Fig. 31), and contained

Figure 31 Godwin's water-level recorder in the 'Godwin Triangle', July 1994

numerous *Frangula* seeds, he was prompted to ask whether mice might play a role in transporting the fallen fruits. Some simple experiments proved this to be highly likely, and the discovery of caches of buried stones, forgotten and germinating *en masse*, confirmed the idea.

FRANGULA DIE-BACK

One of the most conspicuous features of the carr at Wicken Fen since the 1920s has been the dying out of tall *Frangula* bushes in fairly mature carr. Godwin[12] noted that it was possible to find bushes that had been killed within the last one or two days, in the middle of summer, with wilted but still green leaves hanging from the branches. Stripping off the bark revealed that a black coloration extended for some distance in the wood and bark and, where it ringed the branch, wilting and death had occurred. These patches could be traced to snags around the base of dead lateral shoots, a typical point of entry for fungal pathogens. The fungi involved were identified by G. C. Stevenson as a *Fusarium* species, which when inoculated into *Frangula* rapidly produced the characterisitic black patches and killed branches an inch in diameter within six months, and *Nectria cinnabarina*. Both are aggressive wound parasites, and other saprophytic fungi would undoubtedly follow in their wake.

The die-back of *Frangula* could open the way to development of *Rhamnus* carr, producing the pattern observed by Godwin in some mature areas of carr of the apparent replacement of one species by the other. Here, as in the case of the attack by *Galerucella* beetle on guelder-rose, there seems to be an example of the outcome of competition being influenced by a third biological agent.

Although the carr recovered from this attack, two other catastrophes have befallen the *Frangula* since. The first was the coppicing of a large proportion of the shrubs during the early years of the Second World War (Chapter 11). The stumps regrew, but another wave of die-back swept through the *Frangula* carr in the 1980s, although this time the cause is uncertain. The result has been that a large proportion of the *Frangula* standing on all parts of the Fen is now dead wood (Fig. 32) and is therefore highly vulnerable to fire during the dry months of the year. In the autumn of 1991, a spark ignited a large area of carr west of Drainers' Dyke; the fire ripped through the dead, dry shrubs at a height of about 50cm from the ground, reducing the bushes to charcoal, but leaving the ground flora and fauna virtually unscathed.

Whatever the cause of the recent decline, it seems that this episode is now over. Will the *Frangula* carr recover? After the fungal epidemic of the 1930s, regeneration was good, but this occurred in the virtual absence of deer, notorious for preventing regeneration by their grazing in other types of woodland. Today, both roe (*Capreolus capreolus*) and muntjac (*Muntiacus reevesi*) are frequently seen on the Fen, and a few individual red deer (*Cervus elaphus*) have recently been sighted. Although deer are undoubtedly present in considerable numbers, their impact on woody vegetation is relatively slight: *Frangula* is once again the most vigorous colonizer of sedge- and litter-fields.

Figure 32   Dead alder buckthorn (*Frangula alnus*) on Wicken Poor's Fen, July 1994

THE CARR SEED-BANK

The battle against carr has been one of the major preoccupations of management since 1913[14] and clearance has been a consistent practice during the last thirty years (see Chapter 11). The aim has been to re-establish the species-rich herbaceous communities which existed on the Fen in the late 19th century. In view of the considerable investment in time and effort that scrub clearance represents, it is reasonable to ask how likely it is that this aim could be achieved.

The vegetation that develops following the removal of the carr will be derived from three main sources: from plants that survive the period of shading in the vegetative state; from buried or surface dormant seed (the 'seed-bank'); and from seeds carried into the area from surrounding habitats. Of these three, the seed-bank is most likely to represent the vegetation that preceded the carr, but it has until recently remained rather an unknown quantity. Do the seeds of the herbaceous species of litter-fields survive in the seed-bank below carr at Wicken? If so, would they germinate after clearance in sufficient quantities to recreate vegetation resembling that of former years?

The seed-bank, like a pollen deposit (see Chapter 10), contains clues to the previous vegetation of a site. Unfortunately, this record becomes blurred as time elapses, because the seeds of different species survive for different periods, and successive vegetation types contribute their seeds to the seed-bank. The loss of species from the seed-bank would have clear implications for management practice at Wicken Fen: those areas most recently colonized by scrub should contain the largest and most representative reserves of herbaceous seeds, and should therefore be given priority in any programme of clearance. Terry Rowell set out to test this prediction as part of his doctoral research on the history and management of the Fen.[15]

Patches of carr in three different age-categories were identified from a series of aerial photographs of Verrall's Fen taken between 1927 and 1977:[16] 'young' (less than 32 years old); 'intermediate' (32–50 years old); and 'old' (more than 50 years old). Samples of peat were taken in early May (when all the seeds present should have been vernalized), removed to the laboratory, where all roots and rhizomes were sifted out, and the emergence of seedlings was recorded over the next 13 months. Meanwhile, the existing ground vegetation in each of the patches was surveyed for comparison with the emerging seedlings. The ground cover in old carr proved to be quite different from that of the other patches, being much sparser, more completely dominated by nettles, and lacking *Calamagrostis canescens*.

A total of 35 species or genera emerged from the seed-bank (Table VI). Common nettle (*Urtica dioica*) accounted for 40 per cent of all seedlings, and rushes (*Juncus* spp.), rough meadow-grass (*Poa trivialis*), purple loosestrife (*Lythrum salicaria*) and brookweed (*Samolus valerandi*) were also abundant. However, many characteristic fen species were poorly represented (e.g. *Molinia caerulea* and *Cladium mariscus*) or absent (e.g. marsh pea (*Lathyrus palustris*) and *Peucedanum palustre*). A single seedling of fen violet (*Viola persicifolia*) emerged from a peat sample from old carr, producing the first record for this species on the Fen for 64 years (Chapter 7).

The results suggest that, whilst the seed-bank of older stands of carr evidently retains a range of species similar to that of younger patches, the proportion of seeds belonging to 'non-fen' species increases with time (Fig. 33). This may preclude the successful re-establishment of typical 'sedge' and 'litter' herbaceous communities on areas now occupied by all but the youngest scrub and clearly indicates that future clearance efforts should be confined to the newest patches. Even so, the resulting herbaceous vegetation is unlikely to be identical in composition to that previously present, as the reinstatement of the Godwin Plots study has shown (see Chapter 5).

There is no doubt that a good case can be made for recreating the lost diversity of open habitats by removing carr and bringing the new fields under a regular cutting regime. But manpower is limited and, it could be argued, the carr is itself a valuable and fascinating fen habitat. The buckthorn scrub at Wicken Fen is highly prized by entomologists, because both *Frangula* and *Rhamnus* are foodplants of the brimstone butterfly (*Gonepteryx rhamni*), which can be seen in large numbers during spring and summer (Chapter 8). Carr is also valuable habitat for birds, particularly woodcock, grasshopper warblers, woodpeckers and owls (Chapter 9.4). However, it is the 'lower' flora that show the clearest positive responses to the development of the carr habitat on the Fen.

Table VI. The relative abundance of species emerging from the seed bank in carr. From Rowell (1983a), (extracted from Tables 9.2 & 9.5)[15]

Species	Category*	Relative abundance (%) emerging seedlings
Urtica dioica	C	42.1
Juncus spp.	H	10.3
Lythrum salicaria	H(C)	9.8
Poa trivialis	C	9.5
Samolus valerandi	H	8.1
Solanum nigrum	A	4.4
Lysimachia vulgaris	H(C)	4.2
Epilobium hirsutum	H(C)	2.2
Eupatorium cannabinum	H(C)	1.7
Carex spp. (including *Cladium*)	H(C)	1.1
Phalaris arundinacea	H(C)	1.1
Thalictrum flavum	H	0.9
Frangula alnus	C	0.7
Rhinanthus minor	H	0.6
Mentha aquatica	H(C)	0.5
Chenopodium album	A	0.4
Calamagrostis spp.	H(C)	0.3
Galium uliginosum	H	0.3
Hydrocotyle vulgaris	H	0.3
Chenopodium rubrum	A	0.2
Molinia caerulea	H(C)	0.2
Sambucus nigra	C	0.1
Solanum dulcimara	C	0.1
Phragmites australis	H(C)	0.1
Stellaria media	A	0.1
Salix alba	C	<0.1
Crataegus monogyna	C	<0.1
Plantago major	A	<0.1
Rosa spp.	C	<0.1
Persicaria maculosa	A	<0.1
Rhamnus cathartica	C	<0.1
Lamium purpureum	A	<0.1
Viola persicifolia	H	<0.1
Linum catharticum	H	<0.1
Rubus spp.	C	<0.1

*H   species characteristic of herbaceous fen vegetation, and not usually, or never, found as vegetative plants under scrub;

H(C) species characteristic of herbaceous fen vegetation, but often present as vegetative plants under scrub;

C   species characteristic of scrub vegetation;

A   'alien' species, not normally components of fen vegetation

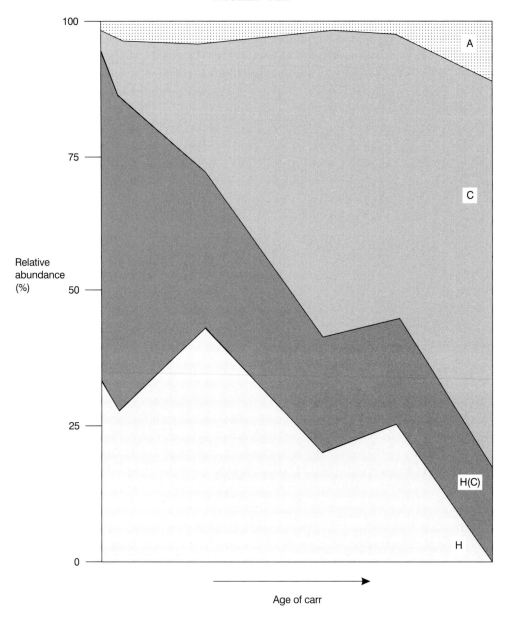

Figure 33 Changes with time in the seed-bank underlying carr.[15] The stands of carr are arranged along the horizontal axis according to their positions on the first axis of ordination of the seed-bank flora; this axis is highly correlated with age, with young stands to the left and old stands to the right. The seed-bank species are grouped according to the categories listed in Table VI.

CARR FERNS, MOSSES AND LICHENS

Records of ferns at Wicken Fen bear witness to the ecological changes associated with the spread of carr. Babington's 1860 list gives only two species for Wicken Fen: the adder's-tongue (*Ophioglossum vulgatum*), and the marsh fern (*Thelypteris palustris*, but called by him '*Lastraea thelypteris*').[2] For a hundred years these two ferns constituted the total Wicken list, but in 1962 Max Walters recorded a single clump of the lady fern (*Athyrium filix-femina*) 'in old carr behind the small brick-pits', and in 1968 the two commonest British ferns, male-fern (*Dryopteris filix-mas*) and buckler fern (*Dryopteris dilatata*), were discovered in the same region[3] (Fig. 34). In the following year, many plants of male-fern were discovered in a patch of old carr on St Edmund's Fen.

The pattern was obvious: as the carr developed into woodland, characteristic woodland ferns were appearing in the undergrowth. Ferns have dust-like spores, and they can easily colonize newly-available microhabitats. This process seemed to be continuing at Wicken, for in 1971 the first record of narrow buckler-fern (*Dryopteris carthusiana*) was made in the same area and, in 1976, A. C. Leslie recorded scaly male-fern (*Dryopteris affinis*) from alder and willow carr on the Fen.[3]

The history of the adder's-tongue is completely different. It was for many years

Figure 34   Ferns in alder buckthorn (*Frangula alnus*) carr near the Brickpits, 23 July 1964

(between 1952 & 1972 at least) to be found near the wind-pump near the Fen entrance. It has not been seen there for some time, but is now abundant in compartment 21 on the margin of the reserve (see Chapter 11). This small, easily overlooked species is obviously intolerant of tall fen vegetation.

Changes in the moss flora of the Fen have been equally dramatic and reflect very clearly ecological trends. Paul Richards' 1932 account of the Fen's moss flora[17] records only twenty species. Michael Proctor's checklist for Cambridgeshire of 1956 added only a few more.[18] However, in 1963, several calcifuge species, which grow on acid soils low in calcium, were found by J. M. Lock in carr near the Brickpits.[19] These included *Calypogeia fissa*, *Campylopus flexuosus*, *Dicranum scoparium*, *Hookeria lucens*, *Orthodontium lineare*, *Plagiothecium denticulatum*, *Polytrichum longisetum*, *P. commune*, *P. formosum*, *Sphagnum fimbriatum* and *Tetraphis pellucida*. Further records of some of these mosses have since been made in other parts of the Fen.

Calcifuge mosses occupy three main microhabitats within the carr, all potentially leached of nutrients and acidified, and in which substantial acidification has been confirmed by pH measurements. When *Molinia* is overgrown and killed by carr, the tussocks persist for some time as hummocks, which are eventually broken down by normal decomposition and scratching by pheasants. The hummocks near the Brickpits had almost disappeared by 1975, and had gone completely by 1989. Similar transient habitats are formed by dead *Frangula* stumps and piles of dead *Cladium* leaves.

A second, less ephemeral, type of locality is found in the parts of the Fen with the ridges and furrows of old peat-diggings. The ridges stood above the winter water-level in the 1960s and 1970s, and often bore calcifuge mosses. The furrows, flooded with calcareous ground water during the winter, are generally filled with *Calliergon cuspidatum*.

Extensive areas of calcifuge mosses have sometimes developed where the fen surface was high enough to escape flooding with calcareous water in most winters. *Atrichum undulatum* and *Mnium hornum* were often the first colonizers, with species of *Sphagnum* and *Polytrichum* appearing later, but often these latter species grew directly on the peat surface, without clear evidence of any pioneers. Large parts of compartments 2, 4, 5 and 13 developed in this way (see map Appendix A).

Are these calcifuge mosses relics of a formerly more widespread flora, or are they recent arrivals? There seems to be no direct evidence for the occurrence of *Sphagnum* at Wicken Fen prior to 1963, indeed there is much evidence to the contrary.[20] In 1845, Jenyns noted that *Sphagnum* was not a component of the local fen peat[21] and its conspicuous absence from the Fen was commented on by Evans in 1911[22] and Richards in 1932.[17] There is, however, a good record of the development of a rich calcifuge moss flora as a result of 30 years of monitoring of Godwin's experimental areas. It seems unlikely that these mosses developed from relict plants or buried spores, as the richest sites were within carr and completely undisturbed. Furthermore, pH profiles show that acidification is confined to the surface layers: borings made by H. J. B. Birks in 1978 through the peat beneath *Sphagnum* on St Edmund's Fen revealed that the mosses were growing on a 10cm-deep layer of highly humified fen peat overlying shell marl, which in turn overlay 3m of alkaline peat made from *Phragmites* and/or *Cladium*.

Moss spores and fragments can be carried far by the wind, and it is probable that long-distance dispersal must have been responsible. Some of the species are abundant to the east in Breckland, where many are recent arrivals, presumably mainly from western Britain. Accidental introduction seems unlikely: most visitors stay on the droves and sedge-fields, where calcifuge mosses are absent, and very few indeed go to St Edmund's Fen, where the mosses were abundant.

The peak of occurrence of calcifuge mosses at Wicken Fen seems to have been in the mid 1970s. Various factors appear to have contributed to their recent decline, including the state of the carr. One rich area in compartment 5 was accidentally burned: the fire not only damaged the mosses directly, but also, by killing the *Frangula* canopy, allowed the field layer to thicken up and shade them. The opening of the carr canopy by *Frangula* dieback has similarly allowed much more vigorous growth of higher plants beneath it; when this field layer collapses during the winter, it forms a mat over the surface, shading any ground-living mosses during what must be their most important season of growth. Changes in water-levels may also be implicated: in wet autumns and winters, calcareous ground water now covers the peat surface in many parts of the Fen.

Lichens, as symbioses of fungi and algae, hardly qualify for inclusion as flora, but these too show a response to changing habitat availability. A list of thirty-nine species of lichens at Wicken Fen was compiled by J. R. Laundon in 1972.[23] In his introduction to this list, Laundon says there are no old records from the Fen, the earliest record being made in 1960. This might in part be due to a neglect of lichen studies but it must also be true, as Laundon says, that 'the shrub and tree colonization of the Fen during the present century has provided extensive habitats for corticolous (bark-inhabiting) lichens; such habitats were previously much more restricted, so that the lichen flora is probably richer now than at any time in the past.' However, the carr is not the only new habitat on the Fen: of the 39 species in Laundon's list, no fewer than eight were recorded only 'on the concrete post by the windmill'. In 1991, Laundon revisited the Fen and noted that although the lichen flora had changed little during the intervening 20 years, there had been a small decline in the lichen vegetation. He comments that this decline 'is because the trees and shrubs have grown older, and many have now died...When the shrubs die the bark falls off and the lichens go with it'.[24]

WOODLAND

Near the Brickpits, where the gault clay reaches to within centimetres of the surface, there is an extensive area with hawthorn (*Crataegus monogyna*) scrub and a small woodland with mature pedunculate oak (*Quercus robur*) and ash (*Fraxinus excelsior*) and a number of old apple-trees near the former brickworkers' cottages. This patch of woodland has been there at least since the early 19th century (Chapter 10). There are also scattered large individuals of ash and white willow (*Salix alba*) and an extensive grove of downy birch, but otherwise trees are not a major feature of the Fen's landscape.

Some of these trees have developed from deliberate plantings, and some from un-intentional beginnings: the line of willows along Sedge Fen Drove are alleged to have arisen from the stakes put in to mark the National Trust plots or even from posts set up for 'sugaring' for moths (see Chapter 8). Birch-trees were planted at the western end of Sedge Fen Drove at the beginning of the century and spread slowly at first.[12] However, in the 1970s and 1980s, birch was spreading rapidly by seed (see Fig. 36, p. 113); this coincided with the peak abundance of calcifuge mosses, indicating a phase of acidifi-cation of the Fen surface. Many of these birches are now dying, in parallel with the decline in the mosses, perhaps because they have reached the end of their natural life, but also perhaps because of increased winter wetness on the Fen. Trees are also dying on both St Edmund's and Verrall's Fens, and this can almost certainly be attributed to the raising of the water-table by the waterproofing of the Fen's boundary banks (Chapter 11).

Perhaps the most surprising feature of the woodland at Wicken is the scarcity of alder (*Alnus glutinosa*). This species is generally associated with the carr/woodland tran-sition in wetlands. Indeed, comparison of Wicken Fen's woody vegetation with the National Vegetation Classification scheme reflects the unexpectedness of this situa-tion: the nearest equivalent of Wicken's assemblage is the 'alder–meadowsweet sub-community' of willow–birch–reed woodland (Table V). What is more, a pollen profile taken from the Fen's peat shows that alder has been very abundant in the vicinity of Wicken Fen in the distant past (see Fig. 53, Chapter 10). Today, alder at Wicken is vir-tually restricted to planted trees, in the grove at the west end of Sedge Fen Drove and on the other side of the Lode on Evans' Fen. In 1936, Godwin noted that these planted trees were showing no regeneration,[12] but seedlings are now occasionally encountered.

Woodland undoubtedly adds to the diversity of habitats found on the reserve, but it seems not to form part of the natural mosaic on the wettest parts of the Fen. Living trees, and their dead trunks and branches, are important habitats for birds and insects (Chapter 8) at Wicken. Should trees be planted? The planted row of bay willow (*Salix pentandra*) running from Sedge Fen Drove up to Spinney Bank has matured to produce an impressive display of specimen trees. These magnificent trees provide an intriguing insight into the way management policy has changed at Wicken Fen and at other nature reserves in the past few decades: bay willow is not native to the Fen and current management policy would not countenance the planting of this 'alien' species (Chapter 11).

Specimen trees are otherwise few in number and are cherished for their contribu-tion to the landscape on the fringe of the reserve. One of the Fen's largest trees, a hybrid black-poplar (*Populus × canadensis*), another 'alien', was uprooted by the gale that struck southern England in October 1987. The tree was hauled upright and has appar-ently recovered.

In the north-east corner of the Fen just off the reserve, on a field that has recently come out of arable cultivation, a mixture of native trees that already occur on the Fen, such as ash, oak, alder and grey willow (*Salix cinerea*), has been planted with an under-storey of hawthorn, blackthorn (*Prunus spinosa*), alder buckthorn and guelder-rose. The intention is to increase the number and diversity of trees in the marginal land adjoining the reserve and to create warm sunny glades for the benefit of insects. The field still has the appearance of a tree nursery, but butterflies and other insects are already foraging in large numbers in the sheltered grassy patches.

References

1 Wallis (1904), p. 220
2 Babington (1860)
3 Wicken Fen Local Committee botanical records
4 West (1898)
5 Evans (1925), p. 90
6 Yapp (1908), p. 79
7 Ibid., p. 80
8 Godwin (1929), p. 148
9 Godwin (1936), p. 82
10 Godwin & Bharucha (1932), p. 185
11 Ibid., p. 181
12 Godwin (1936)
13 Godwin *et al.* (1974)
14 Wicken Fen Executive Committee Minute Books (1913)
15 Rowell (1983a), Chapter 9
16 Photograph files, Wicken Fen archive
17 Richards (1932)
18 Proctor (1956)
19 Lock (1963)
20 Rowell & Harvey (1988)
21 Jenyns (1845)
22 Evans (1911)
23 Laundon (1973)
24 Laundon (13 February 1991, letter in Wicken Fen archive)

PART THREE

Flora and Fauna

7

BOTANICAL RECORDS AND
FLORISTIC STUDIES

S. M. WALTERS

EFORE the middle of the 19th century, there are hardly any records of plants that can be localized with certainty to what we now call Wicken Fen. Indeed, the names 'Wicken Fen' or 'Wicken Sedge Fen' do not appear at all in the earlier Cambridgeshire Floras, neither in the first by Ray, published in 1660,[1] nor in its successor by Relhan.[2,3,4] Of course, we can find generalized records referring to famous Wicken plants in these early works, such as Ray's statement about bog-myrtle (*Myrica gale*) that it grows 'in the fens in the Isle of Ely in many places abundantly'; but the records by Babington, especially those published in his *Flora* of 1860,[5] constitute the first substantial body of information. Since Babington's time, however, we have a fairly continuous botanical record up to the present day.

Three published lists of the vascular plants of Wicken Fen are available: the first appears as an appendix in Babington's Flora of 1860; the second was compiled by Max Walters and published as a check-list pamphlet in 1967;[6] the third, published in 1994, is an updated, annotated version of Walters' list.[7] This check-list is based upon a card index of all traceable records which Walters began to compile in 1950, and which is still kept by the Botanical Secretary. A computerized version of the records was produced by Michael Lock in 1985, copies of which are available to research workers and others. The records cited in this chapter are to be found in this file, unless otherwise stated.

Information on particular species covers well over a century, and in a few cases, such as marsh pea (*Lathyrus palustris*), actually verifies that the plant has been at Wicken Fen for more than 150 years. Most records tell us nothing about the abundance of the species concerned, but Babington's 1860 list is a valuable exception, for in it he indicates with an asterisk those species 'which most abound' in Wicken Fen, and he further comments on the dominant role of *Cladium* in the sedge crop there.

One striking feature of the plant records is that weeds and ruderals in general are badly recorded, probably because most recorders feel that they are alien to the Fen. The case of the common daisy (*Bellis perennis*) illustrates this under-recording. Our first record for Wicken is by P. D. Sell 'on the track by the brick-pits' on 15 May 1954; it was subsequently recorded in 1982 and 1984, and 'on path by Drainers' Ditch, May 1985' by J. M. Lock. This is a familiar and widespread plant confined to the well-trodden paths at Wicken, and it seems very doubtful that its very late first record can be taken as good evidence that it is a recent arrival on the Fen. A similar case is ground-ivy (*Glechoma hederacea*) first recorded by H. Godwin on 24 August 1948 as 'in places abundant to dominant (on ground) below *Crataegus*', and subsequently confirmed in 1951, 1957, 1982 and 1985. There is good reason to believe that most recorders before 1950 were simply inclined to ignore very common plants that were in their opinion not 'characteristic of the Fen'.

The theme of this chapter concerns the interesting conclusions that can be drawn from a comparison between what Babington recorded and what we can find on the Fen today. No attempt has been made to summarize all the floristic information in the records. Instead, a number of plant species, or groups of species, of special interest have been selected and the links between their history (as revealed by the botanical records) and general ecological changes on the Fen are examined.

RARE FENLAND SPECIES

Fen orchid (*Liparis loeselii*) (Plate 3, Fig. 4)

Throughout the late Victorian and Edwardian period, the presence of rare fenland plants at Wicken Fen contributed greatly to the Fen's attraction for naturalists. One of the most remarkable of these plants was the fen orchid, now a nationally rare and legally protected species, but, alas, extinct at Wicken.

The history of *Liparis loeselii* in Cambridgeshire goes back to John Ray, who knew it well on 'Hinton and Teversham Moors' near Cambridge, and who gave a very accurate and detailed description of it (the first published British reference to the species) in his Flora of 1660.[1] By 1860, the drainage and destruction of 'moor' habitats in the area meant that Babington, in his *Flora*,[5] was already treating the fen orchid as extinct in the whole county. Soon afterwards, however, he learned that the plant was still growing at Wicken: the evidence was provided by 'Mr. H. E. Fox of Trinity College', who found two specimens there. Its existence at Wicken Fen was confirmed in 1867,

1896 and 1908. The botanist N. D. Simpson included in his field note-book a detailed sketch map of where he saw it growing on the Poor's Fen on 24 July 1913.

It is evident from the sparse and guarded references in print that those naturalists around the turn of the century who knew exactly where *Liparis* grew at Wicken kept the secret to themselves. That secrecy was a sensible precaution, as is evidenced by the fact that C. E. Moss took a specimen for the University Herbarium in 1910 – the only Wicken specimen to be found there. J. E. Lousley visited the Fen on 22 June 1935, and collected and pressed a specimen, which he placed with two photographs in his herbarium (now at Reading) and labelled 'abundant in a fen adj. Wicken Fen'.

From the fragmentary evidence, it appears that there were at least two different areas of Wicken Poor's Fen in which *Liparis* grew. The last *Liparis* known at Wicken was probably that seen by Charles Raven in 1945, who visited the Poor's Fen locality which had been known to the Cambridge botanists at least as early as 1939, when T. G. Tutin saw it. When Max Walters searched the site in 1950, there was a good deal of suitable habitat, but no *Liparis*.

It is not too difficult to fill in the ecological background of the extinction of *Liparis* at Wicken. An invaluable clue is given by the account of a field meeting in 1835 of the 'Swaffham Prior Naturalists' Society', a remarkable organization formed by the children of the talented Jenyns family at Bottisham Hall, not far from Burwell and Wicken Fens. The minutes of their visit to Burwell Fen record:

'We had very good sport both in plants and insects. *Ophrys* [*Liparis*] *loeselii* was found in great plenty. Between four hundred and five hundred specimens were brought home. It was growing in the grass and moss among the pits where they cut turf. There were two bulbs to each plant, and the bulbs were scarcely in the ground at all, so that we picked them out easily with our fingers'.[8]

It is tempting to conclude from this extract that gross over-collecting was responsible for the decline of the fen orchid, and, whilst the Victorian collecting mania cannot have helped this or many another rare plant, the real reasons for both the abundance and the decline are to be sought in the species' very specialized ecological requirements. From what we know of its surviving habitats in East Anglia, it is clear that *Liparis*, like several other Fenland rarities, flourishes in an open community where competition from the main fen dominants is not too intense. Such transient 'open' communities, in which cushions of fen mosses grow, are characteristic of stages of natural succession after traditional turf- or peat-digging. In 1835 on Burwell Fen and the surrounding peat-lands (including parts of what is now the Wicken Fen nature reserve) there was an active peat-digging industry (Chapter 10). The demise of this industry in the 1930s roughly coincides with that of the fen orchid.

Fen violet (*Viola persicifolia*) (Plate 4, Fig. 1)

The other nationally rare and legally protected species at Wicken Fen is *Viola persicifolia* (*V. stagnina*). The history of the fen violet at Wicken is unique. Marked by

Babington in his list of Wicken plants as one of the species which 'most abound there',[5] it was already very rarely seen before the turn of the century, and was considered extinct by all botanists working at Wicken from the 1920s onwards.

In 1951, Max Walters set up a small experimental plot near the Brickpits, primarily to study the differential growth of *Eleocharis* species under different soil water-levels. He took the opportunity to test whether *Viola persicifolia* plants taken from Woodwalton Fen nature reserve would grow in the bared peat in the Wicken plot. Only three plants were involved in this experimental introduction, which was abandoned in 1952 and the only surviving plant removed. Walters noted, however, that seedlings of species not present in the surrounding fen vegetation, especially *Carex serotina* (now *C. viridula* subsp. *viridula*, yellow-sedge), had appeared in the plot, apparently from dormant seed. If this sedge, a very local plant of disturbed peat at Wicken, re-appeared when peat was bared, then other species, including the supposedly extinct violet, might yet do the same.

In May 1980, Terry Rowell spotted a *Viola* among seedlings growing in peat soil samples taken from beneath scrub on the Fen (see Chapter 6). This seedling was grown on in the University Botanic Garden, and produced a typical mature plant of *V. persicifolia*. This dramatic 're-incarnation' of a supposedly extinct Wicken plant was followed closely by the discovery, on Verrall's Fen, in 1982, of a large flowering population of *V. persicifolia*, together with a small number of another violet, the rare *V. canina* subsp. *montana* (heath dog-violet).[9] The latter species had never previously been recorded at Wicken, although it was known to grow at Woodwalton, and formerly elsewhere in the Fens.

This remarkable 'new' violet population at Wicken has been studied each year, and its behaviour seems to be essentially similar to that known at Woodwalton. Any disturbance of the peat-fen communities produces locally bare peat habitats in which dormant *Viola* seed (and that of other species, such as *Juncus articulatus* (jointed rush)) can germinate and establish seedling plants. These *Viola* plants can flourish for one or two seasons, producing both open and cleistogamous flowers (the latter forming ripe fruits without fail), then the surrounding tall fen vegetation closes over the violets, and they remain inconspicuous until some new disturbance.

Although the broad outline of this behaviour is now clear, many questions remain unanswered. One concerns the vegetative persistence of *Viola persicifolia*, which characteristically produces long thin underground stolons in the peat: how important is vegetative propagation relative to spreading by seed? Another concerns the precise conditions under which the dormant seed in the upper layers of the peat will germinate and succeed in establishing new plants. Two factors related to habitat are evidently involved: one is the temporary availability of bare peat, but the other, perhaps equally important, is the adaptation of the plant to seasonal flooding following by drying.

The *Viola* population at Wicken has recently been managed by a programme of summer cutting of the mixed fen vegetation and bush clearance from marginal carr. The result of this policy, as judged by the flowering of the violet in May and June 1990, seemed to be satisfactory, and a rotational treatment, designed to provide some cyclical interference to enable new seedlings to establish themselves, was planned for future years. However, in 1993, no plants were found at the site, and the future of the fen violet at Wicken Fen seemed very uncertain, particularly as the species had also disappeared at Woodwalton Fen. However, in 1994, many seedlings have emerged from an area cleared of scrub near the Wicken '*Viola* field'. The fen violet is now being studied by Jane Croft as part of English Nature's Species Recovery Programme: fifty plants grown from Wicken seed have been planted on the Sedge Fen in experimental plots and appear (in March 1997) to be well established.

In the light of this recent history, what are we to make of Babington's record that in 1860 *Viola persicifolia* (or '*V. stagnina*' as he called it) was one of the really abundant plants on the Fen? The probable explanation is that at that particular time the Fen – or at least that part of the Fen which Babington saw – temporarily presented a habitat ideally suited to an abundant flowering of the violet. The likely cause of its decline would be the abandonment of once active and widespread peat-digging. The history of the fen violet might then resemble the local and temporary abundance of *Liparis* some thirty years earlier on Burwell Fen. The spread of tall dominant plants, especially *Frangula*, which was obviously rapid in the 1870s and 1880s (see Chapter 6), would eliminate the violet, at least so far as any flowers were concerned.

The history of the fen violet at Wicken focuses attention on a somewhat neglected phenomenon in nature reserve management: the significance of the reservoir of dormant seed and the role of disturbance in releasing it into growth. Most rarities at Wicken are rare precisely because they are unable to retain a permanent niche in the dominant fen vegetation types. We should therefore regard the production of long-lived seed, capable of remaining dormant for many years in the upper peat-layers, as a positive adaptation likely to be important in the ecology of many Wicken species.

Fen ragwort (*Senecio paludosus*) (Plate 4, Fig. 2)

The fen ragwort has also returned to Wicken Fen after a long absence. However, while the fen violet has come and gone in the same place apparently in response to changes in local conditions, the fen ragwort had been missing for so long that the probability of it ever reappearing naturally on the Fen was vanishingly small. That this magnificent plant is once again to be seen on the Fen is the result of a reintroduction carried out by an English Nature Species Recovery Programme team led by Terry Wells.

Senecio paludosus was first recorded in Britain by John Ray, who said: 'We have found it in many places in the Fens, as by a great ditch side near Stretham Ferry'.[1] The 19th-century records for the plant are almost exclusively for the area of fenland around Ely. It was recorded many times on what is now the nature reserve at Wicken Fen and the last record from Wicken, made by Babington in 1857,[10] is generally accepted as the last properly-documented evidence for the species growing in the wild in Britain. Babington also recorded that some material was collected from the Fen and cultivated in the Cambridge University Botanic Garden. There is some possibility that the species survived in the wild much later than 1857, perhaps into the 20th century; the documentary evidence from the period is tantalizingly inconclusive.[11]

In July 1972, *Senecio paludosus* was rediscovered growing in a fenland ditch within its known former range in Cambridgeshire by T. W. J. D. Dupree.[11] The length of ditch containing the plant was put under the protection of the Cambridgeshire and Isle of Ely Naturalists' Trust. The plants successfully set seed and the ripe fruiting heads were collected as the stems died back. The ripe seed and a very small proportion of the root-stock of the non-flowering plants were planted in the University Botanic Garden. There is now a good stock in cultivation, including one plant growing in the Demonstration Garden at Wicken Fen.

In 1991, seeds were collected from the ditch site and grown on in cultivation. Fifty seedlings were planted out in May 1992 in an open site on the edge of a shallow pond in the centre of Wicken Sedge Fen. The plants were set out on a hydrological gradient: one row was at the edge of the pond, with the water-level at the top of the basal rosette, another row 15cm higher and a third slightly higher again. Half the site was fenced against deer grazing and half left open. The plants grew rapidly, flowered well and set seed. There seemed to be little if any difference in performance in this first year of plants in wetter or drier situations. However, many of the plants were later found to have been heavily grazed, both within and outside the fenced area. The culprits were thought to be slugs and it was evident that plants surrounded by water were the least affected. This seems to be a case of hydrological conditions influencing plant performance through an unexpected intermediary.

Fen ragwort is currently thriving at Wicken Fen and we hope that it has an assured future here, where its population can be monitored and the surrounding vegetation managed in a way conducive to the plant's survival. The future of the plant in the broader fenland countryside is less certain. Given the history of its apparent extinction in Britain and rediscovery, how likely is the fen ragwort to reappear in other fenland sites? The plants found near Ely in 1972 could not possibly have been derived from seed persisting on that exact site over several decades, because the ditch in which it was found was newly constructed in 1968. It may have spread there from a site nearby, in which case new sites may yet be found. It does, however, seem incredible that such a tall, distinctive plant could go undiscovered, given the level of botanical recording in Britain. It is not impossible that the plant was reintroduced to the Fens from continental stock by a well-meaning but misguided enthusiast, or even as seeds on the feathers or feet of birds. It seems unlikely that the seed can remain viable over very long periods of time and then germinate following disturbance, but the history of the fen violet suggests that such possibilities cannot be dismissed out of hand.

Marsh pea (*Lathyrus palustris*)

Another of the famous Wicken Fen rarities, the marsh pea (Fig. 35), is still locally frequent there.

In the Cambridge Botany School Herbarium there is a specimen from Wicken dated 1834, which is the earliest known localized record for any Wicken plant, and Babington's Journal records, for 5 July 1851, that he and friends 'walked by the river-

Figure 35 Marsh pea (*Lathyrus palustris*)[12]

side (from Waterbeach) to Upware, and along the Spinny bank across the fen to a house near Wicken. Examined Wicken Fen, finding Lathyrus palustris, Stratiotes, Arundo Calamagrostis, Cladium etc.'[13]

For more than 150 years we have a steady trickle of records, mostly, like Babington's, unlocalized except to 'Wicken Fen', but we know that the plant was on Adventurers' Fen in 1921, and St Edmund's Fen in 1957, and it is a reasonable assumption that it was widespread on much of the present nature reserve from much earlier times.

Ray did not know *Lathyrus palustris* in Cambridgeshire, and the first county records are in the 1820 edition of Relhan's flora,[4] where it is recorded for 'Swaffham Fen' and 'Reche Lode'. The 19th-century drainage of much of the remaining fenland outside the Wicken area brought about its local extinction, and for generations botanists have seen it only in Wicken Fen.

Miss P. Cammell carried out a survey of the marsh pea at Wicken from 1972–74,[14] and showed that it was usually to be found growing at the edges of the droves and lodes, and was largely absent from the main areas of vegetation on the Fen proper, whether these were dominated by carr, sedge or reed. She also found that one of the largest populations was in the rough hay-meadow community in compartment 21, outside the limit of the Fen proper (see map, Appendix A). The occurrences of *Lathyrus* seemed to depend on reduced competition from the taller fen dominants such as found in 'mixed fen' communities. In spite of careful study, she was unable to decide the spatial limits of vegetatively-spread individual plants and, though seed from plants on the Fen germinated relatively easily in the University Botanic Garden, she was not able to find undoubted seedlings on the Fen itself.

Because the marsh pea at Wicken is typical of the edges of rides and droves, one's impression of its overall abundance is probably exaggerated. The relatively closed communities of mature *Cladium* and developing carr are quite unsuitable for it. This, of course, has the happy consequence that it remains a 'rare' plant that one can guarantee to see without difficulty in flower at Wicken in July and August.

Fibrous tussock-sedge (*Carex appropinquata*)

Wicken is particularly rich in sedges (Cyperaceae), and has no fewer than 17 species of *Carex* on the list, most of which are still to be seen on the Fen. One of the rarest is *Carex appropinquata*, a densely tussock-forming sedge resembling a smaller version of the much more widespread greater tussock-sedge (*C. paniculata*). Its persistence at Wicken illustrates the importance of the nature reserve in continuing to supply habitats for wetland species formerly more widespread in Britain but now rare or local. A recent note by R. W. David,[15] which gives details of all known British and Irish localities for this sedge, emphasizes that in many earlier-recorded places it is now no longer possible to find the plant. David says that his 'observations in the field suggest that *C. appropinquata* is less tolerant of drought, shade and competition than is *C. paniculata*'. Like many rare plants, its exact habitat requirements are presumably quite specialized, and there is evidence of decline at Wicken Fen in recent years: at the time of the original record (1885), A. Fryer recorded that it was 'abundant', but such statements are not easily interpreted. *Carex appropinquata* is rather inconspicuous, and particularly so when not flowering, so the size of the Wicken population is not easy to determine. The most recent estimate[16] is that the Wicken population consists of about 60 plants in two patches in carr on the south side of Gardiner's Drove.

Fen dandelion or narrow-leaved marsh-dandelion (*Taraxacum palustre*)

Taraxacum palustre is a distinctive plant with very narrow, often almost entire leaves, and appressed outer involucral bracts. It was first described from 'Hinton Moor' near Cambridge (a locality long since built over) by Israel Lyons in 1763. It was familiar to Relhan, and later to Babington, but it is not recorded for Wicken by the latter. C. E. Moss seems to have been the first Cambridge botanist to record it for Wicken Fen in 1909, and in the 1930s the plant was well known to A. H. Evans and other botanists. In the 1940s there was a small population on Sedge Fen Drove together with other *Taraxacum* microspecies, which were not separately distinguished at the time. This population declined through the 1950s and seems now to have died out, but a larger population was discovered around 1950 in North Breed Fen.

In May 1972, William Palmer and Max Walters surveyed the Breed Fen population, and estimated more than 100 discrete flowering clumps scattered through the wetter part of the field. A similar number of flowering plants, restricted to the wetter (lower) half of the field nearest the Fen proper, was counted on 29 April 1974 by the Botany School field class. On 7 May 1975, a similar exercise produced a count of fewer than 50 flowering clumps, mostly near the present site of the William Thorpe Building. There was a particularly wet spring in 1975, and flowering may have been delayed.

No detailed figures are available for 1976–78 but, in 1979, Max Walters counted about 40 plants in flower and young fruit, mostly at the south-west corner of the field. In 1981, John Harvey began his 5-year study of the population.[17] Over the period of the study, the plant had an extremely restricted distribution, with all but a handful of plants being confined to an area of 30m by 18m. Even within this area, the plants showed a very clumped distribution. The study strongly suggests that the spread of the fen dandelion may be largely clonal: only one putative seedling was recorded in the whole five-year study, and, in three of the five years, between 60 and 90 per cent of all flowering heads had suffered predation, probably by small mammals, and little or no seed was set. The size of the population also varied widely, with 403 rosettes recorded in 1982, but only 163 in 1985.

One of the aims of this study was to develop a management regime that might ensure the survival of the species at Wicken Fen or to increase the size of the population. As clonal growth seemed to be important and regeneration from seed rare, Harvey recommended 'a regime of close and regular mowing' for the lower area of the field where the population is now found. In spite of this specific treatment, the fen dandelion has declined further and it has not been possible to find any plants since 1992. It seems that the 'fen dandelion' field has become drier over the last decade, with oxeye daisy

(*Leucanthemum vulgare*) becoming established in large numbers in recent years, and it is possible that this has not favoured the dandelion. The fate of *Taraxacum palustre* is a matter of great concern to the Management Committee and a new research project is now under way to raise plants from Wicken seed and try to discover why the fen dandelion has declined. If the project is successful, plants will be introduced and the habitat managed in an attempt to help the population become firmly re-established.

SPECIES CHANGING IN ABUNDANCE AT WICKEN FEN

The botanical records, although essentially floristic in emphasis, make it possible to detect changes in the abundance and distribution of certain species that can sometimes be of great ecological significance. While it is of considerable interest to record the occurrence of the rare fen species, it is perhaps more instructive from an ecological point of view to enquire into the changing fortunes on the Fen of some of the more common plants, especially those that are among the dominants of the main vegetation types.

Marsh-orchids and spotted-orchids (*Dactylorhiza* (*Dactylorchis*) spp.)

Among the most conspicuous and attractive plants on the Fen in May and June are the *Dactylorhiza* spp. The common species at Wicken is the early marsh-orchid *Dactylorhiza incarnata* (*Orchis incarnata*, *O. strictifolia*), first recorded by Babington[5] as *O. incarnata*, and one of the plants said by him to 'especially abound there'. The common flower-colour at Wicken Fen is the typical flesh-pink one, but a range of colours from white to a rich, deep purplish-red is exhibited every year somewhere on the droves. This colour-range seems to have been first recorded at Wicken Fen in 1900 by W. J. Cross, who placed specimens of both the white and the red-purple variants in the Herbarium of the Botany School in Cambridge.

In 1923, A. H. Evans[18] commented that: 'The drainage has left many spots, not wet enough for the full growth of the roughest vegetation..., where the common marsh Orchids have undoubtedly increased, especially *Orchis incarnata*'. Whilst we may reasonably question Evans' interpretation of the cause, we can accept his observation that marsh orchids flourished with the increased management of the Fen under the National Trust. Marsh orchids are locally common in 'mixed fen' vegetation that arises on the edges of rides, and the present regular cutting extends their habitats further (see Fig. 21 & 26).

Another result of the increase in this habitat has been that three other *Dactylorhiza* species now occur at Wicken. The first of these, the southern marsh-orchid (*D. praetermissa*), was recorded by Evans in his list of 1923[19] and confirmed by Max Walters in 1978. It is a very handsome orchid with large red-purple flowers in which the labellum is flat and broader than *D. incarnata*, and is locally common in fens in lowland England (such as Triplow Meadows in Cambridgeshire). Its 'arrival' at Wicken Fen, where it now grows mixed with *D. incarnata*, emphasizes how the wild orchids, with their widely-dispersed dust-like seed, can appear in suitable new habitats. The related spotted orchids seem to be showing a similar spread to Wicken. The common spotted-orchid of the calcareous soils of Cambridgeshire, *Dactylorhiza fuchsii* (Plate 4, Fig. 3), was first recorded [as *Dactylorchis*] for Wicken Fen by Evans in 1911, but not subsequently verified until 1986, when P. D. Sell recorded a single plant by the path by Drainers' Dyke.[20] In the same year, the Warden, Tim Bennett, discovered eight plants of the heath spotted-orchid *D. maculata* ssp. *ericetorum* (Plate 4, Fig. 4) at the west end of Sedge Fen Drove; a specimen is in the Herbarium of the Cambridge Botany School. This last-named orchid is new, not just to Wicken Fen, but to VC29 (Cambridgeshire) as a whole; it is the common spotted orchid of acid soils of the north and west of Britain, and its appearance at Wicken in the area where other somewhat calcifuge species are found (see *Myrica gale*) is of special interest.

Small-reed (*Calamagrostis*) spp.

Changes in the composition of the fen 'litter' community over the past century (Chapter 5) have been noted amongst the dominant grass species as well as among the more spectacular herbs. Purple moor-grass (*Molinia caerulea*) has declined greatly, while two species of *Calamogrostis* have become much more abundant.

The purple small-reed, *C. canescens* (*C. lanceolata* of earlier authors), and wood small-reed, *C. epigejos*, are now frequent at Wicken Fen, and their relative abundance and behaviour under different conditions have ecological significance. This is true both of their changing frequencies at different periods of the Fen history, and also of their differential behaviour in the various fen habitats at any one time.

A detailed study of the two species at Wicken Fen (and at Woodwalton Fen) was undertaken by K. E. Luck in 1959–64. In her PhD thesis she summarizes and comments on the historical records for *Calamagrostis* on the Fen:

'apart from the relative sparseness of the records themselves, the situation is further complicated by such difficulties as: a) taxonomic confusion between *C. epigejos* and *C. lanceolata*; b) the possibility of the plants not flowering during certain periods, making recognition difficult. Absence of mention is difficult to interpret; c) lack of many estimates of abundance rather than mere presence'.[21]

The third point is, of course, true for virtually every species recorded at Wicken before the present century. Even frequency records usually fail to include any information on size or degree of vigour of the plants, although such observations could be crucial in interpreting floristic changes in an ecological way.

The other two points are more specific to *Calamagrostis*, although they are relevant to grasses and sedges in general. The identification problems posed by 'sterility' (the failure to flower) are considerable. The two *Calamagrostis* species are difficult to distinguish with certainty on purely vegetative characters; in particular, though the upper leaf surface (hairy in *C. canescens*, glabrous in *C. epigejos*) is usually a good field character, it is not always so. Even when fertile, the inflorescences of *C. epigejos* could easily be confused with those of *C. canescens* when the plants are growing in sub-optimal conditions. Luck also points out that the absence of records for either species may be due to the persistence of the grass in a non-flowering state under relatively unfavourable conditions such as prolonged flooding or waterlogging, or shade created by bush colonization.

The first verifiable record for *C. epigejos* is that of Babington in 1855 for Wicken Fen itself. This specimen, in the Cambridge University Herbarium, has been verified by Luck so that Babington's statement, both in his *Flora of Cambridgeshire* proper and in the Wicken List appended to it, that only '*C. lanceolata*' (i.e. *C. canescens*) occurred at Wicken, must be assumed to be incorrect. In fact, there are no 19th-century records supported by herbarium specimens for *C. canescens* at Wicken Fen, though a small number of reliable botanists obviously looked for it, distinguishing it from the *C. epigejos* known to be there.

Negative evidence about *C. canescens* on the Fen continues into the present century, and the first reliable botanist to state that he saw both *Calamagrostis* species at 'Wicken Fen' seems to be N. D. Simpson, in a notebook he kept between 1909 and 1913. By 1923[19] both species are being regularly listed, and Godwin and Tansley[22] include both (using the names *C. epigejos* and *C. lanceolata*) in their 1929 list of the 'more prominent species' which become established in the 'secondary succession' that follows bush clearing.

Summing up the evidence, Luck observes that *C. epigejos* seems to have spread at Wicken Fen during the last decade of the 19th century, and that 'between 1909 & 1923 *C. canescens* seems to have become established on the Fen, some 55 years later than *C. epigejos*'. She comments that 'since *C. canescens* is more often [than *C. epigejos*] a plant of wet peaty habitats .... it seems somewhat surprising that it should have been so much later than *C. epigejos* in arriving at Wicken...'. Her analysis concludes 'Since about 1940 it seems that both *Calamagrostis* spp. have spread over most parts of Wicken Fen where local conditions are suitable .... possibly bush clearance [has] favoured the spread of both species.'

The evidence from the monitoring of the Godwin Plots (Chapter 5) suggests that the two species may respond rather differently to mowing regimes, *C. canescens* being among the dominant herbaceous species in the uncut plot but rare in the mown plots, and the reverse being true for *C. epigejos*.

Black bog-rush (*Schoenus nigricans*)

The history of *Schoenus nigricans* at Wicken Fen provides a contrast with that of the *Calamagrostis* species. This very characteristic plant of wet peaty soils was known to all the early Cambridgeshire botanists, and first recorded for Wicken by Babington, as one of the plants 'that most abound there'. In 1910 C. E. Moss recorded it from Wicken Poor's Fen, where it was next recorded by E. F. Warburg in 1938. How much of the plant survived on the Poor's Fen into the 20th century is speculation, but in 1908 Yapp[23] states that at Wicken he had 'only seen a single tuft, by the side of Wicken Lode', which implies a very considerable decline in the second half of the 19th century. Max Walters discovered a few tufts in a small area of the Poor's Fen in 1950, and observed these till 1954. This seems to be the last record made at Wicken Fen.

The decline of *Schoenus nigricans* is understandable in the light of its behaviour in other fen localities, and in the nature reserve at Chippenham Fen in particular. There, its local persistence is strongly linked to regular cutting of the 'mixed fen' vegetation in which it grows, thus preventing the dominant species of typical mixed fen or reed-swamp from shading it out. The local abundance of *Schoenus nigricans* at Wicken in the last century might then reasonably be interpreted as a temporary recolonization phase following an opening up of the vegetation by extensive peat-digging.

After more than 35 years, it is tempting to suppose that the black bog-rush is extinct at Wicken. The same was assumed of the fen violet; the history of this supposedly extinct species should alert us to the possibility of *Schoenus nigricans* re-appearing in suitable micro-habitats from dormant seed.

Bog-myrtle (*Myrica gale*)

Of the handful of calcifuge angiosperms on the current Wicken Fen checklist, the best-known is the aromatic shrub *Myrica gale*, (Fig. 36), a characteristic species of acid bog and moorland in the north and west of the British Isles. In the light of John Ray's assertion that it 'grows in the fens in the Isle of Ely in many places abundantly'[1], it is perhaps surprising that Babington never saw the plant at Wicken, and, at the end of his Wicken list of 1860, mentions it as one of several plants 'which either are, or were formerly, natives of the Fen, ... not yet noticed in Wicken Fen'.[5] Indeed, he seems never to have seen bog-myrtle anywhere in Cambridgeshire, judging it to be 'destroyed by

Figure 36   Bog-myrtle (*Myrica gale*) (foreground) and the birch grove, July 1994

drainage and cultivation', though we have evidence that it persisted at Wimblington Fire-lots (a relict peat-fen) until 1895.

The first record of bog-myrtle for Wicken Fen was made by Albert Hosking, who recorded both male and female plants 'at the NE side' of Wicken Fen in 1901. Yapp, in his pioneer study of the Wicken vegetation[23] (Chapter 5), confirms that this is a recent discovery, saying the plant is 'now to be found there'. It was known to recorders from the Cambridge Botany School throughout the inter-war period, and, in 1954, Max Walters mapped three distinct patches on the Sedge Fen, including the best-known site at the Drainers' Dyke end of Sedge Fen Drove. These patches still survive, and indeed have been managed over the years by the removal of competing carr, mainly *Salix cinerea*. In 1988, Tim Bennett discovered a new site near the Godwin plots, about 200m north of the main site.

A number of other calcifuge angiosperms appear to have been lost from the Wicken Fen list during this century. These include two carnivorous plants, the lesser bladder-wort (*Utricularia minor*), and the round-leaved sundew (*Drosera rotundifolia*), although the latter is known only from a single record of about 1900 for which there is no support-ing herbarium specimen. Is there any evidence that acid peat occurred in the recent past on the Sedge Fen? Rowell and Harvey, in their description of the ecological devel-opment of the reserve,[24] critically examine the evidence provided by plants and an-imals characteristic of acidic soils and conclude that our records of such 'indicator species' are of little value in settling the question. Even *Myrica gale* may be a poor indi-cator of former acidic conditions on the Fen, as it occurs in Norfolk on peat of pH up to 7.0.[25]

Charophyta

Some aquatic species have also shown changes in response to patterns of management on the Sedge Fen. The charophyte algae, or stoneworts, have been relatively well recorded at Wicken Fen. This is true in the British Isles generally, mainly because it has been a long tradition of the Botanical Society of the British Isles, which is very active in field recording, to include this extraordinary group of algae as 'honorary vascular plants'.

Babington gives two species, *Chara hispida* and *C. vulgaris*, in his Wicken list. Critical work began at Wicken when H. and J. Groves visited the Fen in 1881 and 1882, and recorded as such the first species of *Nitella*, including the rare *N. tenuissima*, for which Wicken Lode became the best-known British locality. In 1920, Groves and Bullock-Webster state *N. tenuissima* to be 'most plentiful in the fenlands of Cambridgeshire, its headquarters apparently being in Wicken Lode'.[26]

Nitella tenuissima is now very rare, having disappeared along with the rest of the rich charophyte community from Wicken Lode in the 1950s (Chapter 3). However, it reap-peared in 1957 in water-filled experimental peat-cuttings on the Sedge Fen and again in 1979 in similar circumstances.[27] In August 1992, a small patch of *N. tenuissima* about 60cm across was spotted in 50cm of water on a peaty shelf at the edge of Wicken

Lode.[28] Shortly afterwards, the Lode vegetation was cut and the patch could not be refound, but it seems highly unlikely that the species will have been wiped out in the Lode, and we expect it to reappear in due course.

The luxuriant carpet of charophytes that once occurred in Wicken Lode included another nationally scarce stonewort species, *Chara pedunculata*. The last record for this species in the Lode dates from 1949. However, a single clump of *C. pedunculata* was found in 1990 in one of the sections of Gardiner's Ditch that had been re-excavated in the previous decade.[29] The history of both these species at Wicken Fen illustrates the tendency for charophytes to appear sporadically following the disturbance of wet peat and again suggests that the ability of propagules to lie dormant in the peat may be a crucial factor in determining whether or not certain species will re-establish themselves when degraded fen habitats are restored.

SPECIES ALIEN TO THE FEN

In addition to the common weeds and ruderals alluded to in the introduction, the Wicken Fen records contain several examples of alien species, including a number of North American origin, whose appearance at the Fen is part of their spread in Britain as a whole. Some of these are aquatic plants, and these are described in Chapter 3.

Michaelmas-daisy (*Aster novi-belgii*)

Aster novi-belgii ('*A. salignus*'), was first recorded at Wicken Fen in 1864, by J. Brown, who said there was 'one large patch not far from the houses'. Several botanists around the turn of the century were interested in the plant, and there was some speculation that it might be native to the Fen. In 1939, Evans recorded that the plant was seen by Hiern 'at the village end of the Fen, then used as cottage gardens', and was obviously of the opinion that the plant was a garden escape. He noted that it 'is now quite established there, and has increased to fill a space of 20 or 30 yards square, though there were at first only two or three clumps, which had hardly increased by 1877.'[30]

Generations of Cambridge botanists have paid their respects to '*Aster salignus*' at Wicken Fen: it continues to hold its own amongst the mixed fen vegetation on Milner-White's Fen (compartment 19) not far from the entrance, flowering in August and September. In his taxonomic revision of *Aster* for *Flora Europaea* of 1976, P. F. Yeo supported the view of the 19th-century American taxonomist Asa Gray that the Wicken Fen plant in the Herbarium of the Cambridge Botany School is *A. novi-belgii*.[31] He treats *A.* × *salignus* as a hybrid between the North American species *A. novi-belgii* and *A. lanceolata*. A detailed treatment of the naturalized Michaelmas-daisies of North American origin is available in the third edition of Clapham, Tutin & Moore.[32]

The Wicken Fen aster continues to fascinate Cambridge botanists. In 1989, David Briggs and co-workers published a detailed account, in which the historical evidence is meticulously assessed.[33] This seems to be the only case of an obviously alien garden plant becoming effectively naturalized on the Fen.

American willowherb (*Epilobium ciliatum*)

Epilobium ciliatum (*E. adenocaulon*) is now common apparently throughout Cambridge-shire (and indeed much of England) but was not recognized in the county until as late as 1946. Its arrival at Wicken Fen could be predicted, but is not very accurately dated in the early 1970s. By 1976 it was recorded by Max Walters as 'well established on disturbed ground in several parts of the Sedge Fen' and already hybridizing with the native *E. parviflorum* (hoary willowherb). It is now probably the commonest *Epilobium*, except for *E. hirsutum* (great willowherb), to be seen on the Fen.

Slender rush (*Juncus tenuis*)

The very distinctive slender rush was first recorded at Wicken Fen by Mrs G. Crompton and Max Walters on 13 July 1988, as a single fruiting clump on the drove by the Brickpits. This North American species is now widely naturalized in the north and west of the British Isles, but relatively uncommon in Eastern England. There are a few other Cambridgeshire records, the oldest being that at Gamlingay (1919).

The arrival of this new wetland species at Wicken Fen, ready to take its place among the seven native species of *Juncus* already on the Fen's list, emphasizes that the flora of the nature reserve may be continuously enriched by natural immigration. Unlike the case of *Bellis perennis*, we can be reasonably sure that *Juncus tenuis* is a real new immigrant, not a plant previously overlooked or misidentified. The reason one can say this with some confidence is that Wicken Fen has been continuously botanized since the end of the second World War, and that the flora of the more accessible rides and droves in particular is subject to scrutiny, not least by teachers eager to demonstrate the characteristic species of the Fen to groups of students. Since the species of *Juncus* are known to be sensitive indicators of ecological factors, they always attract some attention. It is, of course, true that many demonstrators using the Fen for less specialist teaching would avoid comment on grasses, rushes and sedges, and prefer to concentrate on the more familiar 'wild flowers'; but Wicken Fen is no ordinary nature reserve in this respect (Chapter 12), and University and sixth-form school teaching provides a continuous year-by-year check on all the vascular flora in a way that does not happen in most other nature reserves.

The fate of the single clump of this new *Juncus* can easily be monitored, and its initial spread, if it occurs, can be accurately recorded. We have rather little information on these early stages of spread of alien species, and well-organized nature reserves such as Wicken Fen provide ideal opportunities.

Swamp meadow-grass (*Poa palustris*)

Not all aliens to the Fen fit into this pattern of reflecting the spread of the species in Britain generally. A remarkable and, as yet rather mysterious, case concerns the meadow-grasses (*Poa* spp.)

The only species of *Poa* for which there is a 19th-century Wicken record is *P. trivialis* (rough meadow-grass), included by Babington in his list of 1860.[5] There is no reason to doubt this record, since the plant is still frequent on the Fen, and is indeed the common meadow-grass there. No new *Poa* records were made at Wicken until Max Walters made a floristic survey in the early 1950s, which yielded both *P. pratensis* and *P. annua* (smooth and annual meadow-grasses) at the entrance to the Fen. Both these grasses might be expected to be among the 'aliens' to the Fen vegetation, and were (and probably still are) more or less restricted to trampled paths and droves. More surprising, however, was his discovery in September 1952 of a small patch of the rare swamp meadow-grass (*P. palustris*), never previously recorded in the vice-county, at the edge of carr by Sedge Fen Drove. A second patch was discovered in the following year some 50m from the first. A search of the herbarium material of '*P. trivialis*' in the Cambridge Botany School revealed a sheet of *P. palustris* collected on the 'Main Drove' (Sedge Fen Drove) at Wicken by R. A. Lewin in 1941, and originally determined as '*?Agrostis*'. This remains our total experience of this rare grass at the Fen.

Poa palustris was not recognized as a native British plant in the 19th-century Floras, and even as late as 1922 the plant is given for only four widely-scattered riverside localities in the British Isles, and is said to be 'probably introduced'.[34] The discovery of the grass in quantity at Woodwalton Fen in 1951 heightened awareness of its existence, and therefore led to its detection at Wicken Fen and caused a revision of attitude. *P. palustris* is now, according to Clapham, Tutin & Moore[32] said to be 'Native. In a few fens in East Anglia, very local', and otherwise naturalized in scattered localities. However, C. E. Hubbard, in his standard work on British grasses,[35] continued to incline to the view that 'its occurrence in the British Isles may be due entirely to its past cultivation here as a fodder grass'.

There remains a considerable mystery, because neither at Wicken nor at Woodwalton Fen has the grass been recently recorded. Was it in both places a relatively transient and recent introduction? It is true that in Woodwalton in 1951 and subsequent years the grass was locally common on spoil from newly-cleared ditches, and was not so evident when the vegetation closed in. Again we are forced to the conclusion that recording of all but familiar and unmistakable plants remains patchy, and subject to the limitations of the observers. We need systematic monitoring of all plants (and animals), and we are very far from this ideal state.

CRITICAL SPECIES

Groups of species that present particular difficulties in detailed classification have naturally received some attention at Wicken Fen. Three examples, which amply demonstrate the value of long-term recording, concern the spike-rushes (*Eleocharis* spp.), the docks (*Rumex* spp.) and the nettles (*Urtica* spp.)

Spike-rushes (*Eleocharis* spp.)

The spike-rushes are relatively inconspicuous members of the Sedge family Cyperaceae, and it is not perhaps surprising, therefore, that the early records are sparse and at times unreliable. The widespread common spike-rush (*Eleocharis palustris*) grows at Wicken Fen, accompanied by two other species, one of which, slender spike-rush (*E. uniglumis*), is closely related to *E. palustris* and was often not distinguished from it by earlier botanical recorders. Curiously, Babington does not even record *E. palustris* from Wicken Fen, though he obviously knew the plant elsewhere in Cambridgeshire, and states that it is 'not uncommon throughout the County'.

The first record for *E. uniglumis* at Wicken was made by Max Walters on 30 July 1945 on Sedge Fen Drove, and the plant is still frequent there, especially on the middle part. The population is cytologically heterogeneous, with some individuals having 46 chromosomes (the usual number elsewhere), some having *c.*92 and others *c.*62–74, and is unique in this respect.[36] A study of Wicken Fen specimens labelled '*E. palustris*' in the Cambridge Botany School herbarium has shown that *E. uniglumis* was there in 1910 (collected by C. E. Moss) and 1923 (collected by H. Gilbert-Carter), though not recognized as distinct. *E. uniglumis* belongs to a small group of Wicken Fen plants that elsewhere in Britain are much more characteristic of coastal habitats; other species in this category are the brookweed (*Samolus valerandi*) and distant sedge (*Carex distans*).

The third species of *Eleocharis* growing on Sedge Fen Drove at Wicken is the smallest one, few-flowered sedge (*E. quinqueflora*) (*E. pauciflora* of earlier Floras). Max Walters' record, also made on 30 July 1945, was the first of this species in Cambridgeshire in the present century and the first at Wicken Fen. There is, however, some doubt about the early records, for Babington records '*Scirpus caespitosus*' in his Wicken list; he may well have seen *E. quinqueflora* and misidentified it. Unfortunately, there is no specimen in the Cambridge herbarium that might substantiate this, so the earlier existence of *E. quinqueflora* at Wicken Fen remains unproven.

E. quinqueflora is still locally abundant on Sedge Fen Drove, and indeed seems to have increased over the half century that the plant has been known there. It also occurs now in quantity on both Christy's and Thomson's Droves, both of which date from about 1928 (Chapter 11). This spread is undoubtedly associated with the 'opening-up' of the Fen droves with the greatly increased maintenance and traffic, and the consequent creation of more of the transient bare-peat habitats that the species needs.

A fourth *Eleocharis* species at Wicken Fen is ecologically quite different. This is the needle spike-rush (*E. acicularis*), a fine grass-like plant that typically grows submerged on the peaty floor of the lodes and only flowers and fruits when portions of the plant are thrown out on to the dry land. Again, Babington failed to record this plant for Wicken (though he knew it in Roswell Pits, Ely), and the first record for the Fen was made in 1888 by A. Bennett,[37] who stated it to be 'plentiful'. In the 1940s and '50s, *E. acicularis* was abundant in summer in Wicken Lode, and indeed its submerged grass-green carpet was demonstrated every year to students without difficulty. It has since gone through a phase of being greatly reduced, possibly because of the turbidity of the water which reduces the available light for the bottom-rooting plants. Following the ban on boat traffic in the village end of the Lode (Chapter 3), *E. acicularis* appears to be increasing again.

Docks (*Rumex* spp.)

The only dock recorded by Babington for Wicken was the great water dock (*Rumex hydrolapathum*), the food plant of the large copper butterfly (Chapter 8), which still occurs by ditches on the Reserve. Babington was quite familiar with the two other dock species characteristic of wet, peaty habitats, the golden dock (*R. maritimus*) and the closely-related marsh dock (*R. palustris*), and indeed recorded both species from the vicinity of Cambridge, so the absence of any Wicken record seems significant.

The first Wicken Fen record for either species is that by R. H. Lock in 1900: there is a herbarium specimen in Cambridge, from which it is clear that the plant was correctly identified as *R. maritimus*. Godwin noted that *R. maritimus* came up abundantly on mud thrown up from the Lode when it was cleaned 'in the 1930s'. There was no record of *R. palustris* at Wicken until 1952, when Max Walters recorded it in 'a ditch on E. Adventurers' Fen' in 1952, and again 'in several places on the margin of Mere' on Adventurers' Fen in 1956.

In a survey of the developing vegetation in and around the Mere, both *R. maritimus* and *R. palustris* were recorded in September 1959 'in duck-trodden open areas by Mere'. This seems to be the most recent record of *R. maritimus* for the Fen. Records for *R. palustris* on Adventurers' Fen continue, however: in September 1971 it was abundant in open, recently flooded ground on Brett's and Trevelyan's Pieces, occurring with pink water-speedwell (*Veronica catenata*). J. M. Lock found it to be 'still there but infrequent' in August 1985, and it was discovered to be abundant in several places on disturbed ground on Adventurers' Fen in July 1990. On this occasion, some plants with sufficiently advanced flowers were certainly *R. palustris* but no undoubted *R. maritimus* was seen.

Whilst the broad outline of this history makes some sense ecologically, several intriguing questions remain. Both species are strongly associated with wet, disturbed habitats at Wicken Fen, and are never to be found in the ordinary closed communities. Indeed, most occurrences follow artificial dyke- or pond-digging, when mixed peat and mud areas are temporarily created (Godwin seems to be the first botanist to have noticed this at Wicken). In the light of this, Babington's omission seems ecologically explicable: there were presumably no large-scale ditch excavations going on at Wicken when he began his visits in the middle of the 19th century, though local peat-digging by hand was providing habitats for other rare species (see *Viola persicifolia*). Evidence from the occurrence of the two *Rumex* species elsewhere in England suggests strongly that pure peat soils, unmixed with mineral soil, do not provide suitable habitats generally.

What seems to be quite mysterious is the nature of the distinctive ecological preference of *R. palustris* versus *R. maritimus*. Certainly, as Lousley and Kent make clear,[38] the latter does not (in England at any rate) 'show any preference for maritime conditions'. They do, however, say that *R. maritimus* is 'rare and decreasing', whilst making no comment under *R. palustris*. The general picture suggests that *R. maritimus*, but not *R. palustris*, has shown a decline in Cambridgeshire. What we now see on Adventurers' Fen, then, may be in line with the national picture for these two species. More careful study is needed.

Nettles (*Urtica* spp.)

There is no mention of the common nettle, *Urtica dioica*, in Babington's Wicken List. Yapp dismissed it as 'alien' to the Fen,[23] and Godwin and Tansley[22] also treated it as one of several 'aliens' associated with the artificial raised banks of lodes. By 1939, nettles were common in the characteristic undergrowth under dense carr, and indeed are listed by Godwin and Tansley in 1929 as 'frequent' in such communities, as they are today.

Max Walters recalls that, when he was first introduced to the Fen in 1939, Humphrey Gilbert-Carter (then Director of the University Botanic Garden; see Fig. 66, Chapter 11) was pointing out to students that the typical Wicken shade nettle was a tall, narrow-leaved variant that, in its extreme form, almost completely lacked the stinging hairs for which the plant is famous. He used the varietal name 'inermis' for such plants. The first published reference to the Wicken plant seems to be that of A. J. Wilmott in 1948.[39] By 1951, Walters had noted: 'the narrow-leaved, stingless variety is common on the Fen, particularly by Drainers' Dyke and Spinney Bank.'

This variant has recently[40] been recognized as *Urtica galeopsifolia* (or, since subspecific rank may be more appropriate, *Urtica dioica* subsp. *galeopsifolia*) (Fig. 37), a characteristic plant of damp woodland, river banks and fens in Continental Europe. British botanists became aware of this as a result of a visit to Wicken Fen in 1991 by Dr. Dimitri Geltman, a taxonomist in St Petersburg, who has studied the genus *Urtica* throughout its Eurasiatic range. The Wicken Fen populations he deemed 'not to differ from *U. galeopsifolia* as it occurs in Russia'.

In recent years the populations of nettles at Wicken Fen have been the subject of intensive study by Briggs and co-workers in the Department of Plant Sciences in Cambridge.[41,42,43,44] Some of this study is still in progress, but the general picture emerging is that the 'stingless Wicken nettle' is apparently the native variant, whereas the familiar widespread variant with broader leaves and abundant stinging hairs behaves like a recent weed, being more obvious in the disturbed peripheral parts of the reserve or along the paths. The status of intermediate plants (which can readily be found on the Fen) can be interpreted as of hybrid origin. This picture is at least partially confirmed by the demonstration that plants with the general characteristics of subsp. *galeopsifolia* from Wicken Fen, the Norfolk Broads and other British localities are diploid, with 2n=26, the same number recorded by Geltman for Continental material, while typical *U. dioica* is tetraploid (2n=52).

CONCLUSION

If there is any generalization to be made on the basis of these examples, it is the unsurprising one that continued systematic recording would greatly help in monitoring vegetation change. We must, however, accept that much of our floristic information in the future will, as in the past, come from visitors whose interest in the flora is essentially that of an amateur enjoying a hobby. This is not in any way to disparage such record-

Figure 37 Fen nettle (*Urtica galeopsifolia*) at Wicken, September 1994

ing: it provides us with a set of cumulative data (see Fig. 79, Chapter 12) that increases in value as the years go by.

What is increasingly obvious, however, is that the communities of the Fen change relatively rapidly. In particular, the characteristic fenland species for which the reserve is famous are necessarily subject to changing ecological conditions, usually leading to a decline in their rather specialized habitats. The days are gone when legal protection of a nature reserve could by itself be thought to ensure the survival of rare species. We find ourselves managing the remaining populations of rarities with what is often an inadequate knowledge of their ecology. What is worse, we now realize that most rare species owe their scarcity precisely to their low tolerance of competition. We therefore find ourselves reduced to 'inspired gardening' (as is certainly the case for the fen violet) to retain a viable population. Wicken Fen is peculiarly blessed with the strong support of a large number of excellent naturalists (Chapter 12). Even with these resources, however, it has proved impossible to provide the ecological research and monitoring to support effective and informed management of the great majority of the Fen's characteristic species.

References

1 Ray (1660)
2 Relhan (1785)
3 Relhan (1802)
4 Relhan (1820)
5 Babington (1860)
6 Walters (1967)
7 Mountford *et al.* (1994)
8 Swaffham Prior Naturalists' Society (1835)
9 Rowell (1983b)
10 Babington (1857)
11 Walters (1974)
12 Ross-Craig (1954)
13 Babington (1897)
14 Cammell (1975), field notebook in Wicken Fen archive
15 David (1990)
16 David (1991), letter in Wicken Fen archive
17 Harvey (1986)
18 Evans (1923a), p. 43
19 Evans (1923b)
20 Sell (1987)
21 Luck (1965)
22 Godwin & Tansley (1929)
23 Yapp (1908)
24 Rowell & Harvey (1988)
25 Wheeler (1980)
26 Walters (1958)
27 Moore (1986)
28 Preston (1993)
29 Preston (1991b)
30 Evans (1939)
31 Yeo (1976)
32 Clapham *et al.* (1987)
33 Briggs *et al.* (1989)
34 Wilmott (1922)
35 Hubbard (1968)
36 Walters (1951)
37 West (1898)
38 Lousley & Kent (1981)
39 Wilmott (1948)
40 Geltman (1992)
41 Pollard & Briggs (1982)
42 Ibid. (1984a)
43 Ibid. (1984b)
44 Lahav-Ginott (1994)

8

Insects and their Conservation

S. A. CORBET, J. P. DEMPSTER, T. J. BENNETT, R. J. REVELL, C. C. SMITH,
P. F. YEO, I. PERRY, A. B. DRANE AND N. W. MOORE

BECAUSE habitat diversity has been intentionally maintained at Wicken, the Fen still has a rich biota in which changes occurring in the wider countryside can be reflected; and because it has been for so long a focus of attention for biologists, changes in the distribution of some species are better recorded at Wicken Fen than elsewhere. Insects illustrate this situation particularly clearly. Some species are mobile enough to move freely between the Fen and its surroundings. For these, exemplified by bumblebees, detailed recording at Wicken can help to illuminate national trends. Others are less mobile. A few persist as isolated colonies at Wicken Fen after they have been lost from the surrounding area; the swallowtail butterfly persisted in this way until the 1950s.

The individual insects of a species are not evenly scattered over the countryside, but are patchily distributed forming local populations. Close observation of a species over a period of time would reveal an ever-changing kaleidoscopic pattern as individual populations become denser or sparser or even die out, perhaps to be replaced by colonists from other populations nearby. In an area big enough to contain many local populations of a given species, it is unlikely that all will become extinct at the same time. In a small area that does not contain enough populations for local extinctions to be made good, the same species may be at risk. For species present at a few sites on the fens and absent from the surrounding farmland, the future is tenuous, and those with a single population would be eliminated from the whole area by a single extinction. Such was the fate of the swallowtail.

There are important differences between Wicken and the arable land all around. For many species, the Fen is more hospitable: the insect's requirements may be concentrated in, or confined to, the Fen, which therefore represents an island in a sea of unsuitable habitat. In contrast, some species associated with habitation, crops or disturbed land, such as the large white butterfly (*Pieris brassicae*), are present on the Fen as immigrants from breeding sites elsewhere. For them, Wicken Fen may represent a patch of less suitable habitat in a generally congenial matrix.

How appropriate is a model of frequent extinctions of local populations and subsequent re-invasions to the insect populations of a nature reserve? To address this question we need a sequence of distribution records from the reserve and the surrounding country. Wicken Fen is better provided with faunal records than most nature reserves, but without systematic long-term monitoring, extinctions may go unnoticed. Arrivals or re-invasions are more likely to be recorded. Some groups are better documented than others and for these it may be possible to detect changes in populations within the Fen and to compare them with trends in the wider countryside. A useful yardstick for assessing the status of the Fen's insects compared with the national situation has been provided by the publication in 1987 of a *Red Data Book* (*RDB*), containing details of Britain's rare and endangered insects.[1] Particularly well recorded, both on the Fen by local enthusiasts and throughout the country by mapping schemes coordinated by specialist groups or by the Biological Records Centre, are butterflies, moths, bumblebees, flies, beetles and dragonflies, and it is mainly with these groups that the following account is concerned. Records of all orders are, however, kept by the Fen's Zoological Secretary, and a complete list (to March 1997) is published in the separate checklist volume.

BUTTERFLIES AND MOTHS (LEPIDOPTERA)

Swallowtail butterflies (*Papilio machaon britannicus*) (Plate 5, Figs 1–5) were once a major entomological attraction at Wicken Fen, but in the 1950s the local population became extinct, perhaps because of a decrease in the area suitable for its only larval food plant, milk-parsley (*Peucedanum palustre*) (Fig. 38a; Plate 3, Fig. 3), an uncommon plant of open, wet fenland areas (see Chapter 5). That decrease has been attributed to two factors: the spread of carr, reducing open areas from about 120ha to only about 8ha; and improved drainage and falling land-levels in the surrounding agricultural land, which lowered the water-table on the Fen (Chapter 2). Since that critical time, the area suitable for milk-parsley has increased, but natural recolonization by the butterfly is unlikely because the only source of swallowtails, the Norfolk Broads population, is 160km away.[2]

Early attempts to re-establish swallowtails by introducing small numbers of Norfolk individuals did not succeed (Fig 38b). This failure was not due to larval mortality,

Figure 38 (Left) W. S. Farren's photograph of larvae of the swallowtail (*Papilio machaon*) feeding on milk-parsley (*Peucedanum palustre*) at Wicken Fen, 21 July 1901; (Below) the first release on the Fen, by John Smart and Henry Stroyan, of Norfolk stock of swallowtails (*Papilio machaon britannicus*) which had been reared at the Cambridge University Entomological Field Station by B. O. C. Gardiner. Fifty adults and two hundred larvae were released during spring and early summer, 1955.

which was no higher in small experimental populations at Wicken than it was in the Broads. Instead, it was attributed to the state of Wicken Fen's milk-parsley, which grew poorly and had not recolonized newly-created suitable areas. Experiments showed that the plant could survive if transplanted into areas of Wicken Sedge Fen and Adventurers' Fen in which it did not already grow. In a major operation in 1974 involving conservation volunteers, thousands of milk-parsley plants were planted. Despite plant losses due to duck grazing, enough remained to allow the introduction of 228 swallowtails in the summer of 1975. Thereafter, plant numbers fell steadily, and after a promising start, numbers of the butterfly also decreased. Swallowtails were probably extinct at Wicken again by 1980.[3,4]

The swallowtail is currently being reintroduced to Wicken Fen. Eggs collected in Norfolk have been raised in greenhouses and the resulting larvae put out on their food-plants on the Fen in the summer of 1993. A number of adults have been seen flying on the Fen in each subsequent summer and all aspects of the butterfly's growth and survival are being closely monitored. The project, carried out by Dr J. P. Dempster and Mrs M. L. Hall, is in its early stages, but hopes of setting up a permanent population have been set back by two years of drought, in spite of some recent improvement in the growth and flowering of milk-parsley (see Fig. 23, Chapter 5).

The maintenance of large numbers of the swallowtail's food plants depends partly on management of the vegetation. The harvesting of sedge and litter produces open areas, in which *Peucedanum* seed germinates well, but the next cut, 3 or 4 years later, destroys swallowtails present as larvae on the plants.[4] These losses might be made good by reinvasion from adjacent uncut sedge fields if swallowtails were abundant; but when their numbers are small, the local mosaic cannot be maintained by field-to-field movement. On a larger scale, the Wicken population as a whole cannot be saved from extinction by reinvasion from another site because of its geographical isolation.

This study of swallowtails hints at the importance of migration in maintaining local populations. When a population of insects occupies a habitat surrounded by other suitable habitats, mobile individuals will enter the population periodically from outside and breed, so bequeathing their genes to subsequent generations. On the other hand, a population surrounded by inimical countryside is expected to lose mobility: those individuals with physical and behavioural traits favouring mobility would leave the habitat and only the less mobile individuals would remain behind to breed. As Wicken Fen's surroundings became less and less suitable for swallowtails, and the likelihood of immigration diminished, individuals with characteristics favouring mobility must have become progressively fewer. By studying butterflies in museum collections, Jack Dempster discovered that, after the surrounding areas were drained in the early 19th century, the isolated population at Wicken Fen showed morphological changes (such as smaller wings and a narrower thorax) associated with reduced flight capacity. After about 1920 the Norfolk Broads population, too, began to show a similar effect.[2] Rarely has the loss of an isolated population been monitored and understood so fully. The swallowtails of Wicken Fen carry a message for threatened insect populations in general.

Currently about 18 species of butterfly are recorded each year at Wicken Fen, most of them with well-established breeding populations (Plate 5, Fig. 6). In its range of species, Wicken is much poorer than many other nature reserves in Britain, especially those on chalk grassland. However, the highly arable county of Cambridgeshire is undoubtedly one of the most impoverished for butterflies in the country, and Wicken Fen is one of its very best sites. Fens in general support few species, and, for many of those that do occur, the waterlogged conditions provide a suboptimal habitat. Indeed it is quite likely that such species as the meadow brown (*Maniola jurtina*) and small heath (*Coenonympha pamphilus*) have colonized the Fen only since it started to dry out in recent decades. Both are still largely confined to the slightly elevated drier areas at the north-east corner of the reserve.

Apart from the swallowtail, the only true fen species occurring in Britain today is the large copper (*Lycaena dispar*) (Plate 5, Fig. 7). The native race, *L. dispar dispar*, became extinct in 1848 as a result of drainage of its fenland habitat. In 1927, the Dutch race, *L. dispar batavus*, was introduced to both Woodwalton and Wicken Fens. A population has been artificially maintained at Woodwalton Fen ever since, but at Wicken, where the introduction appeared at first to be more successful, the population disappeared with the drainage of Adventurers' Fen in the 1940s (see Chapter 11). The fate of the large copper attracted rather less attention than the demise of the Wicken population of swallowtails, and the extinction at the Fen in the early 1940s of the marsh fritillary (*Eurodryas aurinia*) passed almost without comment. At that time, the fritillary was much commoner than it is now and a local extinction apparently caused little concern. Today, however, the marsh fritillary is very restricted in its distribution and probably more threatened than the swallowtail because of insidious habitat destruction.

The Fen's butterflies have received much more attention since 1979, especially through the Butterfly Monitoring Scheme organized by the Institute of Terrestrial Ecology at Monks Wood.[5] The former Head Warden, Tim Bennett, initiated a series of weekly counts along a fixed transect route covering much of the Sedge Fen each year between April and September.[6] We have more than sixteen years of data. From these counts it is possible to calculate an index of relative abundance for each species[7] and changes in this index from generation to generation or from one year to the next can be compared with changes at other participating sites. In this way we can see how fluctuations at Wicken Fen relate to any regional or national trends. Also, some effects of habitat change on various species are now more clearly understood, because detailed records are kept about any management work carried out at each site during the year.

A significant discovery made in the first year of the Scheme's adoption at the Fen was that the brimstone (*Gonepteryx rhamni*) seems to be a far more mobile species than had pre-viously been thought. In contrast to published information about flight periods, brimstones were seen on the wing almost continuously from early spring until about the end of August (Plate 5, Fig. 8). Analysis of data from other sites confirmed this pattern in wetlands, but showed a different picture in woodland sites. There, brimstones were present for only a relatively short period after hibernation; they were absent during June and July, and then reappeared, tending to be seen for longer into the autumn.[8] The explanation is thought to be that woods, where the two larval food-plants alder buckthorn (*Frangula alnus*) and purging buckthorn (*Rhamnus cathartica*) are absent or sparse, are largely used for hibernation, whereas wetlands, where the two buck-thorns are often abundant, are mainly used for breeding. The rapid decline in numbers at Wicken Fen each autumn tends to support this, since butterflies of the new generation have probably departed to overwinter in the more sheltered surroundings of woodland. An attempt was made to test this theory by individually marking newly-emerged brim-stones on Wicken Fen. Although many were marked, none were recaptured.

Of the other butterfly species for which annual index figures exist, most have fluc-tuated largely in parallel with regional or national changes. However, grassland species like the skippers and browns have shown a marked increase at Wicken Fen over the years, almost certainly as a result of the rigorous cutting regimes introduced during the 1980s. This management pattern has encouraged the less vigorous soft grasses and herbs favoured as larval foodplants. The clearing of glades and the widening of rides (and the creation of glades in new woodland on the Fen's marginal land; see Chapter 11) have also provided many more flowery areas in the sun, favoured by butterflies seeking sources of nectar.

The most marked increase at Wicken Fen has been that of the ringlet (*Aphantopus hyperantus*). In 1979 this was found in only a handful of tiny discrete colonies around the edge of the Sedge Fen, and it did not register at all for the first three years of the tran-sect walk. Since 1982 its index figure has increased steadily and now ringlets are very commonly seen in certain areas. It is a lover of damper, shadier grassland and may be responding to the raised water-levels at Wicken Fen. In contrast, there was a drop in its numbers nationally after the dry summers of 1989–90.

A notable recent addition to the Wicken list is the speckled wood (*Pararge aegeria*), first recorded at the Fen in 1984. Odd sightings in subsequent years suggested that the species had gained a tenuous foothold here and was on the threshold of colonizing the reserve, as it had done at nearby Chippenham Fen. By 1991, it was being recorded routinely on the transect walk and, within two years, had quadrupled its index figure. The Fenland reserves apparently offer islands of thick scrub in a county that has very little woodland.

The collecting of moths at Wicken probably began early in the last century, but no records of these earlier captures were kept until Frederick Bond started to compile lists around 1850. From about this time, Wicken Fen rapidly developed a reputation as a mecca for moth enthusiasts. The pursuit of moths became an important industry in Wicken village, and many of the local people set up as professional 'ghillies' and col-lectors. On warm summer nights, as many as five 'Eddystone Lighthouses' could be seen operating in various parts of the Fen (see Fig. 59, Chapter 10). The efforts of the collectors, although frowned upon in these conservation-conscious days, probably did little harm, and left us a unique legacy of information about species present, fluctua-tions in populations, and of course disappearances.

There have been some sad losses from the species list since those early days. The last specimen of the reed tussock (*Laelia coenosa*) was reputedly captured in 1879 by Albert

Houghton, the Wicken bootmaker, after a long decline in its fortunes in the Fens as a whole. Gone also, it seems, are the marsh dagger (*Acronicta strigosa*) and the many-lined (*Costaconvexa polygrammata*), whose foodplants were hawthorn and bedstraw respectively. The better known gypsy moth (*Lymantria dispar*) was a distinct British form, larger than those found commonly on the Continent. Its caterpillars fed on bog-myrtle (see Chapter 7) and creeping willow rather than on forest trees. The last recorded capture of this form was in 1907.

Despite these losses, Wicken Fen can still boast a number of rare species. The silver barred (*Deltote bankiana*) (Plate 6, Fig. 1) can be seen flying both by day and by night amongst grasses in the more open areas away from the reedswamp. It is resident also at Chippenham Fen, in one bog in Kent and in south-west Ireland. Still breeding at Wicken Fen, but in very few other localities in Britain (*RDB2* 'vulnerable'), is the reed leopard (*Phragmataecia castaneae*) (Plate 6, Fig. 2), whose larvae have powerful jaws and feed internally in the stems of reed.

The marsh moth (*Athetis pallustris*), which is found also on the Lincolnshire coast, may still breed at Wicken Fen, but it is hard to find because of its secretive and unpredictable habits. Its larva feeds by night on meadowsweet, hiding by day in leaf litter, and the male seems to choose cool, wet nights in June to fly, when even the keenest light trappers are reluctant to venture out. Because this species is almost impossible to rear in captivity, very few females have ever been seen. '*Pallustris*' became quite a well-known moth in Wicken village between the wars, and one resident recollects being woken at 3.00 a.m. by Baron Charles de Worms rushing up from the Fen shouting at the top of his voice 'I've got *pallustris*'! Two other uncommon moths to be found at Wicken are the marsh carpet (*Perizoma sagittata*) (Plate 6, Fig. 3), a pretty species whose larvae feed on the seeds of common meadow-rue, and the reed dagger (*Simyra albovenosa*), which lacks the 'dagger' markings usual in this family.

These rarities apart, the varied wetland habitats included in the Wicken reserve provide homes for many species which are uncommon elsewhere in Britain. For example, of the dozen moth species whose larvae feed solely on the common reed (*Phragmites australis*), ten occur commonly at Wicken Fen (Fig 15, Chapter 4) and some of these are listed in the *RDB* 'threatened' categories.[1] The adults of most of these are known as 'wainscots' and are really rather dull in appearance.

A daytime visitor to the Fen would see few species of moth. The wealth of species of the larger moths flying at night, particularly in July, is best appreciated by attracting them to light or 'sugar'. Large day-fliers such as the males of the emperor (*Pavonia pavonia*) and oak eggar (*Lasiocampa quercus*) have been recorded from Wicken Fen, but are certainly not common. Among the rewards for day-time visitors are the lesser cream wave (*Scopula immutata*) and the grass rivulet (*Perizoma albulata*), small pale geometers which are likely to be kicked up by a person walking through grassy areas. The pretty purple-bordered gold (*Idaea muricata*) can also be seen at Wicken, although its principal foodplant, marsh cinquefoil (*Potentilla palustris*), has not been recorded on the Fen for many years.

Whilst the butterflies and larger moths of Wicken Fen have been collected and observed intensively for well over a century, the smaller moths, conventionally known as the Microlepidoptera, have been comparatively neglected until recently, even though the Fen is a rich habitat for many groups. Present and future work on them has a firm base in A. Maitland Emmet's excellent *Annotated Check List* of 1972,[9] which includes 555 of the 1450 or so species known from the British Isles. For nearly a third of the Wicken Fen species, 182 of the 555, there was in 1972 'no recent record'. This does not imply massive extinction. Very many of the smallest 'micros' are extremely difficult to collect or observe, some may exist only at low density or in very small areas, and others pose problems of identification for all except the most expert. Emmet says 'In my sixth year of recording (1971) I registered 26 hitherto unrecorded species, including two in my latest visit in mid-November ... [and] ... confirmed the presence of 20 for which there had been no recent records'. The richness and potential of the Fen can be gauged from Emmet's further remark: 'My own intermittent researches resulted in the addition of three species to the British list; there may be more'. This last is surely true. Not many can approach Emmet's expertise with, for example, the tiny leaf-mining larvae and minuscule adult moths of the Nepticulidae, and few venture on the Fen in mid-November.

The Microlepidoptera of Wicken Fen include several fen specialists and one or two rarities. Typical of fenland pyralids are the abundant reed-feeding *Chilo phragmitella* and the less common *Schoenobius gigantella*, and the beautiful china-mark moths *Nymphula stagnata*, *Elophila nymphaeata*, *Parapoynx stratiotata* and *Cataclysta lemnata*, whose larvae, as their Latin names suggest, feed underwater on various aquatic plants. *C. lemnata* may be seen in abundance at early dusk, flying weakly over any stretch of open water. For much of the summer, a lamp run on a warm night will attract hundreds of the water veneer (*Acentria ephemerella*), which also has aquatic larvae, but which has other extraordinary features. There are two forms of the female moth: one, winged, can fly and joins the males at a lamp; the other, nearly wingless, swims actively beneath the surface of the water from which it emerges to pair with the male on the surface.

Other specialities among Wicken Fen's pyralids are the scarce *Evergestis extimalis*, possibly a wanderer from the Breckland where it is established, its larvae feeding in the seedheads of Cruciferae; the beautiful *Nascia cilialis* on sedges at one of its very few British stations; and most of all *Phlyctaenia perlucidalis*. First recorded in Britain at Woodwalton in 1951 (presumably as a new arrival by migration from the Continent), *P. perlucidalis* is now established in many parts of East Anglia; it seems to have first been recorded at Wicken Fen in June 1984 by R. Fairclough. It is associated with common species of thistle and seems to like damp places but is not strictly a fen insect.

Of interest among the Tortricidae is the vine moth (*Eupoecilia ambiguella*), a scarce insect recorded from southern England, the Midlands and South Wales. One turned up at Wicken Fen on 28 May 1976, and was taken to be a wanderer in that exceptional summer; but a second specimen on 25 July 1989 in another exceptional summer could represent a second generation, a phenomenon that is regular abroad but unknown here. A search for the larva in the fruits of alder buckthorn has not been successful, but the moth is probably established on the Fen, if at very low density.

To maintain this very diverse microlepidopteran assemblage, management should be designed to give a wide range of habitat types. A good example is provided by *Phtheochroa inopiana* (Tortricidae), whose larva feeds in the roots of common fleabane (*Pulicaria dysenterica*). The only note of the occurrence of this species until recently concerns captures in 1885, when it was 'rare at light', not surprisingly since the insect does not fly much after dark. In the 1972 list[9] there was 'no recent record'; but on 5 July 1989 the moth swarmed in the early evening among fleabane in compartment 69 near the northern edge of the Fen (see map, Appendix A). This meadow was a recent creation produced by mowing a year or two before; the removal of reeds and small shrubs allowed the growth of the fleabane and led to the population explosion of the moth. Many of the numerous species of Nepticulidae at Wicken Fen depend on mature deciduous trees, and any loss or decline of these would clearly be serious. To plant a variety of such trees, perhaps on the edges of the Fen, as has been done recently in compartment 68 (Chapter 11), would benefit the Lepidoptera in general.

BEES AND WASPS (HYMENOPTERA)

Bumblebees have declined at Wicken Fen. In the late 1920s Spooner[10] found fourteen species of *Bombus*, the true bumblebees (Plate 7, Fig. 1), especially near the north-eastern margin of the Fen,[11] but today there are only seven[12], in addition to three species of cuckoo bumblebees, *Psithyrus* (Plate 7, Fig. 2). Between 1930 and 1978 seven species of true bumblebees disappeared from the Fen.[12,13] A single specimen of *Bombus distinguendus*, a male, found on *Buddleia* outside the William Thorpe Building in 1980, was probably a casual vagrant.

The well-documented losses of bumblebees at Wicken Fen mirror those in much of east central England. Throughout the region, bumblebee species present before 1960 have been lost, leaving only the seven common species that are widespread throughout Britain.[12,14] These losses, and the parallel decline in Germany, Belgium and France, have been tentatively attributed to agricultural development. In Kent, where the species that have declined here still persist, they are associated particularly with open habitats undisturbed by human activity, such as salt-marsh, sand-dunes, shingle and old meadow.[12] Evidently Wicken Fen, even if it is still suitable for these species, does not provide enough resources to allow them to persist locally and reinvasion is unlikely as there are now no nearby sources of colonists.

A population of bumblebees requires four major resources: flowers as sources of nectar and pollen; nest sites; hibernation sites; and habitats for the male 'patrolling' behaviour that precedes mating. Species differ from one another in their requirements: some prefer deep flowers while others visit open ones; some nest at the soil surface while others nest underground; the male patrol-routes of some species go from tree-base to tree-base while those of others follow hedges. However, all benefit from open sunny habitats where the absence of ploughing allows the establishment of nectar-rich perennial plants; from well-drained rough land for nest sites; from dry banks in which to hibernate; and from a diversity of sheltered habitats with microclimates suitable for patrolling males.

Table VII. Bumblebees and forage plants

Some important forage plants for true bumblebees at Wicken Fen, arranged in descending order of corolla length.
Data from Prŷs-Jones (1982)[13]

Brackets indicate interactions that were relatively rare.

* sometimes robbed through a hole in the corolla

N = nectar   P = pollen

	Long-Tongued Bumblebees				Short-Tongued Bumblebees	Honey-Bees
	Bombus hortorum	*Bombus pascuorum*	*Bombus pratorum*	*Bombus lapidarius*	*Bombus lucorum &* *B. terrestris*	*Apis mellifera*
Lamium album (White dead-nettle)	—	N P	(N)	—	—	—
Symphytum officinale (Common comfrey)	N P	N P	N P	—	N P*	—
Stachys palustris (Marsh woundwort)	—	N P	—	—	—	—
Succisa pratensis (Devils-bit scabious)	—	N	—	—	—	—
Lythrum salicaria (Purple-loosestrife)	—	N P	—	—	—	—
Epilobium hirsutum (Great willowherb)	(N)	N P	(N)	—	—	(N)
Cirsium arvense (Creeping thistle)	—	N	(N)	(N)	—	—
Centaurea nigra (Common knapweed)	N P	N P	N	N P	(N)	—
Eupatorium cannabinum (Hemp-agrimony)	—	N	—	N	N P	N P
Cirsium palustre (Marsh thistle)	N	N P	(N)	N (P)	(N)	—
Frangula alnus (Alder buckthorn)	—	N P	(N)	—	N P	N
Salix spp. (Willow)	—	(N)	N P	—	N	—
Rosa canina (Dog-rose)	—	P	—	—	P	P
Thalictrum flavum (Meadow rue)	—	—	—	—	(P)	P

Table VII shows the main plant species used by bumblebees at Wicken Fen. Generally, long-tubed flowers are used by the long-tongued species *Bombus pascuorum* and *B. hortorum*; the short-tongued species *B. terrestris* and *B. lucorum*, and the agile little *B. pratorum*, use shorter flowers unless they can reach the nectar by robbing, through a hole bitten in the corolla; and *B. lapidarius* favours massed flowers and is often abundant in the Breed Fen hay meadow on common knapweed (*Centaurea nigra*) until mowing removes its forage. Wicken Fen is well provided with nectar-rich perennial flowers with a range of corolla depths, suiting a range of bumblebee species. In the surrounding farmland, forage of comparable value is probably largely confined to the banks of lodes and ditches.

Common comfrey (*Symphytum officinale*) (Plate 3, Fig. 2), a major forage source for bumblebees throughout Britain, is particularly important at Wicken Fen because of its abundance and its long flowering season. It is a rewarding flower on which to watch bumblebees, because of the diverse patterns of flower manipulation shown by different bee species.[15] Nectar is secreted at the base of the tubular corolla. *Bombus pascuorum* and *B. hortorum* can reach the nectar with their long tongues. *B. terrestris* and *B. lucorum* have such short tongues that they must bite a hole in the base of the corolla tube. These holes are sometimes re-used by the little *B. pratorum*, which must otherwise thrust its narrow head into the corolla to reach the nectar. The pollen of comfrey is fine and powdery when dry, and bumblebees shake it out of the anthers by hanging below the flower and vibrating their closed wings with an audible high-pitched buzz.

A typical bumblebee nest is made in a dry soft mass of grass or moss underground or at the surface. Most bumblebees cannot collect nesting material for themselves, and they often take over the disused nests of small mammals or even birds. Because of the high water-table, bumblebees are unlikely to find sufficiently dry nest-sites on the peat fen itself, and most nests found in recent years have been on well-drained banks off the north-eastern margin of the fen; one on the fen itself was in a bird's nest in a bush. Piles of litter or peat might offer dry nest-sites on the fen, but these habitats may be rarer now than they were in the past. Today, most of the bumblebees that forage on the Fen probably come from nests at the fen margin. Rough land in Breed Fen Drove and the Lode Lane area may be particularly important to them. Hibernation sites, like nest sites, need to be dry; a high water-table would largely confine hibernation to the fen margins.

The habitat favoured by male bumblebees for the patrolling flights associated with their courtship differs from species to species. Males of *Bombus hortorum* make regular visits to the base of the large willow tree in front of the William Thorpe Building; but, apart from this rather public display, rather little is known of the male patrolling sites used by bumblebees on the Fen.

The most conspicuous social wasp at Wicken Fen is *Vespula rufa*, which is distinguishable from commoner species of Vespidae by a rusty red area at the front of the abdomen. It is widespread in damp and neglected spots, but local in today's much-cultivated landscape. It nests on the ground within the Fen and gathers nectar from the flowers of alder buckthorn, which have a conveniently long season: the bush is still producing flowers as the first berries redden.

Solitary wasps, in particular the Eumeninae, near relatives of the social wasps, are well represented on the Fen. The commonest is *Ancistrocerus trifasciatus*, a species generally associated with swampy conditions. Many members of the large family Sphecidae are excluded from the Fen by the fact that they nest in dry, often sandy, soil. The others nest in rotten wood, beetle borings and hollow stems, and a long list of these has been assembled from the Wicken area. It is based mainly on records published between 1916[16] and 1938.[11] A great many species recorded in this period have not been found here since. There are two reasons for thinking that this may be due to lack of recording. One is that the dearth of repeat records applies to generally common as well as to more local species, and the other is that Jeremy Field's recent work at Chippenham Fen shows that there is still a rich wasp fauna there.[17] It is also possible that such efforts as there have been at collecting this group have not been directed to the best places. Nevinson described the Sedge Fen itself as 'unproductive' and, though it has plenty of dead wood in places, solitary wasps seem to be difficult to find there. Apart from old posts and sheds near the Lode in Nevinson's time there were 'many good species in Adventurers' Fen'[18] but best of all were 'portions near Burwell Fen' on account of 'the large amount of rotten wood, trees and posts'.[16] Solitary wasps and bees, like many other animals, benefit if dead wood is allowed to remain on the Fen.

The modest lists of spider-hunting wasps (Pompilidae) and ruby-tail wasps (Chrysididae) probably reflect a similar history to those of the Eumeninae and Sphecidae. Among solitary bees, too, wood-nesting species are better represented than ground-nesting species, but there is apparently a contingent that corresponds with the bumble-bees, nesting outside the Fen but foraging within it. This is indicated by the number of *Andrena* (Apidae) species recorded, though one of these, *A. labialis*, was reported by Spooner to nest in clay soil in Breed Fen Drove. The other major groups of Hymenoptera, the parasitic wasps and the ants, also have very brief modern lists; the former due to lack of recording, the latter due to the absence of suitably dry ground for nesting.

Wicken Fen provides a habitat for a number of bees and wasps that have special requirements. *Rhopalum gracile*, a wasp species with a local distribution in south-east England, is found only in damp areas. Another sphecid wasp *Passaloecus clypealis* and the small black bee *Hylaeus* (*Prosopis*) *pectoralis* both nest in the galls formed by the fly *Lipara lucens* at the tip of reed stems (Fig. 15). The reeds need to be left standing for two years for these 'squatters' to complete their life cycle. *Macropis europaea*, a bee rather smaller than a honeybee, can easily be spotted visiting the flowers of yellow loosestrife (*Lysimachia vulgaris*) in July and August. This flower is one of several unrelated plants scattered across the world that offer oil instead of nectar to the specialized bees that visit them. *Macropis* nests on the Fen in soil that is probably swamped in winter.

FLIES (DIPTERA)

Among the most attractive of the two-winged flies are the hoverflies, Syrphidae, of which 112 species have been recorded at Wicken Fen (Plate 7, Figs 5–7). Hoverflies exploit a wide range of habitats for their larval development and both the relative abundance of different species and their spatial distribution at Wicken reflect the diversity of the Fen itself. Woodland, a favoured habitat for hoverflies, is poorly represented here. However, the few mature trees at the eastern end of Sedge Fen Drove, near the Brickpits, have associated with them species whose larvae develop in dead wood (*Xylota abiens, Criorhina floccosa*) and aphid feeders such as *Neocnemodon vitripennis*. Because of the frequency of flooding, species whose larvae are associated with the nests of wasps and bees, or with root aphids, are largely restricted to the drier margins of the Fen. On the other hand, species with larvae that develop in wet places are well represented, especially species of *Anasimyia*, *Eristalis* and *Helophilus*. Other hoverfly species which are common at Wicken Fen include *Rhingia campestris*, notable for its long 'snout' and its ability to reach the nectar in deep flowers, and *Syritta pipiens*, males of which hover above flowers where they pounce on feeding females. Wicken Fen has numerous rare hoverfly species, of which perhaps the most notable is *Anasimyia interpuncta* (*RDB3*), first seen there in 1932 and found several times since 1973, feeding on the flowers of kingcups and dandelions, usually in May and early June. This nationally rare species is otherwise restricted to a few sites in East Anglia and south-east England.[19]

Hoverflies have been well recorded over the last 100 years, by Verrall and others from the end of the 19th century until the Second World War, and then by Ivan Perry and others since 1969. Although Wicken Fen is unusual for the continuity and intensity of its recording, it is not easy to recognize invasions and extinctions over that period, because one cannot be sure whether unrecorded species were absent, or simply not found. Seven species lack recent records, but of these some may never have been established on the Fen itself, and others, always rare, may have been overlooked in recent years. *Myolepta luteola*, of which three specimens were found on the same day in 1936, develops in rot holes and has been reared from elm. It may have been lost as a Wicken resident since the ancient elms on the edge of the fen were removed after they succumbed to Dutch Elm disease. New species are continually being found at Wicken, but because of our incomplete knowledge of the Fen fauna it is hard to interpret these new records. However, many are of species characteristic of woodland edge, and may reflect an increase in habitats of that kind on the Fen.[20]

Mosquitoes are among the most conspicuous of the Fen's flies. Although malaria no longer plagues the Fens, Wicken's mosquitoes include species of *Anopheles* which are potential vectors of the disease. Indeed, it was possible to catch malaria, even in Cambridge, at the end of the First World War as infected servicemen returned to University and the Cam's mosquitoes redistributed the parasite.[21] Eleven species of mosquito are known from Wicken Fen. Of ten found in Lewis' survey of 1929–30,[22] nine were refound in studies 50 years later.[23]

The lowering of the water-table over the last half-century has been accompanied by a change in the mosquito community. Among species that depend on very shallow waters, those of permanent pools have decreased and those of temporary puddles have increased. *Culiseta morsitans* and *Coquillettidia richiardii*, which breed in shallow permanent waters, were very abundant in 1930 but rare or absent by 1980. Three species of *Aedes* that lay their eggs in dry regions likely to become flooded have done better: *A. cinereus* remains abundant, and *A. annulipes* and *A. rusticus* were much commoner in the second survey than in the first. *A. annulipes* is a large, handsome mosquito with conspicuous white rings on its legs, but the female bites eagerly and few visitors pause to admire it while it does so. A species that breeds in the water that collects in hollows in mature trees, *A. geniculatus*, was not common in either survey. The few found on the Fen may have come from breeding sites in the village, and so may those of *Culex* species, whose egg rafts and larvae are found in water butts in Lode Lane. With the recent waterproofing of the Fen's perimeter ditches and the raising of water-levels (Chapter 11), we might expect that these trends in mosquito abundance may slow down or even be reversed over the next few years.

The pattern of mosquito/visitor interactions depends on the distribution of visitors, as well as on that of biting mosquitoes. Members of the public participated in a survey in 1980–82 which showed that the three common *Aedes* species were the main visitor biters. Jerry Rudd discovered, in twenty-four-hour man-baited biting catches, that *Aedes* species bite mainly by day (when visitors are available) whereas *Anopheles* species bite by night (when their human diet may be limited to undergraduate biologists, moth trappers and bird ringers).[23,24] Most of the interactions between mosquitoes and visitors took place at the eastern end of the Fen and along Spinney Bank, although mosquitoes (but not visitors) are abundant elsewhere, notably around the old brick-kiln ponds south of Wicken Lode.

One hundred and four species of chironomids, or non-biting midges, have been recorded from the Fen, the main site for Peter Langton's intensive investigations. The Fen owes its overall species richness to the diversity of its aquatic habitats: each individual water-body has its own characteristic and stable chironomid community, which is easily destroyed by episodes of pollution, as happened when pit 78e received nutrient-rich water from outside the Fen (Chapter 3). A nucleus for recolonization should therefore be retained within each water-body when destructive management operations, such as slubbing, are performed (Chapter 11). In the absence of detailed earlier studies of chironomids at Wicken Fen, no long-term trends in species distributions are apparent.

Other groups of flies have not, in general, been studied in such detail as the hoverflies, mosquitoes and chironomids. The Fen is particularly rich in species of Hybotidae, Empididae and Dolichopodidae, whose larvae develop in damp places and wet mud. These have been well recorded in the past, partly because of the special affection that G. H. Verrall and J. E. Collin had for them, but more needs to be known of their current status and natural history on the Fen before useful patterns will begin to emerge. Among the most conspicuous of the dolichopodids is *Poecilobothrus nobilitatus* (Plate 7, Fig. 4), a metallic green fly with dark wings tipped in white, whose posturings in the sun attract attention on patches of bare mud. When shaded by trees these mud patches form the arena for courtship flights of males of *Argyra* species, which flash intermittently as sunflecks catch their reflective silver-dusted bodies. (See also Plate 7, Figs 3, 8.)

One other fly that has received special attention at Wicken is the chloropid *Lipara lucens*, which forms galls on reed (Fig. 15, Chapter 4). The developing larva lives in the hollowed-out stem surrounded by the leaf bases of several internodes that have failed to elongate. These galls, which may be very abundant in reed-beds, were studied at Wicken Fen for many years by George Salt and his students in the Department of Zoology in Cambridge.[25] The less conspicuous galls of the much rarer *L. similis* (*RDB2* 'vulnerable') have also been found[26] and adults of the third British species, *L. rufitarsis*, have been recorded in recent years. The succession of insect species housed by *Lipara* galls includes parasites and inquilines, some of which merely lodge in the abandoned gall. Among the inquilines are two of Wicken Fen's rarest aculeate wasps, *Passaloecus clypealis* and *Hylaeus pectoralis* (q.v., above), while the rare chloropid fly *Cryptonevra consimilis* (*RDB2*) has been reared from the galls of *Lipara similis*.

BEETLES (COLEOPTERA)

Wicken Fen has long been known as a good place for beetles (Plate 6, Figs 6–12). Since the early days of the 19th century, many notable early coleopterists, including the young Charles Darwin when he was at Cambridge, have collected the Fen's specialities.[27] Although the earliest records are sometimes very imprecise in their localities, there are enough of them to permit comparisons between then and now.

Omer Cooper, Perkins and Tottenham drew attention to certain beetle populations which were showing change during the 1920s and '30s.[27] Many of the beetles that were declining then have since been found, but there are some notable exceptions. *Dromius sigma*, a distinctive reed carabid, has yet to be rediscovered, and while it is rash to pronounce a beetle extinct in a particular locality, it is unlikely that it still occurs on the Fen. The large black carabid *Pterostichus aterrimus* (*RDB1* 'endangered'), once common in the Fens, has not been found for many years. Fortunately, other reed carabids are thriving: *Dromius longiceps*, *Demetrias imperialis* (Plate 6, Fig. 6), *D. monostigma* and the bright orange and blue *Odacantha melanura*. Another carabid, *Panageus crux-major* (*RDB1*), which according to Wollaston occurred in 'immense numbers' at Wicken in 1842,[27] has not been found recently on the Fen. The beetle's distinctive black cross on predominantly orange-red elytra would have been noticed by the many modern recorders but perhaps it still occurs on the Fen at a low population density.

Wicken Fen remains the only site in the fenland of Cambridgeshire and Huntingdonshire for the rare small brown carabid, *Trechus rivularis* (*RDB3* 'rare'). Clearly the isolation of these fens during the draining and conversion to arable of the surrounding land has threatened the populations of the rarer species and virtually ruled out natural recolonization. Changes at Wicken, such as the taming of Adventurers' Fen during the Second World War, the encroachment of carr on open areas during the extended period of reduced management (Chapter 11) and the progressive drying of the Fen have undoubtedly led to some casualties among the beetle fauna. Some of the old species from the Fens have become nationally rare: *Pterostichus aterrimus* (*RDB1*), *Chlaenius tristis* (*RDB2* 'vulnerable'), *Spercheus emarginatus* (*RDB1*, probably extinct in Britain), *Hydraena palustris* (*RDB2*), *Oberea oculata* (*RDB1*) and *Lixus paraplecticus* (*RDB1*). It should not be surprising that they are now rare or extinct on the Fen. *O. oculata*, common to the collectors of old but not seen for many years, had been given up for lost when it suddenly turned up in 1984 before a non-coleopterist who photographed a specimen on sallow. There may well be a reasonable population of this attractive red and black longhorn; it is a renowned recluse, hiding under leaves or flying over the sallow and alder buckthorn. Renewed efforts are to be made to establish its status at

Wicken. *Lixus paraplecticus*, an inch-long narrow weevil, sometimes with a golden bloom in new specimens, was a Wicken speciality, and it appears on Omer Cooper and Tottenham's list of 1932.[28] It has not been seen for many years, perhaps because one of its food plants, greater water-parsnip (*Sium latifolium*), has disappeared from the Fen.

Despite these fluctuations and declines the Fen still has a wonderfully rich beetle fauna. Few sights are more dramatic than the two-inch long iridescent greeny bronze cerambycid *Aromia moschata* (Plate 6, Fig. 10), the musk beetle, flying slowly over the sallows on a hot August day, and coming down to rest on a flower. Often seen basking in the sun on flowerheads and low vegetation are the yellow and black longhorn, *Strangalia maculata* (Plate 6, Fig 9), the golden-bloomed grey longhorn *Agapanthia villoso-viridescens* (Plate 6, Fig. 11) and the ashy grey longhorn *Anaglyptus mysticus* with chestnut shoulders to its elytra.

The reeds and sedges lining the lodes and dykes often have a number of the chrysomelid reed beetles (*Donacia* spp.) (Plate 6, Fig. 12) clinging to their leaves. Sometimes the dwarf willows and low vegetation can be infested with the large golden green chrysomelid *Chrysolina graminis*, while on the sallows occur two characteristic fenland weevils with silvery gold scaling, *Acalyptus carpini* and *Dorytomus salicinus*. With so much water, it is perhaps not surprising that Wicken Fen supports a very rich water beetle fauna. Among the more uncommon species are *Agabus undulatus* (*RDB2*) (Plate 6, Fig. 7), with its characteristic orange zigzag markings across the base of the elytra, which can be met with in the Brickpits, and *A. uliginosus*, which occurs in the more boggy areas. All five of the spectacularly large lowland dytiscids have been found: *Dytiscus circumcinctus, D. circumflexus, D. dimidiatus* (*RDB3*), *D. marginalis* and *D. semisulcatus*. While these species occur in more open ditches, the very old, overgrown ditches on the Fen are valuable habitat for beetles (Chapter 3), including such fenland specialists as *Dryops anglicanus* and the hydrophilid *Hydraena palustris* (*RDB2*).[29]

The great majority of the Fen's beetles are small and dull in colour and can be found only by sieving the reed and sedge leaf-litter or by sweeping the vegetation. With a list of over a thousand different species of beetle, Wicken Fen is a most valuable site for Coleoptera. The sustained management effort of recent years should maintain the Fen's diversity of habitats, thus ensuring the survival of its special beetle populations.

DRAGONFLIES (ODONATA)

Dragonflies are essentially tropical insects and require warm, sunny, sheltered places. Thirty-three of the 39 British dragonfly species depend upon still waters for their larval habitat. Ponds are often short-lived and many insects such as the dragonflies that breed in ponds and other transient habitats have evolved exceptional powers of dispersal. Thus dragonflies are quick to exploit new habitats and it is not surprising that all the common species of dragonfly in East Anglia – such as the common darter (*Sympetrum striolatum*) (Plate 7, Fig. 9) – have discovered Wicken Fen and breed there. The ability of dragonflies to find ponds is so great that if a particular common species is not found at a pond, it is fairly safe to assume that the habitat is not suitable for it.

Table VIII. Dragonflies of Wicken Fen in their national and regional context

	Number of species		
	Recorded breeding regularly, past and/or present	Known to be breeding recently	Probably extinct in area
British Isles	42*	39	3
England	37	34	3
East Anglia	29	28	1
Wicken Fen	23	18†	5

* in addition, there are 3 immigrant species that rarely breed in the British Isles
† possibly 17, as the breeding of *Calopteryx splendens* has not been proven.

We are fortunate at Wicken Fen in having records of dragonflies for over a hundred years, and so we can compare the fauna of the past with that of today, and can relate the differences to changes in land use. A comparison of the dragonfly fauna of Wicken Fen with those of the larger areas of which the Fen is part (Table VIII) reveals that, although five species have been lost, about half of all the English species still breed there. For this reason alone Wicken Fen qualifies as a Site of Special Scientific Interest.

The dragonfly species that have been recorded at Wicken Fen (Table IX) fall into four distinct groups: scarce immigrant species from the European continent, which rarely breed in the British Isles – yellow winged darter (*Sympetrum flaveolum*); species whose larvae are usually found in flowing water – banded demoiselle (*Calopteryx splendens*); species whose larvae are usually confined to acid waters – small red damselfly (*Ceriagrion tenellum*), common hawker (*Aeshna juncea*), keeled skimmer (*Orthetrum coerulescens*) and black darter (*Sympetrum danae*); and species whose larvae are found in a wide range of water-bodies and which have a wide tolerance of pH and aquatic vegetation – all other species, of which all but one are still present.

By the end of the first quarter of this century the water-filled peat-diggings had virtually disappeared (Chapter 10) and with them the acid water dragonflies that used to occur at Wicken Fen. If acid water conditions were to be restored to the Fen by peat digging, *Aeshna juncea* would probably recolonize, as it has the new mere in the peat of Holme Fen (Chapter 1). *Ceriagrion tenellum*, *Orthetrum coerulescens* and *Sympetrum danae* are now so rare and localized in East Anglia that it is very unlikely that they would colonize Wicken Fen unaided. In 1990, peat-digging was reintroduced on a limited scale for demonstration purposes. If new peat-diggings were made extensive enough to sustain viable populations of these insects, their reintroduction might be considered (see Chapter 11).

The other species to disappear was the scarce emerald dragonfly (*Lestes dryas*), which breeds in lakes, ponds and ditches with many emergent plants such as *Equisetum* and *Schoenoplectus*. Its disappearance may have been due to loss of its preferred habitat. Some of the existing ditches appear fairly suitable for it, but it may have failed to find them as it is now a rare insect in East Anglia.

Table IX. Dragonflies at Wicken Fen in the 19th and 20th centuries. For the species still occurring at the Fen, breeding habitats and months during which adults may best be seen are indicated.

	Years recorded			Lodes	Large dykes	Breeding habitats		Mere	Months flying
	1850 –99	1900 –49	1950 –	Lodes	Large dykes	Ditches	Brick -pits	Mere	
Calopteryx splendens		*	*	+					6–7
Lestes sponsa	*	*	*		+	+	+		7–8
L. dryas		*							
Pyrrhosoma nymphula		*	*	+		+	+		5–6
Erythromma najas		*	*	+	+				5–7
Coenagrion puella	*	*	*	+	+	+	+		5–7
C. pulchellum	*	*	*			+	+		5–7
Enallagma cyathigerum		*	*		+			+	6–8
Ischnura elegans	*	*	*	+	+	+	+	+	5–8
Ceriagrion tenellum†	*								
Aeshna cyanea		*	*	+	+		+		7–9
A. grandis	*	*	*	+	+	+	+		7–8
A. juncea†		*							
A. mixta		*		+	+	+	+		8–9
Anax imperator		*		+			+		6–7
Brachytron pratense	*	*	*		+				5–6
Libellula quadrimaculata	*	*	*	+	+	+	+		5–7
L. depressa		*	*				+		5–6
Orthetrum cancellatum		*			+			+	5–7
O. coerulescens†	*								
Sympetrum danae†		*							
S. flaveolum‡		*	*						
S. sanguineum	*	*	*		+	+	+		7–8
S. striolatum	*	*	*	+	+	+	+	+	6–10

† species restricted to acid water
‡ immigrant species which rarely, if ever, breeds in the British Isles

Two species present today were not recorded before 1950, and as both are conspicuous insects, it is unlikely that they were overlooked; they are almost certainly new colonists. The black-tailed skimmer (*Orthetrum cancellatum*) breeds in lakes or slowly flowing rivers and dykes with bare patches on their edges, on which the males sun themselves. Gravel pits provide an ideal habitat for *O. cancellatum*, and the species has increased enormously with the great increase in gravel workings in lowland Britain in recent decades. The numerous new gravel pits in the Fens and the Ouse Valley may have provided the colonists of the Mere at Wicken. More recently this species has colonized the new dyke beside Spinney Bank. The very large and beautiful emperor dragonfly (*Anax imperator*) is at the northern edge of its range in the Fens. It is another species which has benefited from the new gravel pits, and like *O. cancellatum* it may have colonized Wicken Fen from them. The recent increase in mild winters may also have favoured it.

The hairy dragonfly (*Brachytron pratense*) (Plate 7, Fig. 10), the only hawker dragonfly which flies in the spring, was once a common insect at Wicken Fen. Then it disappeared for a number of years and has only recently returned, reappearing in several other fenland localities at the same time. It is susceptible to water pollution; improved water-quality in these localities may have allowed it to return. Now that it is back at Wicken Fen, the opening up of more waterways, and their careful management, should ensure its survival.[29] The variable damselfly (*Coenagrion pulchellum*) is another local species which was once much commoner at Wicken and has been centred on ditch 78d and the Brickpits for many years. Improved ditch management (Chapter 11) has meant that this species is also extending its range within the Fen.

Two very local species which were confined to the East Anglian flood-plains may have bred at Wicken Fen in the distant past. The Norfolk hawker (*Aeshna isosceles*), like the swallowtail butterfly, used to occur in the Fens as well as the Broads, but it has long been extinct in the Fens. In the Broads it is mainly found in grazing marshes, in unpolluted ditches which contain water-soldier (*Stratiotes aloides*). This plant is now very rare in the Fens and no longer occurs at Wicken. The Norfolk damselfly (*Coenagrion armatum*) used to be found in the Broads in a few unpolluted ditches containing frogbit (*Hydrocharis morsus-ranae*), a plant last found at Wicken Fen in the 1950s. This damselfly became extinct in East Anglia, and hence in the British Isles, about forty years ago. Both *A. isosceles* and *C. armatum* are under threat in Europe, so it may be worth considering their introduction to Wicken Fen in the future. This should not be attempted until much more is known about their exact habitat requirements.

Meanwhile, there are still many interesting dragonflies to be seen and enjoyed at Wicken Fen. If the Fen is visited at the right time, adult insects of most of its breeding species can be seen within 500m of the William Thorpe Building. What is the right time? Mature males congregate by water during the late morning and early afternoon on warm days; most are aggressive and territorial and so advertise their presence. Females go to water only to mate and lay eggs so they are more rarely seen. Immature adults (which are often quite difficult to identify) remain dispersed away from water, and feed in rides and sheltered places, as do mature males and females when they are not by water, late and early in the day, and when weather is poor. Different species of adult dragonflies have distinct flying seasons, and preferred habitats within the Fen (defined in Table IX). To see a species, visit the right habitat about noon on a fine day in the right season. *Calopteryx splendens* and the broad-bodied chaser (*Libellula depressa*) are rare or only occasional visitors to Wicken at present; one is lucky to see them.

Wicken Fen provides excellent opportunities for studying dragonfly behaviour and ecology. It has recently been used for an interesting study of the territorial behaviour of the four-spotted chaser (*Libellula quadrimaculata*).[30] Peter Convey transferred his project to Wicken in 1986 when the much smaller colony at Quy Fen died out following two severe winters. He uniquely marked and observed 233 individual mature male *L. quadrimaculata* in the area around the Brickpits, following the main emergence periods in early June and mid July. Each of these males might live about 16 days, with some surviving up to 45 days.

Mature males of *L. quadrimaculata* arrive at the water on which they will hold territories about a week after emergence. The territory of this species is used solely for the purposes of reproduction: obtaining females and providing them with suitable oviposition sites. Most of the territories at Wicken Fen were held along lengths of ditches, which are no more than two metres wide, so a single male can effectively patrol both banks and the water between. On the ponds, however, males tended to defend only one shore and the water immediately adjacent. The size of the territory varied with the number of males contesting the area, and this in turn reflected the quality of the habitat: on ditches near the windpump, territories averaged about 6 m in length, but they extended for up to 30 m on overgrown sections of Gardiner's Ditch.

Convey noticed that some males of *L. quadrimaculata* did not show the chasing response to other males characteristic of territory holders. These 'satellite' males perched on reeds within other males' territories and would attempt to mate with females entering the area. If a satellite succeeded, the legitimate territory holder would immediately remate the female. Because of the peculiar arrangement of the reproductive apparatus in dragonflies, the sperm of the last male to mate with a female before the eggs are laid fertilizes most of the eggs. So a satellite is no more than a 'hopeful reproductive'.

The unique marks given to each male enabled Convey to follow the fortunes of individual dragonflies. All of the 38 males seen behaving as satellites were also observed as territory holders on other occasions, sometimes on the same day and even alternating between the two types of behaviour. Satellites are evidently not 'learner' territory holders, as the tendency to show satellite behaviour was not correlated with the male's age. It was, however, linked to his size: males acting as satellites had significantly greater wingspans than those which did not. However, the muscle power of these larger males was not proportionally greater; they would be less manoeuvrable in flight and probably at a disadvantage in aerial disputes with smaller males, which would be able to establish themselves as territory holders, relegating the larger male to the role of satellite.

POSTSCRIPT: MANAGING THE FEN FOR INSECTS

If the Fen is to be managed to enhance insect diversity, an appropriate aim would be to increase the probability that an extinction in one population would be replaced by reinvasion from another, and to promote the persistence of 'island' populations of species that are poorly represented outside the Fen by increasing the area and numbers of particular fen-specific habitats. These include the yellow loosestrife essential for the survival of the bee *Macropis europaea*, the shallow pools and tree holes in which mosquitoes breed, the individual brickpits with their characteristic chironomid communities, and the litter piles beloved of 19th-century beetle collectors. Undisturbed turf and banks at the Fen margins may be important as nesting sites for bees that forage on the Fen but cannot nest there because of the high water-table.

The maintenance of these special species and the restoration of lost species (see Chapter 12) are among the prime objectives of management, and a component of the accepted aim of enhancement of species richness. Another objective is enhanced public appreciation. The long-established and detailed documentation of Wicken's insect fauna, of which only the most-studied groups have been discussed above, and the predictable presence of large, dramatic and beautiful species at sites visible from the boardwalk as well as smaller, less conspicuous ones (see Plate 6, Figs 4, 5), offer excellent opportunities for interpretative material that can help to fulfil this objective.

References

1 Shirt (1987)
2 Dempster *et al.* (1976)
3 Dempster (1976)
4 Dempster & Hall (1980)
5 Pollard (1979)
6 Bennett (1988)
7 Pollard (1977)
8 Pollard & Hall (1980)
9 Emmet (1972)
10 Spooner (1930)
11 Kerrich & Spooner (1938)
12 Williams (1986)
13 Prŷs-Jones (1982)
14 Williams (1982)
15 Saville & Chapman (1988)

16 Nevinson (1916)
17 J. P. Field (pers. comm.)
18 Nevinson (1926)
19 Falk (1991)
20 Unwin (1987)
21 Godwin (1985)
22 Lewis (1932)
23 Rudd (1986)
24 Rudd (1982)
25 Salt (1947)
26 Spooner (1929)
27 Omer Cooper *et al.* (1928)
28 Omer Cooper & Tottenham (1932)
29 Painter (1995)
30 Convey (1989)

9

BIRDS AND BIRD STUDIES

1. INTRODUCTION

C. J. R. THORNE AND T. J. BENNETT

WELL BEFORE the first acquisition of land at Wicken Fen by the National Trust, the area had been of interest to ornithologists, mainly of the collecting type. The earliest records of breeding by Montagu's harrier (*Circus pygargus*), spotted crake (*Porzana porzana*), short-eared owl (*Asio flammeus*), Savi's warbler (*Locustella luscinioides*) and marsh warbler (*Acrocephalus palustris*), come from the 1840s and 1850s (although a number of these records must now be judged doubtful). Rare or scarce species continued to be the main interest for many years, and this is reflected in the emphasis shown in the comments on Wicken Fen in various regional publications in the latter part of the 19th and early part of the 20th centuries.[1] However, the acquisition of the site was mainly because of its fame among entomologists, and to a lesser extent botanists; most bird records were of a rather casual nature and were largely confined to the Sedge Fen, which did not support a great variety of species. Evans,[2] writing in 1923 as the first Secretary of the Wicken Fen Local Committee, even stated that 'the absence of bird life in general is remarkable'. Of the 650 pages contained in *The*

Natural History of Wicken Fen,[3,4] only one per cent was devoted to birds, which may be taken as further evidence that ornithology was not a major interest in the 1920s.

The most attractive area for birds was not really on the reserve at all, but lay beyond Burwell Lode. This land (the South Adventurers' Fen described by Ennion[5]) periodically became waterlogged between the two World Wars. It was never, unfortunately, destined to become National Trust property. In marked contrast, it seems from contemporary reports of Wicken Fen's Management Committee that those parts of Adventurers' Fen north of Burwell Lode, which had been acquired by the Trust as early as 1907, were viewed rather as an extension of the main reserve: thus in 1929, it was reported that 70 acres of litter had been cut there.[6]

MANAGING THE FEN FOR BIRDS

Priority at Wicken always has been, and always should be, given to the Sedge Fen and St Edmund's Fen, as they have not been subject to the intense drainage effort applied to Adventurers' Fen (Chapters 10 & 11). However, it is clear from old Management Committee reports that there have been distinct cycles of emphasis placed on matters of special ornithological interest, which seem to coincide with the influence of particular members of the Committee. The peaks manifest themselves in more thorough accounts of interesting birds noted during the years in question and greater enthusiasm for carrying out management projects designed to further enhance the birdlife.

From the earliest days, the area to the west of Drainers' Dyke ('Verrall's Fen') was set aside 'for the Harriers'. Two pairs of Montagu's harriers were nesting at Wicken in the 1920s[2] and the Committee judged that the best form of management would be to minimize disturbance by restricting access. However, this policy led to deterioration of the habitat, as the open, grassy areas, left uncut, were quickly overwhelmed with carr (Chapter 6). Montagu's harriers have not nested at Wicken since the 1940s. While it may seem that this *laissez faire* approach was counter-productive, the harrier's demise at Wicken occurred in parallel with a decline throughout East Anglia and may have been inevitable. When one considers the financial state of the Fen at the time (Chapter 11), it is hard to see how the Committee could have acted differently.

David Lack's *Birds of Cambridgeshire*[7] of 1934 confirms that the species of most interest on the Sedge Fen at that date were Montagu's harriers (1–2 pairs) and short-eared owls (2–5 pairs), both of which bred regularly, and grasshopper warblers (*Locustella naevia*) which bred abundantly. With only some 700 visitors a year, disturbance was clearly not a problem. But Lack was probably accurately summarizing the views of ornithologists in general when he compared the Fen unfavourably with South Adventurers' Fen and wrote of a wish to see more wetland habitat created at Wicken. He identified the 'low-lying ground at the north-west corner of Burwell Fen' which was 'permanently flooded to a depth of three to five feet' as promising to be the 'best breeding place for water birds in the whole of the fenland', and strongly advised that the National Trust attempt to acquire the land 'which adjoins the Wicken property and provides a type of bird haunt entirely lacking at Wicken'.

In 1938, William Thorpe wrote similarly that 'there is no doubt that the greatest need of Wicken as a bird reserve is the digging of a large mere and the encouragement of reed beds'.[8] The Committee, being well aware that carr invasion was becoming ever more serious (Chapter 6), no doubt noted these comments, were sympathetic, and did authorize some work, although only on a small scale. Almost sixty years later, the ideas and constraints identified in the 1930s that could make Adventurers' Fen 'more attractive to wildfowl' remain almost identical, so that in many ways the true potential of the area has, even now, still to be realized.

In 1938 the first project that was unquestionably aimed specifically at encouraging birdlife was carried out: Barnes' Mere was dug, by hand, between May and September of that year and was named after the then 'watcher' G. W. Barnes and his family (see Chapter 11), who were responsible for the work (Fig. 39). This was sited in Verrall's Fen, and was relatively inaccessible, there being no permanent bridge across Drainers' Dyke at the time. The success of this curiously designed water-body, looking like 'three sides of a square each 70 yards by 10 yards and 4–5 feet deep with bays on the angles 15 yards by 6 yards wide',[6] was regularly documented in ensuing years.

Large numbers of teal (*Anas crecca*), wigeon (*A. penelope*) and mallard (*A. platyrhynchos*), and smaller numbers of shoveler (*A. clypaeata*), pochard (*Aythya ferina*) and tufted ducks (*A. fuligula*), became a regular feature in the winter with total counts of 1500 or more birds noted. In 1946, a hide was erected at the Barnes' Mere to encourage observations of

Figure 39 The Barnes family at work, digging Barnes' Mere, 13 July 1938. The summer water-table at the time lay about 30cm below the surface.

wildfowl. Regrettably, no provision appears to have been made for the long-term maintenance of this water-body, so that today it is surrounded by impenetrable scrub; its outline is hard to follow on the ground and there is rarely any standing water in it.

By the end of 1942, the whole area of Adventurers' Fen had been drained and put under the plough (see Chapter 11). During the war and the immediate post-war period, interesting sightings were apparently rather few: a dead common scoter (*Melanitta nigra*) was found in 1943; wheatears (*Oenanthe oenanthe*) probably bred in 1944; hen harriers (*Circus cyaneus*) were apparently much in evidence in the winters of 1944–45 and 1945–46; and in November 1948 there were sightings of a whinchat (*Saxicola rubetra*) over the course of a week. The farmer responsible for the draining of Adventurers' Fen, Alan Bloom, clearly saw things rather differently: he judged that wildfowl were still plentiful 'in the depths of Wicken Fen' and that the conversion to arable had enlarged feeding grounds, even if it had reduced nesting space.[9]

The encroachment of carr (which was reported as covering 90 per cent of the Sedge Fen by 1950) resulted in the loss of both Montagu's harrier (which probably last bred in 1948) and short-eared owl (1954). This was compensated for by the arrival of long-eared owls (*Asio otus*) (which probably first bred in 1936) and woodcock (*Scolopax rusticola*) (late 1950s), birds characteristic of more wooded habitat (see Chapter 9.4).

A 'piece of news of outstanding importance'[6] to ornithologists was received in 1952, when the Committee heard they were to benefit from the will of Mrs Edith Bouquet. Adventurers' Fen had been finally derequisitioned in that year, and the trustees of the Bouquet estate had decided that the money should be used to create and maintain a 10-acre Mere on the land, with enough left over to allow for the alteration to drains and the construction of sluices, as necessary. There was obvious optimism following the success of Barnes' Mere, which was still proving attractive, but above all there were now the financial resources to proceed with the ideas that the Committee had for so long been planning. After some delay caused by the shortage of suitable equipment (which had been required for repairs following the 1953 East Coast storm surge), work finally got under way in mid-1954 and the project was completed in October 1955 (see Fig. 3b). The grand opening ceremony on 28 November received coverage from both BBC radio and television (Fig. 40). The scheme was carefully planned with the valuable help of Peter Scott and designed on 'the principle that the requirements of nature conservation and agriculture need not always be antagonistic but can be complementary or even mutually beneficial'. The Mere very quickly proved attractive to ducks and, before surrounding vegetation could firmly establish itself, to migrant waders too.

It was intended from the outset that access to the Mere for visitors (which by 1955 had risen to some 1,600 a year) would eventually be marked out. Recent visitors will be only too well aware that this objective is only now being achieved. However, in 1956, a viewing tower (the Tower Hide, Fig. 41), modelled on one at Slimbridge, was erected. Two telescopes mounted on rigid stands were installed for the use of visitors in 1957. The improved visibility clearly helped to increase the reserve's bird list: two ferruginous ducks (*Aythya nyroca*) seen that winter brought the duck total for the Mere to 12 species in its first two years.

Figure 40   A. C. Bouquet with Peter Scott at the opening of the Mere,
28 November 1955

Figure 41   The Tower Hide, emerging from the canopy of buckthorn (*Rhamnus cathartica*)
and elder (*Sambucus nigra*), July 1994

In order to keep the rest of Adventurers' Fen in good condition much of it was put
down to grazing, but in the exceptionally wet year of 1958 grazing was not possible.
Reed and rush invasion was rapid, so that the area was beginning to look again rather
like it had in the 1920s and 1930s. West Adventurers' Fen, particularly, was rapidly
developing into a fully-fledged reed-bed. Probably as a result, bearded tits (*Panurus
biarmicus*) wintered at the Fen for the first time in 1959–60. In 1962 it was decided to
treat the West Adventurers' Fen reed-bed as a truly commercial crop. These reed-beds
have more recently been extended and, by the exclusion of grazing, have been allowed
to cover much of the Mere area and its surroundings. The portion treated commercially is still restricted to the western side of Harrison's Drove as originally intended,
but their greater size (they are now among the largest inland reed-beds in Britain) has
proved ever more attractive to birds (Chapters 4 & 9.4).

In 1964 an Appeal Committee was set up to raise funds for the further development
of Adventurers' Fen, which was to be known as the 'Charles Raven Marshland
Reserve'. Close co-operation between those associated with the Fen and the Ouse
River Board (later effectively the National Rivers Authority) eventually led to the construction during 1969–71 of waterproof banks, which allow the area to be seasonally
flooded without affecting neighbouring agricultural land. However, the chronic problem of controlled discharge of water out of the area and the unwanted drainage effect
of Commissioner's Drain was not resolved. A foretaste of what the Appeal Committee
had in mind was savoured in the wet winter of 1967–68, when much of the future
Charles Raven Marshland Reserve became flooded.

By the summer of 1968 the appeal had reached a total of £49,000, of which some £20,000 had been raised from the public phase launched by Peter Scott, who gave a lecture at Cambridge Guildhall in October 1967. A colour film produced by Robin Crane was also premiered at the lecture and subsequently shown on television and widely used for publicity meetings, giving the whole exercise a surprisingly high profile. This undoubtedly led directly to the marked increase in visitor figures, which were recorded as over 9,000 in that year.

In the summer of 1971, the Royal Engineers based at Waterbeach were invited to carry out a number of earth-moving exercises on Adventurers' Fen in the course of military training. These included the creation of a mound behind the Mere, on which a hide might one day be built and, at the extreme southern tip of the reserve, on Rothschild's Lapwing, the excavation of the 'Sappers Pond'. This pond was intended to be suitable for both ducks and waders; planned with advice from Bert Axell, it was of deliberately irregular shape, with deep and shallow areas, and plenty of 'edge'. However, rather few birds used the area, despite a project carried out by members of the 'Wicken Fen Group' (see below) in early 1974, to create a low cliff for attracting sand martins (*Riparia riparia*) or kingfishers (*Alcedo atthis*) and a wet feeding area for waders.[10]

In 1989, many of the dykes and ditches within and surrounding the reed-beds were reinstated and a number of completely blind lengths excavated. Not only was this programme intended to facilitate more rapid flooding and drainage of the reed-beds, but also to provide valuable new bird habitat in the form of corridors of uncut reed enclosing permanent water projecting well into the heart of the reed fields (Chapter 4).

Major works have also been carried out on Adventurers' Fen by the Anglian Water Authority as part of a flood relief scheme (Chapter 11). The waterproof banks have been strengthened, the possibility of more efficient water control within the area attained and, at long last, full agreement about the discharge of superfluous water into the drainage district has been achieved. A great deal of clay was need for this project; much of it was extracted from a site adjacent to the Sappers Pond. This has created a deep, 2- acre 'Borrow Pit', with islands and irregular shelving shoreline. This has quickly proved attractive to a variety of water birds, particularly little grebe (*Tachybaptus ruficollis*) and tufted duck. Canada geese (*Branta canadensis*) have also taken up residence on the Borrow Pit and are giving cause for concern at the way in which they trample vegetation and edges. Their numbers have been increasing logarithmically at Wicken in the last 25 years, from their first breeding in 1967 up to flock sizes that reached 20 by 1980, 100 by 1986 and 200 by 1989.

The current management plan reaffirms the intention fully to develop the 'Marshland Reserve'. However the rigorous management regime required on the Sedge Fen and Verrall's Fen previously left very little time and manpower to devote to Adventurers' Fen. But a combination of increased staffing and mechanisation now allows many of the objectives on the main part of the reserve to be achieved, and with funds available through a 'Stewardship Scheme' (Chapter 13) it is now possible to channel much more effort into Adventurers' Fen.

When the 'Marshland Reserve' comes to fruition, it will raise many questions of public access and visitor management. Visitor numbers are currently 30,000 per year (Chapter 11). The provision of a totally new range of facilities for visitors on Adventurers' Fen, and further creation of habitat on adjacent former arable fields to attract more birds to be viewed, sounds very appealing. Many visitors are birdwatchers; they are often frustrated by being confined to the Sedge Fen. The challenge is to create a plan for the 'Marshland Reserve' that will allow the satisfactory co-existence of birds and birdwatchers in what is really quite a small area (see Chapter 13).

THE 'WICKEN FEN GROUP'

After the Second World War, there was considerable enthusiasm amongst several undergraduate members of the Cambridge Bird Club, which manifested itself in the first attempt at bird census work at Wicken Fen. A preliminary survey of ecological communities in 1947 was followed by sample breeding censuses in the years 1948 to 1951. Although necessarily limited in scope, this work[11] was an encouraging forerunner to some of the later scientific bird studies.

Species recording became much more systematic when, in May 1961, Lt.-Col. Charles Mitchell was appointed as the Fen's first Warden/Naturalist. A sign that the avifauna of the Fen was receiving serious attention was the publication in 1967 of the *Birds of Wicken Fen* by Graham Easy and Colin Kirtland.[12] This booklet, the fourth of the Committee's Guides to Wicken Fen, was written in the popular format of an annotated checklist. It notes 164 species of wild bird as having been reliably reported within the boundaries of the National Trust Reserve, 78 of which had bred at least once.

In April 1968, the Wicken Fen Ringing Group was formed. Ringing of birds at the Fen, mostly at roosts in the autumn, had previously been carried out sporadically between 1955 and 1965 (by Peter Evans, Sid Fenn, Dave Palmer, Colin Kirtland, Richard Douthwaite and others), but the formal establishment of a Group, comprising up to 35 participating members as well as another 15 'friends', allowed a much more scientific approach to be taken. A major intention of the Group's founders (Michael Allen, Colin Bibby and David Steventon) was that 'information gathered in the course of a sustained ringing programme might be of some use to those involved in the management of the Fen, where precise knowledge of the needs of the flora and fauna is clearly of prime importance'.[13]

Another stimulus had been the national effort ('the *Acrocephalus* enquiry'), set up at that time under the auspices of the British Trust for Ornithology (BTO), to learn more about reed and sedge warblers (*A. scirpaceus* and *A. schoenobaenus*), which are abundant at Wicken. The Group thus embarked on the systematic catching, ringing and recording of birds to monitor the Fen's populations. To further the work, a substantial investment in equipment was required. Funds for this project came from the members themselves, with assistance from industry and from the Committee, which also allowed the Group to erect a discreet hut on Adventurers' Fen to use as a base.

Some 59,000 birds have been ringed by the Group in the 29 years of its existence, and many analyses made. Some of the more obvious results obtainable from ringing are the discovery of migration routes and, if the catching is regular enough, of bird population numbers (see below). Many other studies are also made possible by the catching and subsequent careful analysis of birds in the hand, and a number of these have been reported in the Group's *Reports*. For example, the moulting;[14,15,16,17] growth;[18,19] survival;[20,21,22,23,24,25,26] body temperatures;[27] parasites;[28,29] weights;[30,31,32,33,34,35] and measurements;[36,37] of a wide variety of bird species have been studied. The simple regular retrapping of Wicken birds has also demonstrated surprising longevity for several species (Table X), including the British record for the garden warbler.

Some of the Group's work has also appeared in the more formal scientific literature; this includes studies of bird behaviour that are greatly assisted by the marking, using distinct colour rings, of individual birds.[38,39] Recent exciting work on the co-evolution of the cuckoo (*Cuculus canorus*) and its hosts has been published in the *Scientific American*,[40] thus bringing Wicken Fen bird studies to the widest possible audience (see Chapter 9.3).

The major value of bird ringing, as with any other monitoring system in nature, depends on its continuity, and the Wicken Fen Ringing Group has an excellent record in this respect. All the records and measurements of reed and sedge warblers, of which about 8,500 and 4,000 have been ringed respectively, have been fully computerized. These data have been used to assist work by the BTO on the best way of using ringing recoveries, on a national scale, to estimate survival rates.[41,42,43,44] Despite much fluctuation in its membership, the Group has managed to continue its work to the present day.

The 1970s and 1980s were a productive period for the study of birds at the Fen in general. Regular wildfowl counts on the Mere began in the 1960s and continue to this day; these counts, made mid-month throughout each winter on behalf of the Wildfowl Trust, have given useful and reliable figures (see also Chapter 9.4). The visibility of the Mere, and probably also the accuracy of the counts, has been improved since 1978 by the clearance of much invading vegetation and the erection of the 'Lower Hide' overlooking the Mere in 1980. The Ringing Group established a February 'Owl Count', a census of calling birds, that ran for 10 years (1977–87). They also began an experiment to determine whether wooden or plastic nest boxes would be equally acceptable: sets of boxes were put up first on Verrall's Fen (1973) and subsequently moved to Adventurers' and then to St Edmund's Fens. The birds, mostly blue and great tits (*Parus caeruleus* and *P. major*) but some tree sparrows (*Passer montanus*) as well, much preferred wood; the plastic boxes were withdrawn, but the surviving wooden boxes are still studied.

The Ringing Group's regular netting activities have clarified the Fen status of a number of species, showing, for example that the tree creeper (*Certhia familiaris*) and willow tit (*Parus montanus*) breed regularly in small numbers, and that the goldcrest (*Regulus regulus*) occasionally breeds. Some birds once thought to be rarities, such as redstart (*Phoenicurus phoenicurus*) and pied flycatcher (*Ficedula hypoleuca*), are now known to be scarce but regular passage migrants, while some genuine rarities, such as the barred and great reed warblers (*Sylvia nisoria* and *Acrocephalus arundinaceus*), have made their only known appearance at the Fen in a pocket in a mist net!

Table X. Longest interval, in years and months, between ringing and recovery or retrap

	Wicken Fen Group record	BTO British record
Tawny owl (*Strix aluco*)	10y 8m	25y 5m
Reed bunting (*Emberiza schoeniclus*)	9y 7m	9y 11m
Snipe (*Gallinago gallinago*)	9y 4m	17y 11m
Reed warbler (*Acrocephalus scirpaceus*)	9y 2m	12y 10m
Blackbird (*Turdus merula*)	9y 1m	14y 9m
Bullfinch (*Pyrrhula pyrrhula*)	8y 1m	9y 2m
Garden warbler (*Sylvia borin*)	7y 10m	7y 10m
Willow warbler (*Phylloscopus trochilus*)	7y 10m	9y 11m
Long-tailed tit (*Aegithalos caudatus*)	7y 3m	8y 0m
Willow tit (*Parus montanus*)	7y 2m	10y 4m
Song thrush (*Turdus philomelos*)	7y 0m	10y 4m
Cuckoo (*Cuculus canorus*)	6y 11m	8y 11m
Great tit (*Parus major*)	6y 11m	13y 11m
Blue tit (*P. caeruleus*)	6y 8m	12y 4m
Dunnock (*Prunella modularis*)	6y 8m	9y 3m
Chaffinch (*Fringilla coelebs*)	6y 6m	11y 8m
Sedge warbler (*Acrocephalus schoenobaenus*)	6y 3m	7y 11m
Robin (*Erithacus rubecula*)	5y 11m	8y 7m
Lesser-spotted woodpecker (*Dendrocopos minor*)	5y 9m	6y 3m
Sparrowhawk (*Accipiter nisus*)	5y 5m	9y 8m
Wren (*Troglodytes troglodytes*)	5y 4m	5y 11m
Redwing (*Turdus iliacus*)	5y 3m	7y 2m
Yellowhammer (*Emberiza citrinella*)	5y 3m	11y 10m
Long-eared owl (*Asio otus*)	4y 10m	12y 10m
Redpoll (*Carduelis flammea*)	4y 9m	8y 5m
Chiffchaff (*Philloscopus collybita*)	4y 5m	6y 1m
Starling (*Sturnus vulgaris*)	4y 4m	22y 0m
Blackcap (*Sylvia atricapilla*)	4y 2m	10y 8m
Spotted flycatcher (*Muscicapa striata*)	4y 2m	9y 3m
Lesser whitethroat (*Sylvia curruca*)	4y 0m	5y 8m
Greenfinch (*Carduelis chloris*)	4y 0m	11y 1m
Tree creeper (*Certhia familiaris*)	3y 11m	8y 0m
Kestrel (*Falco tinnunculus*)	3y 10m	23y 10m
Great-spotted woodpecker (*Dendrocopos major*)	3y 9m	10y 9m
Swallow (*Hirundo rustica*)	3y 9m	9y 7m
Woodcock (*Scolopax rusticola*)	3y 4m	12y 4m
Mallard (*Anas platyrhynchos*)	3y 2m	25y 4m
Whitethroat (*Sylvia communis*)	3y 1m	7y 8m
Jay (*Garrulus glandarius*)	3y 0m	16y 10m
House sparrow (*Passer domesticus*)	3y 0m	12y 0m

In 1979 the newly-appointed Warden, Tim Bennett, brought further ornithological expertise to the Fen. Together with Chris Thorne, the long-time Secretary of the Ringing Group, he produced a new edition of *The Birds of Wicken Fen*.[45] This booklet listed 189 bird species, 25 more than did its predecessor of 15 years before, which bears witness to the activities of the ornithologists at the Fen. The increased number of visitors, and their increasing interest in birds, meant that a new edition was soon required;[46] this has details of 195 wild species, 90 of which had bred at the Fen. New bird species continue to be recorded regularly, both as visitors and breeders.

In 1899, the year of the National Trust's first acquisition, a male golden oriole (*Oriolus oriolus*) was recorded at Wicken Fen by A. F. R. (Sandy) Wollaston, a distinguished explorer, who was related by marriage to Charles Raven. It may well be that the golden oriole will before long be added to the list of breeding species. Ninety-two years later, Tim Bennett obtained the first sighting on the Fen of that other most colourful species, the hoopoe (*Upupa epops*). Since then, several other rare visitors have been sighted, amongst them such notable species as spoonbill (*Platalea leucorodia*) and little egret (*Egretta garzetta*). The current tally of birds recorded at Wicken (at March 1997) stands at 202, of which 92 have bred.

2. MIGRATORY MOVEMENTS AND POPULATION CHANGES OF PASSERINES MONITORED BY RINGING

P. M. M. BIRCHAM

Information on the movement and migration of birds that have been ringed can be gathered in three ways: a bird recaptured at the same site ('retrap'); a bird recaptured by another ringer at another site and subsequently released ('control'); or a bird discovered, usually dead or injured, by a member of the public ('recovery'). Many birds are re-caught at Wicken Fen, sometimes on several subsequent occasions, and these are always referred to as retraps. Retrap analysis has been used by the Wicken Fen Group to provide information about aspects of bird biology, such as growth and development, but it is the controls and recoveries that show the movements undertaken by birds.

Not all the birds caught and ringed are travellers, indeed many of the species which contribute substantially to the total of birds ringed at the Fen, such as bullfinch (*Pyrrhula pyrrhula*), blue tit, dunnock (*Prunella modularis*) and wren (*Troglodytes troglodytes*) (each of these species represents more than five per cent of the total ringed) have been shown to be largely sedentary. This is not unique to the site, since these species are nationally known to remain within, or close to, the immediate area where they were raised.

A considerable proportion of the birds at Wicken, however, are migratory and spend only part of the year at the Fen. This not only includes well-known migrants such as warblers, cuckoos, and hirundines in summer, and ducks and thrushes in winter, but also some individuals of species that we consider to be 'resident' such as blackbird (*Turdus merula*), robin (*Erithacus rubecula*) and chaffinch (*Fringilla coelebs*). The main migratory movements are well documented: summer visitors make their way to and from Britain overland as far as they are able, through southern Europe; and the wintering birds, that come to the Fen from northern and eastern Europe, fly more or less directly across the main land mass via Germany and Holland. The two maps (Fig. 42) show the overseas source, or destination, of selected species. They are divided broadly into those ringed at the Fen in summer (Fig. 42a, which shows the sort of routes that summer migrants employ) and those ringed in winter (Fig. 42b, which shows not only the source of some of the birds that winter on the Fen but also, in the case of song thrush (*Turdus philomelos*) and redwing (*T. iliacus*), the areas in which they may spend subsequent winters).

A marsh harrier (*Circus aeruginosus*) ringed as a nestling in June 1985 was found dead in Mauretania in the following October, and a turtle dove (*Streptopelia turtur*), also ringed in summer, was found in Mali. These represent the Group's most southerly recoveries, although a swallow (*Hirunda rustica*) ringed before the Group was formed was recovered in South Africa (see below). One of the reed warblers provided an excellent life history: ringed at Wicken as a young bird in September 1973, it was caught and released in Morocco on 3 November of the same year; it was handled subsequently at the Fen on 20 July 1974 and 17 August 1975.[47] Further interesting examples among the birds ringed while wintering on the Fen include a robin from southern Sweden; a woodcock which was recovered in West Germany (presumably its point of origin); another woodcock which was recovered in Wales during the same winter in which it was ringed on the Fen (showing that some birds from the Continent reach East Anglia in autumn before moving on to winter further west); two bearded tits handled one winter at Wicken were found in Belgium (at the same site) in the winter of the following year; and a brambling (*Fringilla montifringilla*) from the Fen was controlled on Heligoland, probably returning to Scandinavia. A moorhen (*Gallinula chloropus*) ringed in the autumn of 1974 at Wicken and recovered in France in the autumn of 1976 was notable because British recoveries of this species in France are very unusual. Most other foreign recoveries follow well-established national patterns.

An important feature of ringing is that it allows us to find out how long birds take to move from place to place. Almost all recoveries take place long after the bird was originally handled, but sometimes the time span is quite short. The best example of this is a sedge warbler ringed on the Fen on 14 August 1976 which was controlled at Le Migron, in France, a week later.

Studies of the routes taken by migrating birds within the British Isles are particularly fascinating, since they often show entry and exit points and the routes taken across the country. The Wicken Fen Group has gathered some data of this sort about sedge and reed warblers. Despite ringing more than 3,000 sedge warblers and 7,000 reed warblers up to the end of August 1990, the group has had few recoveries in Africa of these species. However, there has been a large number of recoveries in Britain (Fig. 43a). Where these

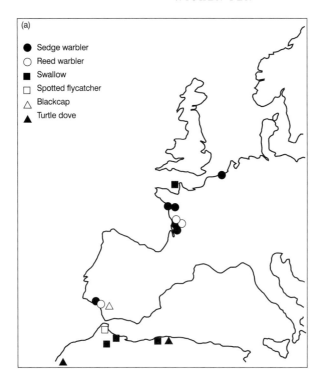

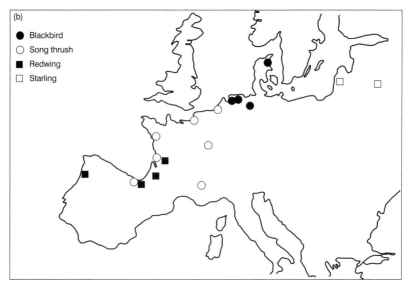

Figure 42 Selected foreign recoveries of birds ringed at Wicken Fen since 1968: (a) birds ringed during the summer: sedge warbler (*Acrocephalus schoenobaenus*), reed warbler (*A. scirpaceus*), swallow (*Hirundo rustica*), spotted flycatcher (*Muscicapa striata*), blackcap (*Sylvia atricapilla*) and turtle dove (*Streptopelia turtur*); (b) birds ringed during the winter: blackbird (*Turdus merula*), song thrush (*T. philomelos*), redwing (*T. iliacus*) and starling (*Sturnus vulgaris*)

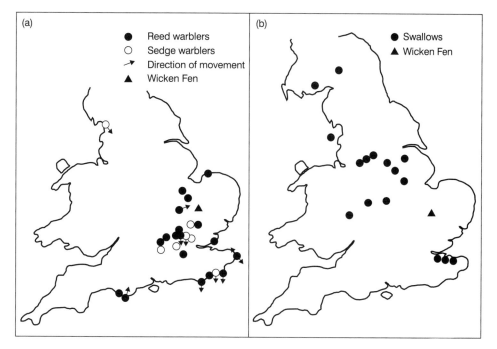

Figure 43   British recoveries of three species trapped at Wicken Fen: (a) reed and sedge warblers
(*Acrocephalus scirpaceus* and *A. schoenobaenus*); (b) swallows (*Hirundo rustica*)

birds have been ringed and recovered/controlled in the same year, directional arrows indicate whether the birds were moving to, or from, the Fen. There appears to be, in general, a migratory movement more or less in a straight line to or from the south with a departure/entry point around the coast centred on the Sussex area.

Further information of this sort is revealed when looking at similar data for swallows (Fig. 43b), which are caught in large numbers in some years at their autumn roosts. These data show a clear pattern of movement through Wicken from northern England, using the Fen as a stopover site on their way out of the country. A notable example was a bird ringed at Wakefield, West Yorkshire on 15 September 1980, controlled at Wicken nine days later and recovered on 11 August 1981 at Huddersfield, just 20km west of its original ringing point. These birds seem to funnel down to Wicken, where the reed-beds provide an excellent roosting site, and then move on south before crossing the North Sea. Ringing showed long ago that British swallows winter in South Africa; one bird ringed at Wicken in August 1962 was recovered in Orange Free State in January 1963.

POPULATION CHANGES OF PASSERINES

In 1970, the Wicken Fen Group became one of the pioneers of what subsequently became known as 'constant effort site' ringing in an attempt to monitor changes in the populations of some species at the Fen. Two schemes have been employed, although they both had the same aim, which was to operate a specific footage of net in the same sites for four sessions each summer.

In the original scheme, which ran from 1970 to 1980, sessions were at roughly four week intervals in the months May–August, and each lasted for about 32 hours. Six areas of the Fen were monitored, chosen to give as wide a cross-section of the representative types of vegetation as possible (Fig. 44a):

A1 (in compartment 22): 140ft of net along the perimeter of water-filled brickpits which contained some reed;

A2 (in compartment 15): 200ft along a ride cut through fen carr with some mature trees such as willow, oak and poplar;

B2 (in compartment 20): 200ft in fen carr which contained more hawthorn but had a wet, reedy area in the centre;

B3: (in compartment 21): 200ft in a drier site where the scrub was denser, and contained no reed or sedge (Plate 8, Fig. 1);

FL: 2 stretches of 100ft along the northern perimeter of the reed-bed on Adventurers' Fen (predominantly hawthorn scrub);

FR: 2 × 100ft along a ride on the southern perimeter of Adventurers' Fen (hawthorn scrub with mature willows).

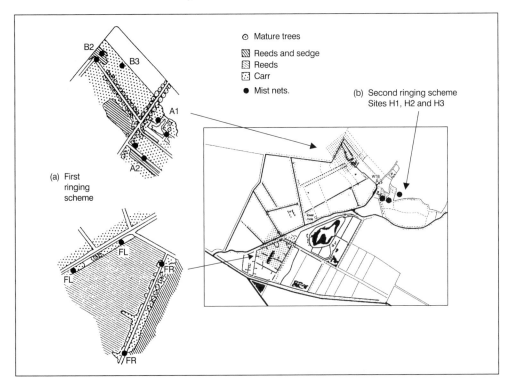

Figure 44   The two standardized ringing schemes: (a) 1970–80; (b) 1982–present (St Edmund's Fen)

This scheme required considerable manpower, since two teams operated simultaneously, and the level of coverage proved difficult to maintain as the active membership of the group declined. In 1980, it was agreed among the membership that some form of monitoring should continue and a more modest plan was devised using sites on St Edmund's Fen.

Whereas the nets in the original scheme were sited well within the Fen, those in the newer scheme are situated on the periphery, and catch birds moving to and from St Edmund's Fen. The vegetation in the new area is mainly fen carr divided into sections by well-cut paths and bordered by arable land with Monks Lode to the south. In general it is dry, but certain areas of standing water remain most of the year. It differs from the previously monitored areas in that it contains more mature trees and in parts is almost woodland, and it also lacks any significant area of reed-bed. One sector of the new area, H3, is an abandoned field in which willow scrub has become established among a mixed flora of typical fen plants. The sub-sites used are H1 (120ft of net), H2 (170ft) and H3 (180ft) (Fig. 44b). These sites have been worked for four hours prior to darkness and four hours after first light once a month from April to July inclusive, every year since 1982.

The problems associated with attempting to use catching totals as a means of estimating population levels are of four kinds. First, the human factor, such as the variation in effort: this is reflected in the way that the original regime had to be abandoned, which was regrettable, since the results were both more representative and more accurate. Secondly, the weather: some sessions take place in overcast windless conditions, which are ideal for mist-netting, while others may be subjected to excessive wind or sunshine, both of which have an adverse effect on catching. The third problem is that the vegetation around the sites changes, sometimes naturally, but sometimes as a result of the management programme, and even a subtle change can radically alter the usefulness of the area for birds and affect mist-netting success. In order to test the efficiency of the standard sites method, a study was carried out in 1974, using a mapping technique to assess breeding birds numbers based on the BTO Common Bird Census, and the results turned out to be encouragingly similar. Finally, there is one other unfortunate disadvantage of the technique: some species which are present at the Fen, such as wood pigeon (*Columba palumbus*) and collared dove (*Streptopelia decaocto*), are not caught in mist nets and are thus not represented in this analysis.

For the purpose of analysis of the data, species comparisons are expressed as a percentage of overall catch. It has proved necessary to use this method to eliminate some of the session-to-session variables which affect catching efficiency. While the duration of each session was controlled, it is important to note that only adult birds were included in the analysis. The annual values for species for which there were significant catches from both regimes over the periods 1970–80 and 1982–93 have been plotted (Fig. 45).

Published accounts of national trends in populations, such as that produced by the BTO and NCC,[55] allow comparison with changes measured at Wicken Fen. Among the common resident species, the Wicken Fen figures for wren, dunnock and robin show relatively stable populations, with a recent fall in dunnock and rise in robin numbers. Wrens have been caught in increased numbers in recent years and the breeding pro-

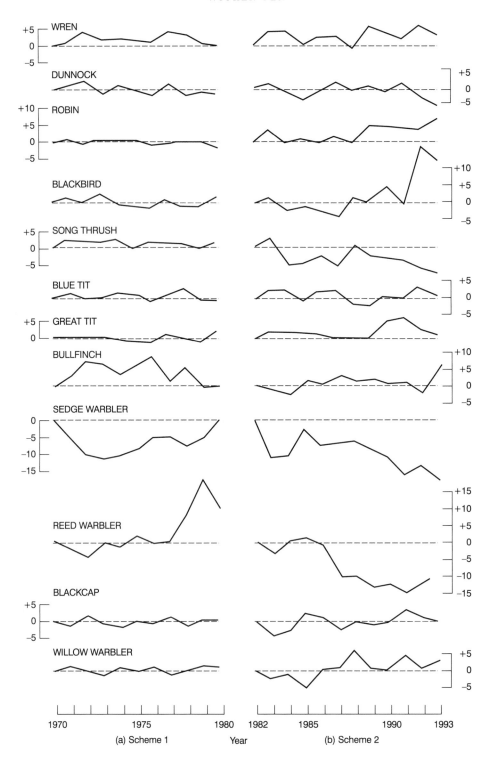

WREN
DUNNOCK
ROBIN
BLACKBIRD
SONG THRUSH
BLUE TIT
GREAT TIT
BULLFINCH
SEDGE WARBLER
REED WARBLER
BLACKCAP
WILLOW WARBLER

1970   1975   1980   1982   1985   1990   1993

(a) Scheme 1   Year   (b) Scheme 2

ductivity has been high. Following two mild winters, the rise in their population is reflected by the 1989 figure of 7.6 per cent of catches, which is the highest since monitoring began. National results show the wren to be susceptible to hard winters and generally fluctuating in numbers more widely than at Wicken Fen. Song thrush have declined markedly at Wicken Fen, with numbers falling to an all-time low in 1993, when not a single bird was caught in the standardized sessions. During recent years, there has been a considerable rise in blackbird numbers, possibly linked with the decline in song thrushes. The BTO trend shows song thrushes to be declining in all habitats since 1982 but with a slight recovery in 1988 which also happened at Wicken Fen.

Some species of warbler show considerable changes, particularly sedge and reed warblers, which together amounted to over a third of all birds caught in the original scheme. The Wicken results suggest a gradual increase in reed warblers up to 1980, and, during the same period, a sharp decline and recovery in sedge warblers. The national trends show a further subsequent national decline in sedge warbler but a gradual rise in reed warbler populations, which contrasts with the situation at the Fen, where our monitoring reveals that reed warblers have continued to decline sharply. Blackcap (*Sylvia atricapilla*) and willow warbler (*Phylloscopus trochilus*) have increased in abundance nationally, the former rather more dramatically than the latter. At Wicken Fen they show similar trends, but willow warbler have increased to a greater degree than blackcap. This may be as a result of subtle changes in the habitat where our monitoring is taking place. Whitethroat (*Sylvia communis*), lesser whitethroat (*S. curruca*) (Plate 8, Fig. 2) and garden warbler (*S. borin*) have been caught only in small numbers but, whereas the first two species show relative stability at present, the garden warbler has suddenly increased dramatically from around one per cent of the catch to seven per cent in 1993.

Spotted flycatcher (*Muscicapa striata*) have decreased at Wicken Fen to such an extent that, since 1988, not a single bird has been caught in the standardized sessions. This reflects a similar trend shown nationally, where the largest decrease happened in 1984.

Most of the tits and finches show characteristic natural patterns of population change. Bullfinch populations seem to have been far less stable over the period of the first scheme than other finch species. Chaffinch numbers remained remarkably stable, but numbers of redpoll (*Carduelis flammea*) and reed bunting (*Emberiza schoeniclus*) have declined, the latter dramatically (Fig. 46).

Among the data that emerged from the original scheme were the clear preferences of certain species for specific parts of the Fen. These preferences were most pronounced in the reed warbler but were seen also in other species, such as whitethroat and lesser whitethroat, both of which were found predominantly in the drier area (B2 & B3) (Table XI).

Figure 45 (opposite page) Changes in the abundance of twelve species caught during standardized mist-netting sessions 1970–1993. The abundance of each species is expressed as a percentage of the total catch for the year and changes are shown in relation to its contribution to the catch during (a) 1970 (scheme 1: left-hand series) and (b) 1982 (scheme 2: right-hand series)[48,49,50,51,52,53,54]

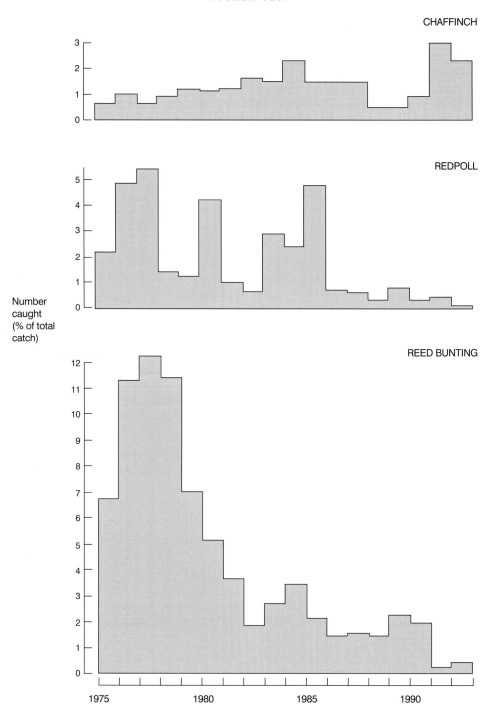

Figure 46 Population changes in three finch species, expressed as percentages of the total catch for the year: (a) chaffinch (*Fringilla coelebs*); (b) redpoll (*Carduelis flammea*); (c) reed bunting (*Emberiza schoeniclus*)

Table XI. Site (vegetation) preferences of selected passerines 1970–73.
Abundance is expressed as percentage of total catch.

Data from Bibby (1973a)[49]	A1	A2	B2	B3	FR	FL
Song thrush (*Turdus philomelos*)	3.1	5.2	8.3	5.5	3.9	4.4
Blackbird (*T. merula*)	4.8	5.2	5.2	11.3	3.9	3.7
Robin (*Erithacus rubecula*)	4.4	4.0	3.4	2.1	1.3	<1.0
Dunnock (*Prunella modularis*)	6.1	10.5	9.7	12.0	6.3	7.7
Reed warbler (*Acrocephalus scirpaceus*)	34.6	14.9	10.9	4.0	27.2	40.5
Sedge warbler (*A. schoenobaenus*)	10.7	10.1	15.0	6.7	16.9	12.5
Lesser whitethroat (*Sylvia curruca*)	1.5	—	2.0	4.3	1.1	<1.0
Whitethroat (*S. communis*)	<1.0	—	2.1	4.0	<1.0	<1.0
Blackcap (*S. atricapilla*)	3.9	2.2	3.3	2.5	3.7	1.5
Willow warbler (*Phylloscopus trochilus*)	1.8	2.0	2.6	3.3	2.6	2.5
Redpoll (*Carduelis flammea*)	2.4	1.6	5.2	3.1	5.5	3.7
Bullfinch (*Pyrrhula pyrrhula*)	10.1	15.7	12.6	10.4	5.0	8.5

Areas B3 (drier) and FL (reed-bed edge) provide the greatest contrast, with very low reed warbler numbers and high numbers of dunnock and blackbird in the former and the reverse in the latter. Song thrushes seemed to prefer B2 and bullfinches were common in all the areas of carr, while willow warblers showed the least marked preference of any species, being caught in similar proportions at all sites.

Equally interesting were the year by year changes at each site (Table XII). It is likely that some habitat change in the area caused a fall in its usage by reed and sedge warblers, since over the six-year period the proportional representation of reed and sedge warblers halved, while the relative abundance of willow warbler more than doubled. The reason for these changes is likely to have been the opening up of the site, which had previously been largely overgrown.

The original scheme (1970–80) provided more consistent results, which is almost certainly due to the larger overall sample (about 800 individual birds per annum compared with only around 150 in 1982–93), but the later studies of St Edmund's Fen at

Table XII. Changes in the population of certain species at standard site A2
over the period 1970–76 (three-year means).

Data from Milwright (1976)[51]	1970–72	1972–74	1974–76
Reed warbler (*Acrocephalus scirpaceus*)	13.1	9.0	7.7
Sedge warbler (*A. schoenobaenus*)	9.5	3.5	4.8
Willow warbler (*Phylloscopus trochilus*)	2.6	4.2	6.6
Bullfinch (*Pyrrhula pyrrhula*)	14.7	16.1	13.7

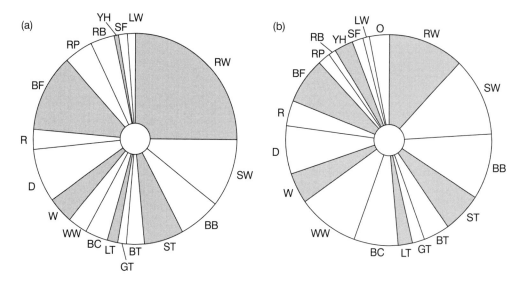

Figure 47   The bird communities of (a) Wicken Fen as a whole; (b) St Edmund's Fen:

RW	=	reed warbler (*Acrocephalus scirpaceus*)	D	=	dunnock (*Prunella modularis*)
SW	=	sedge warbler (*A. schoenobaenus*)	R	=	robin (*Erithacus rubecula*)
BB	=	blackbird (*Turdus merula*)	BF	=	bullfinch (*Pyrrhula pyrrhula*)
ST	=	song thrush (*T. philomelos*)	RP	=	redpoll (*Carduelis flammea*)
BT	=	blue tit (*Parus caeruleus*)	RB	=	reed bunting (*Emberiza schoeniclus*)
GT	=	great tit (*P. major*)	YH	=	yellowhammer (*E. citrinella*)
LT	=	long-tailed tit (*Aegithalos caudatus*)	SF	=	spotted flycatcher (*Muscicapa striata*)
BC	=	blackcap (*Sylvia atricapella*)	LW	=	lesser whitethroat (*Sylvia curruca*)
WW	=	willow warbler (*Phylloscopus trochilus*)	O	=	other species
W	=	wren (*Troglodytes troglodytes*)			

least make it possible to compare the bird communities of the different habitats over the whole Fen (Fig. 47).

The most dramatic difference between the two schemes lies in the population of reed warblers. In the St Edmund's Fen data, their relative abundance is much lower, indicating a less suitable habitat, but it also shows that even parts of the fen carr are used by these birds for feeding or passing through. However, the recent decline in numbers may be due to changes taking place at the monitoring site rather than to a genuine decline of the breeding population in the reed-bed. Sedge warblers are found in similar percentage numbers in both schemes, but recent results suggest that the levels are no longer similar. Blackbirds have a consistently higher relative abundance on St Edmund's Fen as have willow warblers. The habitat differences between the two areas assessed in 1970–80 and 1982–93 is nowhere better illustrated than in the results for the two buntings: the yellowhammer (*Emberiza citrinella*) barely figured in the first period, while the reed bunting was around five per cent of the catch, a situation that was reversed in the latter study.

3. CUCKOOS AND REED WARBLERS

N. B. DAVIES & M. DE L. BROOKE

One of the most remarkable sights on the Fen in summer is that of a reed warbler (*Acrocephalus scirpaceus*) feeding a young cuckoo (*Cuculus canorus*) (Fig. 48). Towards the end of the nestling stage, the young cuckoo overflows the nest and the reed warblers seem to risk being devoured themselves as they bow deep into the cuckoo's enormous gape with food. Out of the nest the situation becomes even more extraordinary as the little warblers often perch on the cuckoo's back in order to reach the mouth of a fledgling eight times their own weight.

Figure 48 Reed warbler (*Acrocephalus scirpaceus*) feeding a well-grown nestling cuckoo (*Cuculus canorus*)

Although the parasitic habits of the cuckoo have long been known, since at least the time of Aristotle writing some 2,300 years ago, it is only recently that biologists have conducted experiments on how the cuckoo manages to trick the host.[56,57] Hosts gain no reproductive reward from a successfully parasitized nest because, on hatching, the cuckoo chick ejects the host's own eggs and young over the side of the nest (Fig. 49). Natural selection should, therefore, favour host abilities to combat cuckoos. This, in turn, will select for more sophisticated trickery on the part of the cuckoo. The result should be an evolutionary 'arms race' leading to ever more intricate adaptations and counteradaptations.

In Britain, cuckoos parasitize four main species of host, the meadow pipit (*Anthus pratensis*) in moorland, the reed warbler in marshland, the dunnock, or hedge sparrow (*Prunella modularis*) in woodland and farmland, and the pied wagtail (*Motacilla alba yarrellii*) in open pastoral country. Individual female cuckoos are thought to specialize on one particular host and in Britain there are therefore, probably, at least four genetically distinct strains of female cuckoo, referred to as gentes (singular gens).[58] Females of each gens lay a distinctive egg type. Pipit-cuckoos lay brownish eggs, matching the pipit's own eggs in colour. Reed-warbler-cuckoos lay greenish eggs mimicking the warbler's greenish eggs. Wagtail-cuckoos lay pale, greyish-white eggs which likewise match those

Figure 49   Young cuckoo (*Cuculus canorus*) ejecting an egg from the nest of a reed warbler (*Acrocephalus scirpaceus*)

of their host. The exception is the dunnock-cuckoo, whose pale spotted egg contrasts markedly with the immaculate blue eggs of the dunnock. Plate 9, Fig. 1 shows, in the left-hand column, the eggs of the five principal British hosts (from the top: robin, pied wagtail, dunnock, reed warbler and meadow pipit), together with a Central European host, the great reed warbler (*Acrocephalus arundinaceus*) (bottom). The central column shows a typical example of a cuckoo egg laid in the nest of the corresponding host.

Wicken Fen is a stronghold of the reed warbler-cuckoo. It is difficult to assess the number of cuckoos on the Fen. In 1985, when our study area extended along Burwell Lode, there were 14 females laying eggs, individuals being recognizable by slight differences in egg colour and markings (Fig. 50). We would guess that about eight female

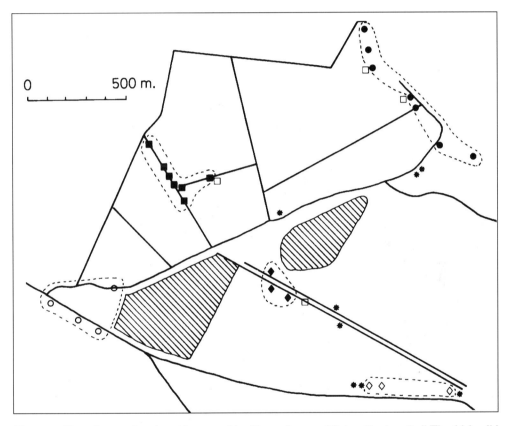

Figure 50 Sites of nests of reed warblers parasitized by cuckoos on Wicken Fen in 1985.[59] The thick solid lines are reed-fringed dykes and lodes where nests were searched for. Not all nests will have been found because the two areas of extensive reed bed (hatched areas) were not searched. Female cuckoos, recognized by their distinctive eggs, tended to lay in exclusive areas (enclosed by dashed lines). For two females, seven eggs were found (closed circles, closed squares). For two females, four eggs were found (open circles; open squares – this female laid over a wide area and her range has not been enclosed by dashes). For two females, three eggs were found (open diamonds, closed diamonds). The eight asterisks represent eight other females for whom just one egg each was found.

cuckoos maintained laying territories on the Fen itself. Of 142 reed warbler nests monitored during egg laying in 1985, 32 (22.5 per cent) were parasitized and in 1986, 12 out
of 132 nests (9.1 per cent) were parasitized.[59] Over the country as a whole, the average
proportion of reed warbler nests parasitized is seven per cent, as measured by the nest
record scheme of the BTO.[60]

Reed warblers occasionally reject a cuckoo egg, either by ejecting it from the nest,
or by deserting the whole clutch. However, in about 80 per cent of cases we found that
the cuckoo succeeded in getting the hosts to accept its egg. How does the cuckoo
manage this? Female cuckoos adopt a particular procedure when parasitizing host
nests, first described in detail for pipit-cuckoos by the brilliant field observations of
Edgar Chance[61] and shown to be the same for reed-warbler-cuckoos by Ian Wyllie's
recent work.[62] This laying sequence can sometimes be observed from the Tower Hide
overlooking the Mere, or along the quieter dykes and lodes. The female cuckoo usually finds a nest by watching the hosts build. Then, a few days later, she parasitizes the
nest one afternoon during the host laying-period, most commonly between mid-day
and 1700 BST. Before laying, she remains quietly on a perch, sometimes for an hour
or more, and then suddenly glides down to the nest. She removes one host egg (sometimes more), lays her own directly into the host nest, and then flies off with the host egg
in her bill. The whole procedure takes less than 10 seconds and it is difficult to believe
that the cuckoo can have laid in such a short time. However a visit to the nest will
reveal the cuckoo egg lying among the warbler's clutch, a little larger than the host
eggs, but matching them quite well in colour and pattern.

To what extent has this cuckoo behaviour been designed, by selection, to defeat host
defences? We studied this question on the Fen by behaving as cuckoos ourselves and
parasitizing reed warbler nests with model cuckoo eggs. Our idea was to vary the different aspects of the cuckoo's procedure to examine the effects on host behaviour. The
model eggs, of the exact size and weight of real cuckoo eggs, were made of resin and
painted to resemble the different colours laid by various gentes.[59] The right-hand
column of Plate 9, Fig. 1 shows our model eggs painted to mimic the corresponding
cuckoo egg. (As robin and pied wagtail-cuckoo eggs are not clearly distinct, we painted
just one type of egg, a pied-wagtail model, shown bridging the robin (top) and pied
wagtail (second) rows. In the case of the dunnock (third row) where there is no colour
mimicry between cuckoo and host egg, our pale blue model egg matches those laid by
cuckoos parasitizing redstart (*Phoenicurus phoenicurus*) in Finland).

In the first experiments we copied the procedure of real cuckoos and 'parasitized'
nests one afternoon during the host laying period, first removing one host egg (under
NCC licence). The results showed that the model egg had to resemble the reed warbler's own eggs in coloration, otherwise it was likely to be rejected. Thus, models
painted to resemble eggs laid by reed warbler-cuckoos were all accepted, whereas
models painted like those from other gentes (e.g. pipit-cuckoos, wagtail-cuckoos), and
therefore different from the reed warbler's own eggs, were rejected in 66 per cent of
the cases. Host discrimination, therefore, clearly has selected for a mimetic cuckoo egg
by reed-warbler-cuckoos. The importance of host discrimination for the evolution of

egg mimicry was further shown by experiments with dunnocks which, unlike reed warblers, showed no discrimination against model eggs unlike their own, thus explaining why dunnock-cuckoos, by contrast, do not lay mimetic eggs.[58]

Why did reed warblers accept badly-matching models in about a third of the nests? There is some evidence from experiments with other species that individuals may learn what their own eggs look like when they breed for the first time. With this knowledge, they are then able to reject foreign eggs from their nest even if they form the majority of the clutch. Thus some species, at least, show 'true egg recognition' rather than simply following a rule 'reject an odd egg'. If poorly matching models (or real cuckoo eggs) were put in the nests of first-time breeders, therefore, they may learn these as part of their own range of egg types and so accept them. Our observations showed that both male and female reed warblers rejected eggs, so under this hypothesis both members of the pair would have to be naïve for acceptance. Ringing recoveries suggest that the annual survival of adult reed warblers on the Fen is around 43–57 per cent[22] which would, in fact, result in approximately a third of the pairs consisting of both male and female first-time breeders, the same proportion we found for acceptance of badly-matching models.

We were encouraged, therefore, to test whether first-time breeders really were more likely to accept model eggs unlike their own. With the help of the Wicken Fen Ringing Group, particularly Chris Thorne and Max Hobbs, birds were colour-ringed to indicate their age. Unfortunately, very few of the colour-ringed nestlings returned as adults in subsequent years and so we were unable to test pairs where we knew for certain that both male and female were young birds. However, for pairs including at least one known experienced breeder the same proportion (33 per cent) accepted badly matching models, as before.[59] Thus we have no support for the idea that naïve breeders are more likely to accept, though further experiments would be useful.

Host discrimination may not be the only selective pressure favouring the evolution of a mimetic cuckoo egg. At six out of the 44 nests parasitized by a cuckoo in 1985 and 1986, a second cuckoo later visited the nest and laid an egg. It would clearly pay the second cuckoo to remove the first bird's egg because usually only one cuckoo can be reared per nest and the earlier laid egg is likely to hatch first, whereupon the first cuckoo chick will eject the other eggs from the nest. Host egg mimicry may evolve therefore, not only by host discrimination, but also because it reduces the chance that second cuckoos will be able to discriminate and remove the first cuckoo's egg from the host's clutch. Some cuckoos visited nests where we had placed a model egg unlike the reed warbler's own eggs and there was, in fact, a tendency for the cuckoo to remove the model rather than one of the reed warbler's own eggs, which suggests that discrimination by cuckoos themselves could play some part in the evolution of egg mimicry.

What about the other aspects of the cuckoo's behaviour? When we placed model eggs in reed warbler nests either at dawn during the host's laying period, or before the hosts began to lay, then even well-matching models were likely to be rejected. Thus the time and stage of laying adopted by cuckoos have been tailored to circumvent host discrimination. The remarkable speed of laying is also important; when we placed a stuffed cuckoo on the warblers' nests, to simulate a cuckoo which was slow to lay, the warblers mobbed it vigorously and were subsequently more likely to reject even mimetic models from their nest. The speed with which the cuckoo lays therefore seems to be adaptive in decreasing the chance that the hosts are alerted. Finally, although the cuckoo's egg is a little larger than the host eggs, it is remarkably small for a bird the size of a cuckoo. Typically, a cuckoo-sized bird would be expected to lay an egg about three times the weight (about the size of a blackbird's egg). When we placed such giant model eggs in the warblers' nests they were often rejected, even when painted to resemble the warbler's own eggs in colour, so again host discrimination has been important.[59]

One part of the cuckoo's behaviour which has apparently not been selected in relation to host defences is the habit of removing a host egg before parasitism. Our experiments showed that host egg removal did not influence whether a model was accepted. Two other likely advantages to cuckoos of removal of an egg are that it increases the efficiency with which the cuckoo egg is incubated and, incidently, provides the female cuckoo with a free meal. Why then doesn't the female remove all the host eggs, and thereby gain even more nourishment? Host responses again provide the answer; when a reed warbler's clutch is reduced too much, the birds desert. It turns out that one or two host eggs is the most the female cuckoo can remove without the risk of causing desertion. Although hosts desert single eggs, they do not desert single chicks (even a single reed warbler chick is cared for). Thus the young cuckoo, by contrast, can eject all the host's eggs without penalty. It is the fact that hosts desert single eggs but not single chicks which means that the cuckoo chick must do the ejecting, not the female cuckoo earlier during laying.

In marked contrast to their discrimination at the egg stage, reed warblers seem unconcerned about the presence of a chick unlike their own. The newly-hatched cuckoo chick is pink, with a bright orange gape, quite unlike the reed warblers' own young which have black skin and yellow gapes with tongue spots. Because cuckoo eggs require less incubation, they hatch about a day earlier than the host eggs. This is probably of advantage to the young cuckoo because it is likely that host eggs are easier to eject than host chicks. As a consequence, the host parents usually do not have the opportunity to compare the cuckoo chick with their own young. Our experiments showed, however, that even when hosts could make this comparison, they still did not discriminate. When we strapped two nests side by side, one with a cuckoo chick and the other with a reed warbler chick, the parent reed warblers happily fed the contents of both nests. It has been suggested that the cuckoo chick provides a 'supernormal' stimulus and so is even more attractive than the warblers' own young. However, in these experiments the warblers fed both chicks with equal frequency and, furthermore would accept strange young of other species in amongst a brood of their own. Thus the cuckoo chick does not provide any special stimuli necessary for acceptance. Rather it seems that the warblers simply do not discriminate at the chick stage and will feed any nestling in their nest, whatever its appearance. Although the cuckoo has had to evolve a mimetic egg to deceive the host, it has not been forced to evolve a mimetic chick. Perhaps chick discrimination is a more difficult perceptual task for the hosts because chicks, unlike eggs, change dramatically in appearance as they grow.

The food brought to cuckoo nestlings, as assessed by prey remains in faeces, is similar to that brought to broods of the reed-warbler's own young, namely flies, especially dung flies (Scatophagidae), hoverflies (Syrphidae), Muscidae and Calliphoridae, and beetles, bugs (both Homoptera and Heteroptera), caterpillars and spiders. A cuckoo chick is also provisioned at about the same rate as an average brood (three or four) of the hosts' own young. This may reflect the fact that the cuckoo's development is geared to a provisioning rate the parent warblers can normally sustain.[63]

Female cuckoos defend territories in which they lay, on average, eight eggs per year, laying on alternate days and often in two 'clutches', separated by several days rest.[62] Although reed warblers are the most common host on the Fen, other species such as sedge warblers (*Acrocephalus schoenobaenus*) and dunnocks are also occasionally parasitized. It is likely that these parasitisms are by reed-warbler-cuckoos, who turn to alternative hosts when they cannot find a suitable reed warbler nest to lay in.

The female cuckoo is also known to plunder host nests that are at the incubation or chick stage, and so too advanced for parasitism, in order to force the hosts to lay again and so increase the availability of suitable nests. We suspect that much of the predation of reed warbler nests on the Fen is due to cuckoo predation for this reason, because many clutches are taken with no obvious sign of disturbance to the nest, which usually accompanies the work of large avian predators such as corvids. Most nests are over water and so probably inaccessible to many mammalian predators. If cuckoos themselves depredated reed warbler nests, it would clearly pay a female to remember the location in her territory of nests she had parasitized and to leave these untouched. The prediction is, therefore, that if the cuckoo itself is a major predator, we would expect nests with a cuckoo egg to suffer less predation. Our data support this prediction; only 22.5 per cent of 40 parasitized nests suffered predation at the egg stage compared with 41.1 per cent of 175 unparasitized nests, a statistically significant difference.

Experiments on the Fen by William Duckworth[39] showed that reed warblers respond to adult cuckoos in a particular manner that reflects the costs of parasitism. Cuckoos are a threat to the nest contents but not to the well-being of the host parents and adult reed warblers readily attacked a stuffed cuckoo at their nest, often landing on it and pulling feathers out. By contrast, they were less ready to approach a stuffed jay (*Garrulus glandarius*) and even less likely to approach a sparrowhawk (*Accipiter nisus*); the former is a danger not only to the nest but also to the adult, while the latter is a danger to the adults only. Furthermore, reactions to a cuckoo more or less ceased once the young fledged (the cuckoo is no threat to fledglings) whereas alarm to a jay or sparrowhawk continued (both are capable of killing fledglings). Clearly then, the reed warbler's different responses to these three predators is adapted to their respective dangers to the nest and the adults themselves.

During our study in 1985 and 1986 there were probably about 250 pairs of reed warblers breeding on the Fen. Assuming each pair produces two clutches per season, there will be 500 clutches laid. With eight female cuckoos resident on the Fen, each laying eight eggs per season, with most in reed warbler nests and a few in the nests of alternative hosts, approximately 60 cuckoo eggs will be laid in reed warbler nests, producing 12 per cent parasitism (close to the observed frequency). The annual survival of adult reed warblers at Wicken Fen is 43–57 per cent.[22] If the reed warbler population is to remain stable, therefore, the 440 unparasitized nests each year must produce 200 to 300 recruits to the next year's breeding population to replace the dying adults. This seems feasible, so it is unlikely that at the present rate of parasitism the cuckoo is severely damaging the reed warbler population on the Fen.

The last cuckoo calls are heard on the Fen in early July and the adults then depart for their winter quarters, south of the Sahara, leaving many nestlings and fledglings still under the care of the reed warblers. The independent young cuckoos leave later, in August and September, never having set eyes on their real parents. It is hoped that Wicken Fen will continue to provide a safe stage for this miracle of co-evolution, where these marvellous interactions between host and parasite will be played for future generations to enjoy.

4. CONSERVATION IMPORTANCE OF BIRD POPULATIONS AT WICKEN FEN

C. J. CADBURY

This last section aims to put Wicken Fen's bird populations and the habitats with which they are associated into a local and national context. First, the habitats for birds at Wicken are compared with their occurrence in the old counties of Cambridgeshire and Huntingdonshire (including the Soke of Peterborough). The characteristic birds of these habitats are then discussed; comparison of their status at Wicken with those attained locally and nationally produces a clear picture of the importance of the reserve in conserving British birdlife.

The bird communities of Wicken Fen largely relate to four main habitats: open water, reed-beds, wet grassland (including grazing marsh, as well as fen sedge and litter fields) and carr. To a certain extent they are hydrologically influenced phases in a vegetation succession on a peaty wetland. However, at Wicken, much of the demarcation between these habitats is maintained by management: control of the water-level, mowing, grazing and scrub removal (see Chapter 11).

Cambridgeshire and adjacent areas have much habitat for wintering waterfowl, some of which occur in internationally important numbers. The grassy washlands which are flooded most winters to take the overflow from the Ouse, Nene and Cam Rivers are an exceptional feature (Fig. 1, p. 2). There are flooded gravel and other mineral workings at 16 sites in Cambridgeshire and many others in neighbouring counties. There is also the huge expanse of Grafham Water reservoir. Apart from drains and dykes, the only areas of permanent open water at Wicken Fen were until recently the Mere (four hectares), a shallow 'scrape' excavated on Rothschild's

Lapwing for breeding waders, and the small flooded brickpits. The Mere has two favourable attributes with respect to wildfowl: its relative freedom from human disturbance and the proximity of feeding areas on the Cam Washes. Recent improvements to the waterholding capacity of Howe's Bank have resulted in there being about 8ha of shallow standing water and swamp on Verrall's Fen. This undisturbed area at the western end of Wicken Fen, is becoming increasingly important for waterfowl.

In Britain, there are few large beds of reed (*Phragmites australis*) away from the main concentration in the Norfolk Broads area and on the East Anglian coast. Only 109 reed-beds of 2ha or more were identified in England and Wales in a survey undertaken by the RSPB in 1979 and 1980.[64,65] Wicken Fen, with about 40ha of reed, was one of these and is the largest in the old county of Cambridgeshire. There are only three other large reed-beds in the county: the RSPB reserve at Fowlmere (20ha); Fulbourn/Teversham Fen (less than 20 ha, most of which is dry with much fen vegetation mixed with impoverished reed); and a reed-choked drain beside the Nene Washes (8ha).

Wet or damp grassland is now a scarce habitat in lowland Britain. After 300 years of land drainage, less than one per cent of the original Fenlands of Cambridgeshire and adjacent Lincolnshire and Norfolk now remain.[66] Even so, Cambridgeshire, with the washlands on the Rivers Ouse (1860 ha of grassland), Nene (674ha) and Cam (152ha), has some of the largest existing areas of lowland wet grassland in Britain. At Wicken Fen there are 53ha of grazed grassland on Adventurers' Fen and 24ha of mixed fen vegetation on the Sedge Fen, which are mown regularly on an annual or longer cycle (Chapter 11); a further 52ha of grazing land is currently being established adjacent to Adventurer's Fen (Chapter 13).

Fen carr, of which there is so much in the Norfolk Broads, is very restricted in Cambridgeshire. Wicken and Chippenham Fens have the only extensive areas where scrub has colonized as a result of the peat drying out and a cessation of mowing (Chapter 6). There are a few sites at Wicken, as on St Edmund's Fen, where the carr has developed into woodland. As a result of wetter conditions, fungus disease that has killed much of the alder buckthorn, and scrub removal, the area of carr on the Fen has declined in recent years. There has been a similar development of carr on damp peat at Woodwalton and Holme Fens in Huntingdonshire (Chapter 1). Elsewhere in the predominantly arable landscape of Cambridgeshire, intensive agriculture has inhibited the spread of scrub, except on poorly drained areas such as at Fowlmere and Fulbourn/Teversham Fens, and on the ancient chalk earthworks of Devil's Ditch and Fleam Dyke.

WILDFOWL

The average peak total (the sum of the maximum count of each species in a winter) of wintering wildfowl at Wicken Fen is in the order of 2,500 compared with 52,700 at the Ouse Washes over the five winters 1988/89 to 1992/93. Populations of six species wintering at the Ouse Washes are internationally important and those of another three species are important in Great Britain.[67] Of the 10 species that regularly winter at

Wicken, none occurs at even nationally important numbers. Nevertheless, few inland wetlands except the Ouse and Nene Washes regularly support over 1,000 wigeon (*Anas penelope*), as Wicken does. Maximum numbers tend to occur at Wicken when the Ouse Washes are deeply flooded, depriving wigeon of grazing. The average peak autumn/winter gatherings for the five winters 1985/86 to 1989/90 on Wicken Mere of teal (*A. crecca*) (240), mallard (*A. platyrhynchos*) (540), and shoveler (*A. clypeata*) (30) are notable in local terms. Peak numbers of gadwall (*A. strepera*) declined from over 50 in 1983/84 to 12 in 1989/90. The national and Cambridgeshire wintering populations of this species have, however, been increasing markedly.[68] The numbers of teal and wigeon at Wicken have declined during the mid 1990s as other sites have become available nearby.

The Mere is largely used by ducks as a roost and daytime loafing site. At dusk, most wigeon, teal and gadwall fly out to feed on the flooded Cam Washes, particularly near Upware only two kilometres away, or, in the case of mallard, to arable fields where there is waste grain and potatoes. Disturbance from wildfowling precludes much daytime feeding by wigeon on the Cam Washes between 1 September and the end of January. Angling and pleasure cruising on the River Cam may also disturb wildfowl throughout the winter.

Six species of wildfowl, including feral greylag geese (*Anser anser*), now regularly breed at Wicken Fen compared with eleven at the Ouse Washes, eight at the Nene Washes and seven at the Cam Washes. These washlands are a stronghold of breeding shoveler in Britain, though numbers fluctuate markedly according to the flood conditions. The average May counts of males for the Ouse, Nene and Cam Washes total just under 300 for the years 1978–89. Up to five pairs have bred at Wicken. The total breeding population in Britain has been estimated to be only about 1,000–1,500 pairs.[69]

The British population of garganey (*Anas querquedula*) has rarely exceeded 50 pairs in recent years. About a quarter of the total occur in the Cambridgeshire/Norfolk Fens. Though the species bred on the Cam Washes on several occasions in the late 1980s/early 1990s, with two pairs in 1993, it breeds only irregularly at Wicken Fen (including probably in 1990 and 1991). Shelduck (*Tadorna tadorna*) have been spreading inland in the Fens and have recently shown signs of colonizing Wicken Fen though breeding has yet to be confirmed.

The overwintering population of cormorants (*Phalacrocorax carbo*) in 'new' Cambridgeshire and the Norfolk section of the Ouse Washes has increased markedly since the early 1970s. The mid-winter total by 1993 probably exceeded 500, and since 1988 a breeding colony has been established at Little Paxton Gravel Pits. In the autumn of that year, cormorants started to become regular visitors to the Mere at Wicken Fen, even in summer. A maximum of 43 has been recorded.

REED-BED BIRDS

Wicken Fen must have more breeding reed warblers (*Acrocephalus scirpaceus*) than any other site in Cambridgeshire. An accurate population estimate is however virtually impossible by normal bird censusing techniques because of the staggered arrival of birds at the breeding sites and the fact that males tend to sing much less once paired. Counts of up to 114 singing males in a single morning indicate that there is also a substantial population at Fowlmere.

Bearded tits (*Panurus biarmicus*) have wintered annually on Wicken Fen since 1959/60 and the species has become an established breeder since 1983 with between one and five pairs. The main concentrations of bearded tits in Britain in the 1960s were in the Norfolk Broads and in coastal marshes of East Anglia and Kent. By 1992, the British population of about 370 pairs was, however, much more widespread outside East Anglia and in consequence less vulnerable to prolonged periods of severe winter weather and heavy snow.[70] In Cambridgeshire, bearded tits have occurred with some regularity in winter at seven sites other than Wicken and breeding has been recorded at three. Reed seed is important in the winter diet of the bearded tit.[71] Wicken Fen, where reed flowers profusely and fen vegetation provides a variety of alternative seed food, is a particularly favourable wintering site (Chapter 4). At least 20 birds have been recorded between October and December in several years. Ringing has demonstrated an interchange of birds between Wicken Fen and sites in Norfolk, Kent and even Belgium.[46]

The first confirmed breeding record of Cetti's warbler (*Cettia cettia*) in Britain was 1972. As part of its rapid expansion in range, the species became established at Wicken Fen for five years 1980–84 with up to four males. The total British population in 1984 was estimated to be 316 singing males, mostly in North Kent and in East Anglia and in marshes on the South Coast.[72] Those at a number of eastern sites, however, were decimated in the harsh 1984/85 winter[73] and the species has not bred at Wicken since. Cetti's warblers have apparently not bred elsewhere in 'old' Cambridgeshire, but have probably done so recently in the Peterborough area. A succession of mild winters in the late 1980s and early 1990s enabled the numbers in Britain to rise again to over 300 singing males. Most of the increase has, however, been in south-west England and South Wales, where climatic conditions are more suitable for winter survival.[69,72]

Savi's warbler (*Locustella luscinoides*) is more typically a bird of wet reed-beds than Cetti's warbler, which tends to be associated into waterside scrub. Having bred at or near Wicken Fen in the 1840s (shortly before its extinction in Britain), Savi's Warbler was not recorded there again until 1954. Subsequently there have been a total of eight or nine singing males recorded in Cambridgeshire, all but two at Wicken, where breeding probably occurred in 1980 and again in 1990. Since Savi's warbler became re-established as a regular breeding species in Britain in the late 1950s, the population has remained very small (10–20 singing males in any one year since 1981) and restricted in its distribution.[72]

The numbers of water rails (*Rallus aquaticus*) breeding in Britain are poorly known because of the bird's skulking habits and the fact that it 'sings' (several short calls followed by a trill) at night. The breeding strongholds in Cambridgeshire appear to be the Ouse Washes, where up to 14 have been recorded, Fowlmere, which usually has four to six pairs, and Wicken Fen, with at least 10 'singing' birds. The flooding of Verrall's Fen has increased the suitable habitat for water rails at Wicken. In winter, water rails are more widely distributed in the county.

There are only three of four sites in Britain at which spotted crakes (*Porzana porzana*) occur almost annually between April and June. One of these is the Ouse Washes, where up to six calling birds have been heard on a single night and breeding has been confirmed. At Wicken Fen there have been one or two calling most springs since 1977, with a maximum of three in 1989, but none in the dry spring of 1990. Breeding has, however, yet to be substantiated. The occurrence of spotted crakes at both Wicken and the Cam Washes (where there were two) in April 1989 coincided with extensive deep flooding of the Ouse Washes. Birds were heard there only when the floods had receded in May. At the Ouse Washes, spotted crakes call from extensive stands of reed sweet-grass (*Glyceria maxima*) in some of the wettest areas. At Wicken Fen they frequent mixed reed and sedge vegetation at the edge of wet carr.

One or two bitterns (*Botaurus stellaris*) still visit Wicken Fen in most years, but only in winter; formerly they were more frequent and occurred at other times of year. Since a pair bred in 1937 there have been hopes that bitterns would do so again. With the decline in the British population to its present critical level of fewer than 20 booming males,[70,74] the chances seem rather slim, in spite of efforts to improve the habitat for them at Wicken. Bitterns that now occur on the Fen are probably immigrants from the Continent,[75] where numbers are now also much reduced.[74]

The British breeding population of marsh harriers (*Circus aeruginosus*) (Fig. 51) underwent a decline and contraction in range in the 1959–71 period. It is now considered that this was largely the result of acute poisoning of adults by aldrin and dieldrin. Subsequently, following the withdrawal of the cyclodiene pesticides from agricultural use, there has been a steady recovery (now about 130 breeding females) and range expansion of the population, especially in East Anglia.[72,76] Summer sightings were frequent at Wicken Fen in the 1980s, and breeding occurred in both 1981 and 1985.[46] Following nest building in 1990, a pair bred successfully on the Fen in 1991 and 1992, rearing three and five young respectively. In 1993, nesting occurred again, but was unsuccessful. In 1995, two pairs each raised three young and, in 1996, there were again two nests and a third female was present (Plate 9, Fig. 2).

Communal roosting by hen harriers (*Circus cyaneus*) on Wicken Fen was first recorded in February 1978 and now occurs each winter, not only at Wicken (maximum 11 birds), but also at the Ouse and Nene Washes, at Woodwalton Fen. and recently in Breckland (Norfolk/Suffolk border). One or two birds have roosted at several other sites in Cambridgeshire. The maximum total for a synchronized count at Cambridgeshire and Huntingdonshire roosts is 22 birds.[77] It has been estimated that between 300 and 750 hen harriers occur simultaneously at winter roost sites in England. Numbers of hen harriers counted at Cambridgeshire roosts have represented 5–10 per cent of these. At Wicken Fen, harriers usually roost among great fen-sedge (*Cladium mariscus*) and blunt-flowered rush (*Juncus subnodulosus*), on the Sedge Fen rather than in reed-beds. The lack of disturbance from wildfowling and other human causes is a feature of many harrier roosts.

Figure 51　Male marsh harrier (*Circus aeruginosus*) dropping down to its nest in great fen-sedge (*Cladium mariscus*) with food in its talons

BREEDING WADERS OF WET GRASSLAND

The 1982/83 Survey of Breeding Waders of Wet Meadows, organised by the BTO in conjunction with the RSPB and NCC, demonstrated how concentrated these birds had become in lowland England and Wales as a result of a massive reduction in habitat. Lowland wet grasslands provide the main breeding habitat for snipe (*Gallinago gallinago*), yet only 2,122 drumming birds (representing about 3,700 pairs) were recorded in the survey. Of these, 628 (30 per cent) were in Cambridgeshire with the main concentration at the Ouse and Nene Washes (Table XIII).[78] During the 1980s, 25–30 pairs of snipe bred at Wicken Fen at a high density of 32–39 pairs per square kilometre on the grazed and annually mown areas. The Fen's peaty soil that remains moist provides suitable feeding conditions throughout the summer for snipe, which need to probe for earthworms and other invertebrate food.[79] Moreover the mowing of the Sedge Fen has extended the available nesting habitat. On the nearby Cam Washes, the average density over six years (1984–89) was 29 pairs per square kilometre. Mown areas of Woodwalton Fen, where conditions are somewhat similar to those at Wicken, also supported a high density of breeding snipe. The monitoring of waders breeding on lowland wet grassland in England and Wales has shown that numbers of snipe have continued to decline overall, particularly in southern England, since 1982.[80] In the early 1990s, there may have been no more than about 12 drumming snipe on Wicken Fen. On the Cam Washes north of Upware, where the annual maximum number of drumming snipe averaged 20 during the 1980s, there were only 13 and 11 in the dry springs of 1991 and 1992 respectively. The number recovered to 20 in the wet spring of 1993.[81]

Table XIII. Breeding wader populations on wet grassland

Data from Cadbury (1983)[82]

	Lapwing (*Vanellus vanellus*) pairs	Snipe (*Gallinago gallinago*) drumming	Redshank (*Tringa totanus*) pairs
Damp/wet grasslands England and Wales 1982	6,869	2,122* (= 3,700 pairs)†	2,353*
'Old' Cambridgeshire 1982	452	628	204
Huntingdonshire 1982	82	99	43
Ouse Washes average 1978–88 (excl. 1987)	214	394	151
Nene Washes average 1978-88 (excl. 1987)	148	203	78
Cam Washes average‡ 1984–89	14	30	17
Wicken Fen 1984–89	12 declined to 5	25–30	5 declined to 1

* Figures include complete surveys of Sussex (1980/81) and the Somerset Levels (1983)
† For interpretation of counts of drumming snipe see Green (1985)[83]
‡ Excluding two fields north of Upware flooded since spring 1988

In areas of intensive agriculture in eastern and southern England, breeding lapwings (*Vanellus vanellus*) now largely depend on what remains of damp, permanent pasture for feeding and even for nesting. Where the predominant crops are autumn-sown cereals, there is often an acute shortage of bare ground for nesting in spring. The largest concentrations of breeding lapwings in Cambridgeshire have been at the Ouse and Nene Washes (Table XIII). At Wicken Fen, suitable short vegetation for nesting lapwings is largely restricted to pasture on Adventurers' Fen (Plate 9, Fig. 3); this area became increasingly overgrown with rushes during the 1980s and '90s. There were 12 pairs in both 1982 and 1983, but only five or six in each year 1988 to 1990. None bred in 1993, but in 1996 six pairs nested following major works to create new scrapes and increased grazing by cattle on Brett's and Trevelyan's Pieces (see Chapter 13). Numbers on the Cam Washes have suffered a decline: on the area north of Upware, there was an average of 14 pairs annually over the six years 1973–77 compared with three pairs for 1986–93. These figures exclude pairs that move their broods to the washland from adjacent arable farmland.[81]

There are estimated to be about 32,000 pairs of redshanks (*Tringa totanus*) breeding in Britain, but nearly 60 per cent of them are on saltmarshes.[84] Inland, numbers of breeding redshanks, having partially recovered from a decline in the 19th century, suffered another marked reduction in eastern and southern England with the resurgence of intensive field drainage in the 1940s. In 1982, 2,353 pairs of redshanks were recorded breeding inland on lowland wet grassland in England and Wales. Cambridgeshire supported about 240 pairs (10 per cent) of these. Even on the washlands, where the majority of the county's breeding redshanks occurs, the densities of 8–12 pairs per square kilometre are much lower than those of over 50 pairs per square kilometre on East Anglian saltmarshes.[84] Four or five pairs of redshanks bred on Adventurers' Fen annually between 1982 and 1987 inclusive, two or three in 1988, only one in 1989, unsuccessful attempts in 1990 and 1991, but none in 1992 and 1993. Between 1988 and 1992, the permanent flooding of two fields beside the River Cam north of Upware (2.2km away) provided excellent feeding habitat for redshanks and attracted two to four breeding pairs. As a result of encroachment by bulrush (*Typha latifolia*) these fields have become largely unsuitable for waders. In 1996, the new scrapes at Wicken attracted a pair, but they failed to breed successfully.

SCRUBLAND BIRDS

As well as having a typical bird community of scrub, Wicken Fen has five species which are rather local in Britain as a whole. The woodcock (*Scolopax rusticola*) (Plate 9, Fig. 4) apparently only became established as a breeding bird at Wicken in the 1950s, probably in association with the development of mature scrub.[46] Up to a dozen displaying (roding) males have been counted there in recent springs. Though woodcock may breed in at least nine damp woodland sites in Cambridgeshire, peaty Wicken and Chippenham Fens have the largest numbers and highest densities. A substantial breeding population occurs in the conifer plantations and relict fens in Breckland, but the densities are probably lower than at Wicken.

Wicken Fen has long been a recognized breeding site for long-eared owls (*Asio otus*). Judging by the results of a series of spring censuses of calling birds in the 1980s, three to five pairs breed annually in the more mature carr. Calling young, however, were heard only in some years. Single pairs are known to occur fairly regularly at three other sites in Cambridgeshire in the breeding season. Strong populations occur in some years at Holme and Woodwalton Fens, in Breckland and in West Norfolk, east of Kings Lynn.[85] Long-eared owls favour sites where there are dense thickets of hawthorn (*Crataegus monogyna*) (as at Wicken) or Scots pine (*Pinus sylvestris*) (as in Breckland) for nesting and roosting, adjacent to open rough grassland for foraging. They seem to avoid competition with tawny owls (*Strix aluco*), 10 to 12 pairs of which also occur on Wicken Fen. In recent years, two pairs of barn owls (*Tyto alba*) have been resident in the vicinity and hunt over the Fen. In Cambridgeshire this species mainly occurs along the rivers in the Fens, particularly around Ely.

Cambridgeshire was until recently one of the few counties in which the lesser-spotted woodpecker (*Dendrocopus minor*) was the most frequent of the three British woodpecker species (see Plate 8, Fig. 4). It began breeding at Wicken Fen only in the mid 1960s as the scrub matured.[46] The lesser-spotted woodpecker population in Cambridge and elsewhere in south Cambridgeshire temporarily increased in the 1970s, possibly in response to the effects of Dutch Elm disease, but has declined subsequently.[86] Those at Wicken Fen exploited the abundance of dead wood provided by a die-back of alder buckthorn over extensive areas of carr in the 1980s. In the 1980s, the Fen's population was about four pairs; in the early 1990s, it was probably only two. The green woodpecker (*Picus viridis*) was an irregular visitor to Wicken Fen until 1990 when two birds took up residence. The closely mown droves may provide suitable feeding sites.

Cambridgeshire is on the northern edge of the breeding range of the nightingale (*Luscinia megarhynchos*),[87] and the dense, scrubby woodland favoured by the species is scarce over much of the county. The total number of singing males in Cambridgeshire fluctuated between 10 and 19 in the 1980s. The Wicken Fen population, having declined to nil in the 1970s, recovered to become the 'old' county's largest concentration with three to seven singing males between 1983 and 1990. Little Paxton pits, Monks Wood, Woodwalton and Holme Fens in Huntingdonshire all had larger populations. At Wicken, nightingales are associated with dense thickets of blackthorn (*Prunus spinosa*).

The grasshopper warbler (*Locustella naevia*) (Fig. 52) is particularly associated with the interface between scrub and rough, tussocky grassland at damp sites. It is therefore not surprising that Wicken Fen had up to 15 singing males which represent about a quarter of those recorded annually in Cambridgeshire.[86] About eight singing males occurred at Fowlmere.

The willow tit (*Parus montanus*) has a discontinuous distribution in Cambridgeshire, occurring mostly in the damper woods from which the marsh tit (*Parus palustris*) is absent. Wicken Fen, with four to five breeding pairs, Ditton Park Wood and Chippenham Fen were among its strongholds in the county.[86]

Figure 52 Grasshopper warbler at nest (*Locustella naevia*)

AN ISLAND OF WETLAND AND SCRUB

Drainage and intensive agriculture have isolated Wicken Fen from other wetland and scrub habitats. The effect of this isolation on most species of birds is much less than on many plants and the more sedentary invertebrates (Chapters 7 & 8). Wildfowl are particularly mobile and, given open water and freedom from disturbance, their numbers on the Mere have quickly built up.

Some colonizations, such as the breeding by marsh harriers, and the re-establishment of the sparrowhawk (*Accipiter nisus*) as a breeding species in 1990 (if not 1989), after the East Anglian population had been decimated by organochlorine pesticides in the 1960s, reflect a national increase. The less frequent occurrence of the bittern corresponds with the decline of the breeding population in Britain and elsewhere in Western Europe.

Other population changes are of a more local nature. Autumn dispersal of young birds has led to the establishment of some reed-bed passerine species (bearded tit, Cetti's warbler), and the increase in woodland scrub has allowed certain scrub species to become established (woodcock, lesser-spotted woodpecker) or to recolonize after a lengthy absence (nightingale).

Influxes of wildfowl at Wicken Fen, fluctuations in numbers of roosting hen harriers and the sudden arrival and apparent departure of spotted crakes, all suggest movements between Wicken Fen and the Ouse Washes when the latter site is flooded. There would probably be few wigeon using the Wicken Mere were it not for the proximity of flooded pasture for them to graze on the Cam Washes. From an ornithological point of view, Wicken Fen should certainly be considered as an integral part of the wetlands of the Fens. The acquisition of 52ha of arable land adjacent to Wicken Fen provides an opportunity to recreate additional breeding habitat for wildfowl and waders characteristic of lowland wet grassland and a feeding area for wigeon (Chapter 13).

References

1 Evans (1904)
2 Evans (1923a)
3 Gardiner & Tansley (1923)
4 Gardiner (1925–32)
5 Ennion (1942)
6 Wicken Fen Executive Committee Minute Books for 1929, 1936, 1952. In Fen archive
7 Lack (1934), pp. 15–17
8 Thorpe (1938)
9 Bloom (1944)
10 Bircham (1974)
11 Muir (1951)
12 Easy & Kirtland (1967)
13 Bibby (1968)
14 Bibby (1977)
15 Green (1974)
16 Thorne (1974)
17 Thorne (1976)
18 Thorne (1973)
19 Thorne (1975)
20 Bibby (1971)
21 Bibby (1973b)
22 Green (1975)
23 Green (1976)
24 Innes (1977)
25 Innes (1978)
26 Redfern (1978)
27 Green (1971)
28 Barnett & Green (1972)
29 Thorne (1971)
30 Bircham (1970)
31 Bircham (1972)
32 Harvey (1969)
33 Hughes (1983)
34 Messent (1969)
35 Naylor (1974)
36 Harvey (1974)
37 Langslow (1971)
38 Davies & Green (1976)
39 Duckworth (1991)
40 Davies & Brooke (1991)
41 Baillie & Peach (1992)
42 Buckland & Baillie (1987)
43 Peach et al. (1990)
44 Peach et al. (1991)
45 Thorne & Bennett (1982)
46 Thorne & Bennett (1989)
47 Bircham (1978)
48 Bibby (1970)
49 Bibby (1973a)
50 Bircham (1983)
51 Milwright (1976)
52 Thorne (1977)
53 Thorne (1978)
54 Thorne (1980)
55 Marchant et al. (1990)
56 Davies & Brooke (1989a)
57 Davies & Brooke (1989b)
58 Brooke & Davies (1988)
59 Davies & Brooke (1988)
60 Brooke & Davies (1987)
61 Chance (1940)
62 Wyllie (1981)
63 Brooke & Davies (1989)
64 Bibby & Lunn (1982)
65 Everett (1989)
66 Thomas et al. (1981)
67 Owen et al. (1986)
68 Fox & Salmon (1989)
69 Gibbons et al. (1993)
70 RSPB (unpublished reports)
71 Bibby (1974)

72 Spencer & the Rare Bird Breeding Panel (1993)
73 Lack (1986)
74 Day (1981)
75 Bibby (1981)
76 Day (1988)
77 Clarke (1986)
78 Smith (1983)
79 Green & Cadbury (1987)
80 O'Brien & Smith (1992)
81 Cadbury (unpublished)
82 Cadbury (1983)
83 Green (1985)
84 Cadbury et al. (1987)
85 Kemp (1981)
86 Bircham (1989)
87 Sharrock (1976)

Aerial photograph of Wicken Fen, 30 August 1988

1. (Above left) Newly-harvested sedge field with panicles of *Cladium mariscus* in foreground, July 1992; **2**. (above right) Species-rich litter in July with yellow loosestrife (*Lysimachia vulgaris*), purple-loosestrife (*Lythrum salicaria*) and wild angelica (*Angelica sylvestris*)

3. (Left) Sedge Fen Drove in winter

1. Water-violet (*Hottonia palustris*), seen here growing densely in a fen ditch, July 1990

2. Common comfrey (*Symphytum officinale*), found abundantly in the 'mixed sedge' community, is a major forage source for bumblebees

3. Milk-parsley (*Peucedanum palustre*), the larval plant of the swallowtail butterfly, has declined disastrously this century at Wicken but action has been taken to reverse this process

4. Fen orchid (*Liparis loeselii*), was last recorded at Wicken in 1945. This specimen was photographed at Catfield, Norfolk, on 28 June 1977

1. Fen violet (*Viola persicifolia*), a nationally rare species. Thought extinct at Wicken in the 1950s, it reappeared on disturbed peat in the 1980s and is now the subject of an active management programme

2. Fen ragwort (*Senecio paludosus*), believed extinct in Britain since 1857 but rediscovered in July 1972 near Ely, where photographed, the source of the material reintroduced to Wicken Fen

3. Common spotted orchid (*Dactylorhiza fuchsii*), first recorded at Wicken in 1911 but not verified until refound beside Drainers' Dyke in 1986

4. Heath spotted-orchid (*Dactylorhiza maculata* ssp. *ericetorum*), photographed at Wicken Fen, 8 July 1986. A new record for Cambridgeshire as well as for the Reserve

1. Swallowtail butterfly (*Papilio machaon britanicus*) at rest on flowers of red campion (*Silene dioica*), Hickling Broad, Norfolk; 2. Swallowtail egg on *Peucedanum* leaf; 3. First-instar larva, black with indistinct white banding; 4. Pupa attached by its girdle to a reed-stem; 5. The nearly full-grown, fifth-instar swallowtail larva has very distinctive green and black patterning; 6. Green-veined white (*Pieris napi*) on cuckooflower (*Cardamine pratense*), one of eighteen butterfly species recorded annually at Wicken; 7. Large Copper (*Lycaena dispar batavus*), reintroduced in 1927 but extinct at Wicken in the 1940s, may be reintroduced in the future; 8. Brimstone (*Gonepteryx rhamni*) on common fleabane (*Pulicaria dysinterica*) in compartment 69. Both larval foodplants (*Rhamnus cathartica* and *Alnus glutinosa*) are common on the reserve

1. Silver barred (*Deltote bankiana*); 2. Reed leopard (*Phragmataecia castanea*); 3. Marsh carpet (*Perizoma sagittata*); 4. *Xanthostigma xanthostigma*, a snake-fly; 5. *Sialis lutaria*, an alder fly; 6. *Demetrias imperialis*, a reed carabid beetle; 7. *Agabus undulatus*, an uncommon water beetle; 8. *Anthocomus rufus*, a wetland species of malachite beetle; 9. *Strangalia maculata*, a commonly-seen longhorn beetle; 10. *Aromia moschata*, the longhorn 'musk beetle'; 11. *Agapanthia villosoviridescens*, a local longhorn beetle; 12. *Donacia sparganii*, a chrysomelid reed beetle

1. *Bombus lapidarius*, a long-tongued 'true' bumblebee; 2. *Psithyrus vestalis*, a cuckoo bumblebee; 3. *Stratiomys singularior*, a soldier fly; 4. *Poecilobothrus nobilitatus*, a long-headed fly; 5. *Criorhina floccosa*, a hoverfly; 6. *Volucella bombylans*, a bee-mimicking hoverfly; 7. *Sericomyia silentis*, a hoverfly; 8. *Sicus ferrugineus*, a bee-killing fly; 9. Common darter (*Sympetrum striolatum*); 10. Hairy dragonfly (*Brachytron pratense*)

1. (Above) Mist-net erected at site B3 in compartment 21; **2.** (top right) Lesser whitethroat (*Sylvia curruca*), which migrates SE to the Middle East and E. Africa, ringed in August 1996; **3.** (lower right) Jay (*Garrulus glandarius*), a generally non-migratory species, ringed in August 1996

4. Great-spotted woodpecker (*Dendrocopos major*), the commonest resident woodpecker, ringed in May 1992

5. Kestrel (*Falco tinnunculus*), female in the hand, ringed in May 1992

1. (Left) Eggs of six hosts of the cuckoo (*Cuculus canorus*); (centre) corresponding cuckoo eggs; and (right) five model eggs put in nests for experimental purposes (see Chapter 9.3 for details)

2. Marsh harrier (*Circus aeruginosus*) nest and young. Their disparate size is due to the intervals between hatching, a strategy which enables the strongest to survive when food supplies are short

3. Lapwings (*Vanellus vanellus*) again breed in small numbers in pasture land on Adventurers' Fen

4. Woodcock (*Scolopax rusticola*) are supremely well camouflaged on the nest due to their cryptic plumage

On the Fens – Sedge cutting at Wicken Fen, early morning. Painting by Robert Walker Macbeth (1848–1910)

1. Members of the Local Management Committee and Advisory Panel, at the Annual Meeting, 1992: (standing, left to right) G. Lohoar (Deputy Head Warden); A. Vine; S. Ward (National Trust); S. M. Walters; N. W. Moore (Chairman); T. J. Bennett (Head Warden); J. M. Lock; F. J. Bingley; P. W. Richards; I. Perry; S. P. Tomkins; D. Almond; F. S. J Hollick; C. J. R Thorne; (seated) S. A. Corbet; J. O. Mountford; L. E. Friday (Secretary); I. G. Crompton; P. F. Yeo; D. J. Kiddy; N. A. Straw; P. Langton

2. The Fen staff in front of the boathouse on the occasion of the presentation to Ralph Sargeant of the National Trust's medal for 25 years' service, March 1997: (left to right) N. Wicks (Assistant Warden); M. Chatfield (Property Manager); M. Lester (Reserve Warden); A. Hair (Education/Interpretation Officer); C. Laidlaw (volunteer); R. Sargeant (Warden); M. Cornell (Warden); D.-J. Challenger (Secretary); C. Weightmann (Education/Interpretation Officer); J. Sykes (fundraiser); O. Thursby (Assistant Warden); S. Wiseman (Assistant Warden); M. Denyer (volunteer)

1, **2**. Waterproofing Spinney Bank, November 1988. (Left) Inserting the polythene membrane in the trench; then, (right) backfilling to render the membrane secure and protect it from damage

3. Cutting submerged weeds in Wicken Lode – the NRA boat in action. The Lode must be kept navigable.

4. Carrying off the sedge harvest, a crop now sold exclusively for thatching

1. (Right) Ralph Sargeant cutting reeds with the Olympia rice-cutter, January 1989

2. (Left) Loading reed bundles on to the Fen boat for transporting to the village end of the Lode and stacking until taken by the thatcher

3. (Right) Litter has either to be burnt, as here; sold for baling, for which there is limited demand; or allowed to rot in specially reserved areas

1. (Left) Path cleared by conservation volunteers through incipient woodland on Verrall's Fen, 1994

2. (Below) Adventurers' Fen contains a variety of habitats – open water, reed-beds and grazing marsh, December 1992

1. (Right) The boardwalk, seen here in winter, can be used in all seasons, even in ordinary shoes

2. (Below) Wicken Lode following a heavy frost, January 1993

1–3. (Above) Fen Cottage in a state of disrepair, 1989; (centre) thatching with reeds harvested from the Fen; (right) applying clay and lime daub to timber and lattice of south gable

4. (Below) Aerial view of the newly-restored Fen Cottage, looking south along Wicken Lode, with the Sedge Fen behind, March 1990

PART FOUR

The Human Dimension

IO

THE HISTORY OF THE FEN

T. A. ROWELL

INTRODUCTION

HISTORY CAN help us interpret much of what we see in the landscape. At Wicken, we might enquire about the origins of the ditches, the embankments, or the old peat-diggings which can be discerned on the ground and are so very clear from the air. How old are the Brickpits? How long has sedge been harvested here, and is it true that the Sedge Fen was extensively dug for peat during the last century? Why was the Fen not drained like the rest of the Cambridgeshire Fenland? Why is it still here? How was it managed in the past, and would this information help us manage it today?

Wicken Fen was perhaps the earliest site of natural history interest to have its history explored, by A. H. Evans in the first volume of *The Natural History of Wicken Fen* published in 1923;[1] the history of relatively recent management practices were researched by Godwin & Tansley, and presented in a later volume published in 1929.[2] Interest in the history is evident in many of Godwin's writings, culminating in an apparently definitive exposition in his *Fenland: its ancient past and uncertain future* published in 1978.[3] The history of the Sedge Fen outlined here is based on researches made in the early 1980s. It is very different from either Evans' or Godwin's versions, which were not based on extensive historical research.

Historical documents, researched in libraries, record offices and private collections, are the key to the history of Wicken Fen.[*] Amongst them have been found clues and answers to all these questions. Deeper ecological questions cannot, unfortunately, be answered in this way. The clues in this case may be found in the very stuff of the Fen itself.

The peat you walk on, formed from preserved remains of the plants that grew here over the centuries, is itself a record of the development of vegetation. Also buried here is evidence of periods of inundation indicated by intercalations of shell marl, and a record of the local vegetation both on and off the Fen in the form of preserved pollen. The specialized disciplines of pollen and macro-fossil analysis can take us way beyond the recent history afforded by documents and other more obvious relics. They allow us glimpses of those vegetational and climatic changes which have occurred since the last Ice Age.

The National Trust property at Wicken Fen spans a parish boundary – between Wicken and Burwell – and takes in many formerly separate properties and pieces of common land. Each has an essentially separate history. Most effort has been expended in exploring the history of the Sedge Fen, because it is the most intact area and is biologically the most interesting section of the property. The Sedge Fen will therefore figure largest in what follows, and each historically separate section of the property will be dealt with individually. First, however, it is useful to examine the role of the crop which gave the Sedge Fen its name and has been instrumental in the survival of the site.

SEDGE – AN ANCIENT CROP

The Sedge Fen appears to have survived, as we shall see, because of its importance to the local economy. The significance of the site was based on its main products, sedge and, to a lesser extent, peat. The significance of peat is well understood; it was an important fuel before the general availability of coal, and the peculiarities of its extraction in the East Anglian Fenland have been admirably described by Godwin.[3] Sedge, however, is generally little understood, and it is worth examining its past use in some detail.

In East Anglia, sedge is the great fen-sedge, *Cladium mariscus*. The tough, long and narrow leaves are the part which is harvested (see Plate 10). According to most guides to the uses of plants, these were used solely for either thatching or kindling. Today, the sedge harvested from Wicken Fen is exclusively a thatching material, most frequently ridging roofs that are otherwise covered with reed. As a ridging material, sedge is much more flexible than reed, and more durable. It is, however, still occasionally used to thatch a complete roof. Thatching is undoubtedly an historical use for sedge, and it is quite possible that it was used as such in prehistoric times.

---

[*] Full references to all the documents quoted are to be found in Rowell (1983a)[4]; only the principal sources are identified here.

The use of sedge as kindling is, perhaps, underselling its former status. Sometimes, sedge was the principal fuel purchased by the bakehouses at the Cambridge colleges in the 17th century, and a mid-18th-century guide to the town[5] listed 'Sedge, with which the Bakers heat their ovens' as one of the 'Necessaries of Life' with which the town was well supplied. Every college had a sedge loft or house, and special equipment was required to handle the bundles as the leaves can rip open flesh with their saw edges. A leather sedge-glove survives in the Folk Museum at Cambridge. Sedge was also used for drying malt. In the 19th century, there are numerous references to its use for fire-lighting, until the advent of resin firelighters killed this practice.

Sedge was used as litter in a wide variety of situations. Its toughness no doubt made it ideal for this. It has been used indoors in domestic situations in the Cambridge colleges, on roadways and, around 1900, for strewing on the gallops at Newmarket during frosty weather to give improved purchase for racehorses' hooves. No doubt it found use as farmyard litter, too.

Other uses for sedge have also been noted. During the repair of the roof to the tower of St Mary the Great at Cambridge in 1593, sedge was bought in specially to 'laye upon the Leads of the Church to save the Leadds when the slate of the Steple was taken downe'. More sedge was bought to cover and, presumably, to protect, the new work on the tower. All this was in addition to the temporary thatch of sedge that the tower sported at this time.[6]

Sedge was sometimes used locally with bushes to fill land drains,[7] in the same way that stone, branches, furze, bracken, twisted straw or bean straw were all used in other parts of the country. Here and in Sweden, cut sedge has been used as fodder, or to bulk out feed. During the 1870s, some of the chief consumers of sedge appear to have been brickmakers. Some sedge was cut at Wicken for covering bricks while drying, but the demand for that purpose was declining at the beginning of the present century.

Sedge was sold by the 'hundred', a unit that consisted of 120 bunches or bundles. Sedge land produced something between five and fifteen hundreds (600–1,800 bunches) annually. Once cut and bundled, any sedge not intended for local use was transported from the Fenland villages to Ely, Cambridge, and neighbouring villages by barge. Tolls were levied on the passage of sedge on the Cam in the 18th and 19th centuries. In Cambridge, sedge was unloaded at the Quay opposite Magdalene College. Close by, at the end of Thompsons Lane, were the Sedge Yard and Sedge Hall. In earlier times, sedge was stacked in the streets where, in 1410, the 'seggerekes' were regarded as a nuisance.

During much of the 20th century, sedge has been cut at Wicken outside the growing season (Chapters 5 & 11). This form of management was thought to be traditional by the early conservation managers of the Fen. This is strange as, in the Norfolk Broads where sedge is also cropped, it is cut during the growing season. Collation of the rather meagre historical information that does exist on the time of cutting on the Sedge Fen provides an interesting story.[8] For instance, the manor court at Wicken ordered, during the 1650s, that the Sedge Fen should be 'laid out' (i.e. divided up amongst the commoners) in late April. Laying out was followed by cutting, which had to be completed by Midsummer's Day. Fines were levied at rates rising from two to ten shillings per hundred during that decade.

In the late 18th century, an agreement was made between landlord and tenant of part of the Sedge Fen that went to great lengths to ensure that the crop was cut at the correct time.[9] They agreed that cutting in any year was to take place only between March and August. If the season did not allow the crop to be cut at this time without injuring the land, then the crop was to remain standing until the following March–August. Of further interest is the agreement to cut sedge at three or, more usually, four years old. Clearly, adverse seasons could mean the crop reaching an even greater age. These historical data indicate that, in the past at least, sedge harvesting at Wicken was on the same basis as in Norfolk, i.e. every four years, during the early to mid growing season.

Little is known about the men who cut, transported, or sold the sedge. Trade directories are silent on the sedge trade until 1864 when Robert Aspland of Wicken began to advertise his services as a sedge merchant, and continued to do so until 1916. Aspland owned more than 48 acres of the Sedge Fen at one time or another, but sold most of it to the National Trust in 1916.

The drainage of large sedge-producing areas around Whittlesey Mere (see Fig. 1, p. 2) and on Burwell Fen during the first half of the 19th century must have curtailed the supply of sedge severely. Whereas formerly whole gangs of barges had delivered sedge to Cambridge, by 1860 only single boats were occasionally seen. By then, Wicken Fen was the major source of the commodity. Nevertheless, the local trade in sedge, litter, and reed was still strong between 1856 and 1875, but declining demand began to bite during the '70s and '80s.[10] While, in 1879, virtually every building in Wicken itself, outhouses included, was thatched with sedge, by 1916 these were few and far between as the older cottages were replaced by modern houses of brick and slate.[11]

This decline continued until, in 1932, sedge from the Fen could no longer be sold at all for thatching.[12] Eventually, the market revived, though much of the good sedge had been lost in the meantime. Today, a relatively small area is cut for this traditional crop which once covered most of the site.

THE SEDGE FEN

Prehistory

The peat that is the substance of Wicken Fen began to form about 4,500 years ago. At that time, large trees grew in the stiff, gault clay soil, and two radiocarbon dates obtained from such trees (so-called 'bog oaks', see Fig. 73, Chapter 11) preserved in the peat of Adventurers' Fen showed dates of $4,380 \pm 140$ and $4,605 \pm 110$ years BP (before the present). Bog oaks found north of the Sedge Fen have been dated to 4,200 BP.

Analysis of peat stratigraphy in a section taken by Godwin from Sedge Fen Drove, close to Drainers' Dyke, shows the gross development of the Fen (Fig. 53). A layer of wood peat at about 330cm depth associated with a preponderance of alder pollen

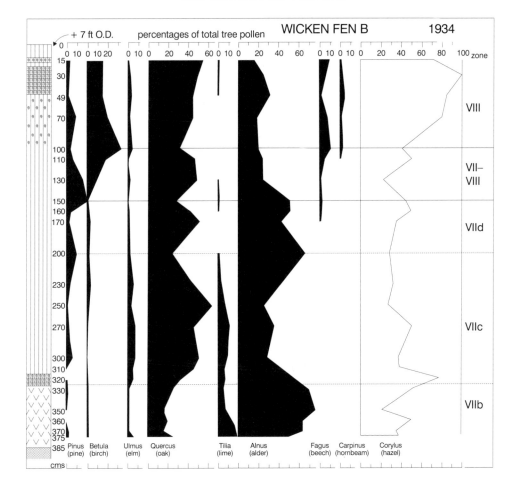

Figure 53   Pollen diagram from a core taken in the Main (Sedge Fen) Drove at Wicken Fen in 1934.[13]
The left-hand column indicates soil types: vertical bars = sedge peat; dots = shell marl; v = wood peat;
hatching = clay.

indicates a relatively dry period. The wood peat is overlain by sedge peat with many shells at the base of the layer. A period of relative dryness can be detected in the later increase in alder pollen, though this is not reflected in the nature of the peat (the Fen still does not support alder to any extent). Near the top of the section, shells become abundant, and from 49 to 12cm depth is a stiff, white, shell marl which formed under open-water conditions. This is overlain by a further thin layer of sedge peat.

Mapping of the shell marl over part of the Sedge Fen (Fig. 54) shows how the area of open water, present probably during Roman times, lay on the Fen. The white marl, so obvious against the black peat, has helped clarify aspects of the recent history of the Fen. In many places where peat has been dug on the Sedge Fen (Fig. 55), the marl is present in the baulks between the trenches and absent, as expected, from the trenches

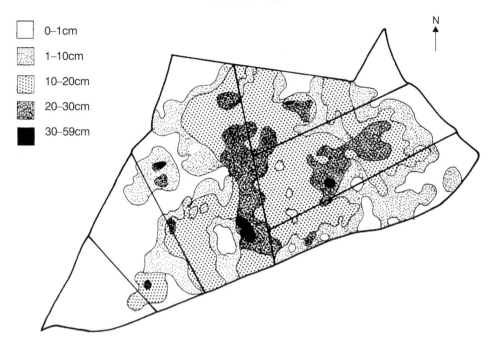

Figure 54   The distribution of shell marl on the Sedge Fen[4]

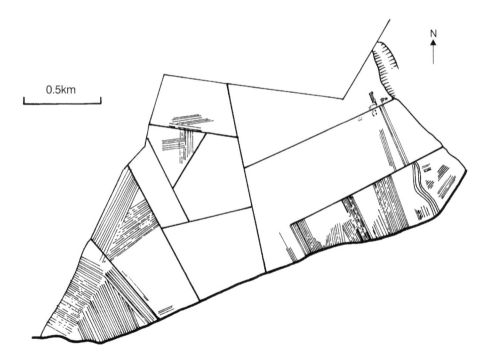

Figure 55   Relict peat trenches on the Sedge Fen as indicated by aerial and field surveys[4]

themselves (although these have refilled with peat to above the level of the marl). Peat extraction on some areas of the Fen was clearly not intensive enough to have involved removal of the baulks, and these areas were probably cut over only once. The furrows which cross Sedge Fen Drove might be peat trenches, but the presence of continuous marl through both ridge and furrow suggests not. More likely, they are the result of traffic damage. The absence of marl, or evidence of its being cut through, largely cor-responds with areas known to have been dug for peat, and follows boundaries known to have been established since the mid-16th century. The presence of thick marl often confirms conclusions drawn about land use from aerial photographs and documents – that much of the Sedge Fen has not been cut for peat since at least the mid-16th cen-tury. Intriguing areas, which do not correspond with known boundaries and where the thick band of shell marl suddenly disappears, might indicate the presence of older peat-diggings or turbaries.

While analysis of the stratigraphy shows the prehistorical development of the Fen (and how much more would a study of the plant and animal macro-fossils in the peat reveal?), study of the pollen content gives a guide to local vegetation (Fig. 53) and, therefore, to environmental conditions. Plants are not the only organisms with remains preserved in the peat; in *The Natural History of Wicken Fen*, Marr records some of the fossils of larger vertebrates found in Burwell and Reach Fens.[14] So the Fen carries not only a record of its own history, but also a record of the environmental history of the surrounding area. Human history may also be preserved in peatlands, as the discovery of Lindow Man, and many other human remains, so dramatically demonstrate.

The scientific importance of the undisturbed peat profiles at Wicken Fen should not be underestimated. As most of the Fenland peat has now been lost, they are an irre-placeable resource for the history of Fenland development and the local environment.

Early documented history

The peatlands to the south of the Wicken Ridge have been developing over the past 9,500 years. We do not know when people began to use the wetlands here, but their first major effect on the area seems to have been the development of large navigable waterways. Wicken Lode is one of a number of these man-made channels in the area, all believed to have been constructed in Roman times. The construction of the lode will have altered the drainage pattern around what is now the Sedge Fen and, indeed, will have effectively created the Fen as a distinct unit separate from the large tract to the south. Similarly, the construction of Monks Lode partitioned off the small area known today as St Edmund's Fen (see maps in Appendix A).

Centuries divide this early use of the wetland from our first record of the area we now call the Sedge Fen at Wicken. In 1279, the commoners of Wicken had 'a marsh ... of one league in length and a half a league in breadth extending from Upware to the village of Wicken', according to the Hundred Rolls. This reference, undoubtedly to the present Sedge Fen, unfortunately lacks any indication of the use to which the land was put. At about the same time, there was 'a marsh in Upware called Frythfen' which was given to Spinney Priory (on the site of the modern Spinney Farm to the north of the Sedge Fen). The frequent occurrence of the element 'frith' in the field names to the north of the Sedge Fen (through the 17th, 18th and 19th centuries) suggest that this was where the marsh was located.

A 'Sedge Fen' is the subject of several entries in the early manorial records for Wicken, the earliest dated 1419. This land was clearly common land where fines were levied for 'cutting sedge in the Segge Fen and allowing it to lie to the grave damage of the marsh' or for having cattle on the Fen. Unfortunately, the manorial records do not tell us where this Segge Fen was. The name tells us only that sedge grew there, and could be as transient, or otherwise, as the crop. Was it actually the modern Sedge Fen? There are a few clues.

Spinney also had a 15th-century interest in a 'Seggefen' as well as another marsh called 'Jankynsfreth'. These were detailed in 1449 and, a century later, the estate still included 'Segefennis ... and frythefennis'. Later still, in 1609, Spinney owned a 40-acre piece of the Sedge Fen, an area which can be identified on the ground today. This small portion of the Sedge Fen, owned by Spinney, seems to have a reasonable connection with the 15th-century common land of the same name. The Sedge Fen and Frith Fen also seem to be well demarcated throughout into areas corresponding to the modern Sedge Fen and the modern Spinney Farm.

The early situation seems to have been, therefore:

(i)   a marsh in the late 13th century, stretching from the Upware ridge to the Wicken ridge (apparently taking in the modern Westmere Farm), and managed as common land for unknown purposes;

(ii) another marsh to the north corresponding to the modern Spinney Farm;

(iii) the harvesting of sedge from the common Sedge Fen in the early 15th century;

(iv) a 40-acre piece of the otherwise common Sedge Fen owned by Spinney Priory.

The 'undrained' fen – 1600–1666

Wicken Sedge Fen is often cited as a remnant of the undrained Fenland. This is a relative concept; as part of the Fenland, the reserve cannot escape the effects of the massive drainage scheme that controls water-levels and allows agriculture to flourish in these low-lying lands. The whole reserve area has been under the influence of drainage schemes for at least three and a half centuries. With the pressures to drain, and much of the land around being drained, it is an interesting question why the Sedge Fen escaped cultivation.

Under the influence of Charles I, work to drain the East Anglian Fenland was carried out between 1630 and 1637. The draining necessitated the making of surveys and maps, and from these we can gain an insight into the lie of the land at that time.

From William Hayward's pre-drainage survey, made in 1635–36, the following descriptions can be gleaned:

'Wickin Towne, a comon Fen more east, called Broadfen and Sedgefen: betwene the several north, and Wicken Lode south.....437–2–0.'[15]

This area included most of the present Sedge Fen, delimited by the Lode to the south,
Upware Ridge to the west, Spinney Bank to the north, and Little Breed Fen to the east
(A on Fig. 56).

'Sir Edward Peyton, a severall adjoyning more to the north-east: butting east upon the
Lode.....40–0–0.'

Clearly, this refers to the 40 acres in the Sedge Fen identified earlier as belonging to
Spinney (B on Fig. 56).

'The same towne of Wickin, a small comon adjoyning more north, called Broadfen;
extending east a little beyond the Lodes end.....20–1–0.'

This is Little Breed Fen (C on Fig. 56).

'Isack Barrow, Esq, a severall more west, betwene the SedgeFen south, and his owne
ground north, butting west upon the high ground. This peece is imbanked on both sides,
both north and south.....57–0–0.'

An area of sedge land outside the Sedge Fen itself on the other side of Spinney Bank
(D on Fig. 56).

'The same towne of Wickin, a litle comon more east, at the east end of Sir John Peyton's
40 acres aforesaid; by the Lode south, east and west.....61–2–0.'

This is Edmund's Fen (E on Fig. 56).

'The same towne [i.e. Burwell], another common ffen adioyning more west: betwene
Wickin Lode north, and Burwell high lode south; with a narrow gory point westward, at
the meeting of the two lodes.....1434–0–0.'

This describes Adventurers' Fen.

From Hayward's records we learn that all the areas of the reserve we are familiar
with were present and correct, except that the Sedge Fen was a little larger than today,
which can be explained by the inclusion at that time of Westmere Farm on the western side. Hayward's survey also tells us that the land on the northern side of the Fen
was embanked where it ran against the Fen, and this is confirmed by cartographic evidence in Jonas Moore's map of the allotments to the Adventurers.[16] Spinney Bank is
therefore at least 350 years old, and probably older still. An earlier map, dated 1604,
does not show the bank itself, but clearly indicates its junctures, both east and west,
with the high land. It is important to understand that the purpose of the embankment
was to keep the land to the north dry rather than to keep the Fen wet. At any time, it
would have been of advantage to the Spinney estate, which has been a farm since 1538
and occupied since the early 13th century, to embank its lands against the floods which
afflicted the area regularly.

The deal made with the speculators (the so-called 'Adventurers') who supplied
finance for the draining was that they would receive drained land in return. Out of the

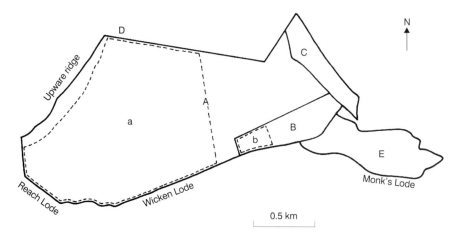

Figure 56 Land use in the early 17th century[15,17,4]

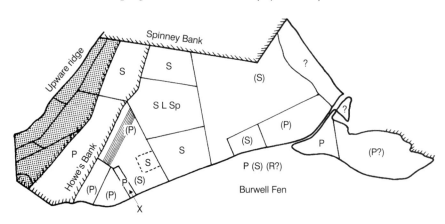

Figure 57 Land use in the 18th century[4]

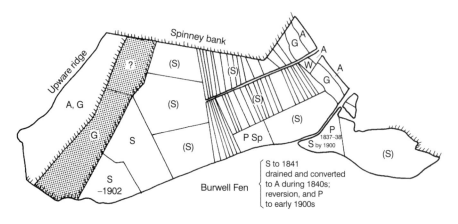

Figure 58 Land use in the 19th century[4]

Sedge Fen they got a large part of the common land, and about a third of the 40-acre plot that belonged to Sir Edward Peyton:

'Out of the common fen ground of or belonging to Wickin, in the said county of Cambridge, four hundred and fifty acres, [that is to say] out of the common fen, called the Sedge Fen or Broad Meadow, three hundred acres at the western end thereof, abutting upon Reach Lode, the hard lands of Wickin, and the imbanked several grounds of Isaac Barrow, Esq.'[17] (a on Fig. 56)

The residual 150 acres was elsewhere in the parish. The boundary between the Adventurers' land and the remainder of the Sedge Fen was to be Drainers' Dyke, which was probably dug at this time.

'Out of a several sedge fen of or belonging to Sir Edward Peyton, Knight and Baronet, fourteen acres at the west end thereof.'[17] (b on Fig. 56)

This was part of the 40 acres, and was to remain a distinct parcel for several centuries.

'Out of the common fen grounds of or belonging to Burwell and Reach in the said county of Cambridge, seven hundred acres at the north-west part of the same fens abutting upon Wickin Lode and Reach Lode.'

In other words, Adventurers' Fen.

When the draining was completed in 1637, the land to be awarded to the Adventurers was graded into five 'sorts', sort 1 being the best grounds and sort 5 being the worst. A large part of the Sedge Fen and the adjacent part of Burwell Fen were classed as sort 2, 'The middle sort of Grounds discharged of the Sea Floods of the River Ouse'. The aim of the draining was to produce land free from flooding in summer, but the enterprise was ruled defective in 1638 and further work was delayed by the Civil War.

A second attempt at draining the entire Fenland began in 1649. Over the next four years, the Adventurers' capital was used to try to convert the Fens into 'winter grounds' that would be free of floods all year round. At the completion of the work, the areas of the Sedge Fen and Burwell Fen were, at last, allotted to the Adventurers. Now, compared with the best winter grounds in the Fenland (sort 11 in the new grading scheme for drainage tax), the Sedge Fen was very poor sort 2 land, and Burwell Fen was even worse, graded as sort 1.

Figure 56   Topographic details of Wicken Sedge Fen as described by William Hayward 1635–36[15] (solid outlines and capital letters); and allotments to the Adventurers as described by the St Ives Law 1659[17] (dotted outlines and lower case)[4]

Figure 57   Brackets indicate that only indirect evidence is available for the stated land use. A broken line indicates that the exact position of the boundary is unknown. Hachures indicate embankments. The shaded area was being drained by a windpump by 1780. P = peat; S = sedge; L = litter; Sp = 'slop'; R = reed; X = 'plot 623', referred to in the text

Figure 58   The shaded area was drained between 1849 and 1886, bringing the western boundary of the Fen to its present position of Howe's Bank. A = arable; G = grass; W = wood; other symbols as used in Figure 57

Poor winter ground it may have been, but as summer ground it undoubtedly fulfilled the aspirations of the inhabitants of Wicken who, in common with many other Fenlanders, had objected violently to the whole idea of the drainage of their fens. So much so, indeed, that anti-drainage riots in Wicken have been cited as antecedents of the English revolutionary movement of the 17th century.[18] The bountiful nature of the undrained Fenland has been frequently referred to; it provided fish, fowl, fuel, thatch, grazing, and many other useful products. Effective drainage would have meant not only the loss of these natural products, but a change to a whole new way of life based on extensive arable farming. As very poor summer ground, conversion of the Sedge Fen and the adjacent part of Burwell Fen could be discounted for the time being.

The dissatisfaction of the inhabitants of Wicken with the results of the drainage work, for which they had paid dearly, is reflected in petitions made to the Adventurers at the end of the second phase. They complained that the works in Wicken were insufficient and endangered the land rather than improved it. Not surprisingly, the Adventurers disagreed, judging the fens of Wicken, including the Sedge Fen, improved. That the Sedge Fen was never improved to the point of becoming winter ground is borne out by a report to the Bedford Level Corporation (BLC) – the organization instituted to maintain the works implemented by the Adventurers. The writer found no evidence that any attempt had ever been made to protect the Sedge Fen from winter floods, to which it had always been subject.

Immediately after the second phase of drainage, the commoners of Wicken were cutting sedge from the Sedge Fen. This they did following the 'laying out' of the Fen which took place on 24 April in 1658 and involved the division of the area to be cut between the commoners. Then the sedge had to be cut and cleared from the Fen by Midsummer's Day. Fines were levied for failing to clear sedge from the allotted portions, and these could exceed the retail value of the crop.

The practice of cutting sedge may well have been continuous since the early 15th century. We do have, however, intriguing references that seem to allude to the cutting of peat. William Hayward's survey[15] actually names the large block of Fen we know as the Sedge Fen as 'Broadfen and Sedgefen', with another 'Broad Fen' on the eastern side which corresponds directly with the modern Little Breed Fen. Another survey made about the same time refers to a block of land called 'Sedg and Turfe Fen' and this can, in turn, be linked with the name 'Broad Meadow'. The only reasonable conclusion is that peat was being dug from some part of the Sedge Fen during the first half of the 17th century. This is likely to have been the western side, where most later extraction was concentrated, particularly as much of the central and eastern shell marl is undisturbed (see above). The present understanding of the disposition of land use on the Sedge Fen is shown above (Fig. 56).

The enclosure of the Fen – 1666–1800

The continuation of sedge cutting after the Adventurers' draining activities were complete suggests that there was little real effect on the Sedge Fen. As indicated above, however, a large portion of the Fen, previously common land, was commandeered and given to the Adventurers. It comprised all the land to the west of Drainers' Dyke, plus a small area alongside the Lode subsequently known as the Fourteen Acres and which had been in private hands anyway. The Dyke itself created the first major sub-division of the Fen at the beginning of a period that was to see it cut into many separate pieces. Drainers' Dyke was undoubtedly a work of the Adventurers and probably served the dual function of dividing the Adventurers' land from the remaining common and of carrying away drainage water from the Spinney estate. A windpump lifted water over Spinney Bank at its western end, but whether there was another serving Drainers' Dyke is not known.

Instead of being divided up and allotted for sedge cutting as before, this large area of Adventurers' land was now out of the control of the manor court and in private hands overseen by the BLC. The BLC ruled that peat-digging was forbidden on Adventurers' land (because it caused flooding and undermined the works maintained by the Corporation) but this did not stop it from happening. By 1722, the Adventurers' land on the Sedge Fen had been divided into seven or eight separate areas. Although one area adjacent to Drainers' Dyke was sedge land and a small area on the western edge had become arable, most was somewhat ambiguously listed as 'Fenn Meadow or Pasture'. It was in this condition that the Adventurers' land was bought in its entirety by Thomas Swale of Mildenhall. He would eventually cause far-reaching changes to his new acquisition.

Swale threw up two banks across the Fen. The most westerly marked what must have been more or less the boundary of the peat proper with the mineral soil of the Upware Ridge. The more easterly bank was what is now known as Howe's Bank on the present western boundary of the Sedge Fen. He also seems to have embanked along the edge of the Lode at this point, to fully protect the area.

By 1780, the westernmost part of the area had gained a more extensive ditch system, and was being actively drained into the Lode by a windpump. Between the two banks, crops of sedge and peat had been taken. Outside the embanked area, Swale subdivided much of the land nearest the Lode, and sold it on. Much of it was dug for peat, and the remains of the trenches can be found on the ground today and are clearly visible in aerial photographs (see for example, Fig. 60). Much of this land was later re-amalgamated into two large blocks subdivided by New Dyke. The subdivision of the Fen over this period accounts for many of the major internal boundaries. These subdivisions, and accompanying land use, are shown in Fig. 57.

When they lost that large area of their common fen to the Adventurers, the people of Wicken had their remaining common land in the Sedge and Edmund's Fen permanently subdivided amongst them. This permanent subdivision occurred elsewhere in the Fens, at for example Soham and Swaffham Prior, and was encouraged by the General Drainage Act of 1663 in order to improve agricultural efficiency. The subdivision at Wicken is mentioned in the records of the manor court which ordered on 18 April 1666 that 'before 25th April a part or portion of the marsh called sedge fen shall be allotted to every holding having common in the marsh.....'. A map showing the subdivision of Edmund's Fen still exists[20] (see Fig. 61), and confirms that the strips of Fen which were later acquired by the National Trust were indeed those set out for the commoners in 1666. We get similar confirmation for the Sedge Fen by later descriptions of the strips in the manor court records. In total, there were fifty-two strips on both Sedge and Edmund's Fen, of about 1.75 acres (0.7ha) and 0.75 acres (0.3ha) apiece respectively.

There are several ecological implications of this subdivision of the Fen. Firstly, to divide the two blocks of strips on the Sedge Fen, and to provide access to them, the broad pathway known as Sedge Fen Drove was provided. This botanically important strip of land has therefore been kept more or less clear, presumably by mowing, since 1666 (Chapter 5); more than 300 years of continuous management with a clearly dated beginning. Secondly, the instigation of permanent plots with, eventually, out-of-phase management will have given the vegetation of the Fen a new small-scale pattern of structural diversity very different to the peripatetic nature of the old 'laying out'. Thirdly, until the historical work outlined here had been completed in the early 1980s, it was presumed that the strips originated as 19th-century enclosures. We must now ask how important to the wildlife interest of the Fen did those strips become between the 17th and 20th centuries? Is their recent amalgamation into larger management units of ecological significance?

During this period, the inhabitants of Wicken had many problems with the water-level in the Lode; the Lode would become overgrown and silted up so that it went dry in summer, or the sluice at Upware would fail and the fenland would be troubled by flooding from the Cam. They had the opportunity, in 1760, to join the Swaffham drainage scheme but, in company with the inhabitants of Burwell, they declined. The views of the Burwell owners are recorded; they regarded their fens as worth more in terms of sedge and peat than they would be if drained. The attitude of the Wicken owners is likely to have been the same, just as it had been more than a century earlier when the Adventurers were compulsorily draining the area.

The 19th century – reversion, decline, and a glimpse of the future

A question which dogs the history of Wicken Sedge Fen is why did it survive? Why was it not drained like the rest of the Fenland? As we have seen, the answer seems to lie in the value of the natural crops of the Fen to the owners. The pressure to drain must have increased during the 19th century. However, when Burwell Fen (including the Adventurers' Fen part of the reserve) was drained in 1840, the Sedge Fen was still left untouched; possibly, the Wicken owners still clung to their view of the value of the natural crops. Unfortunately, the loss of Burwell Fen left the Sedge Fen at Wicken as the sole source of sedge in the Cambridge area. This may have been a temporary advantage, but the market was soon to fall away.

Following drainage and a brief period of agriculture, the main activity on Burwell Fen seems to have been peat digging. On the Sedge Fen, however, the extraction of peat from the western end seems to have declined so that, by the time of the formal Enclosure of Wicken in 1840, there is little evidence of this former land use.

At the enquiries preceding the Commutation of Tithes in 1839, reference was made to sedge being heaped up and carted from the Sedge Fen, but no mention was made of peat. Similarly, most published descriptions of the Fen during the 19th century refer to the cutting of sedge, but omit reference to peat digging. Indeed Miller, writing in the 1880s, considered that peat digging could not occur unless the site were drained.[21]

This change in land use, from peat extraction to sedge harvesting, can be illustrated by reference to one particular block of land (X in Fig. 57). During the 1740s, this area was divided into narrow strips, the outlines of which are preserved today as relict peat-diggings. They are adjacent to land which was contemporaneously described as turf land, so we can conclude that extraction occurred at about this time. In 1814, the entire parcel was willed to a 'sedge man', and in 1843 it passed into the hands of a local sedge merchant. The land was sold in 1878 and a surviving copy of the sale particulars are annotated 'No more sedge to be cut after a week or ten days'. This capacity of land dug for peat to yield a crop of sedge quickly was noted by Gooch in his *General View of the Agriculture of the County of Cambridgeshire*,[7] and was regarded as an important part of the economy of the Fens. The harvestable sedge growing on the Fen today is all found on areas known to have been dug for peat over the past 250 years. The probable disposition of other land uses in the 19th century is shown in Fig. 58.

Good evidence for peat digging well into the 19th century is available for only one area of the Sedge Fen, the Fourteen Acres (b on Fig. 56). The area was small, less than two hectares judging from relict trenches.

The periodic drainage schemes which temporarily de-watered the fenland to the south of Wicken struck again in the 1840s. Burwell Fen, including Adventurers' Fen, was converted to arable land, but the people of Wicken continued to resist joining these doomed projects. The scheme in Burwell, and a similar one in Swaffham, had the effect of isolating the Sedge Fen as probably the only remaining substantial area of semi-natural fen in the region. Certainly it was the only area now accessible from Cambridge and, as such, it became a centre for the naturalists of the day. Henslow had brought his students to Upware and Burwell (perhaps he even collected in the Sedge Fen itself) but it is only after the drainage of Burwell Fen that we start to get records from the Sedge Fen at Wicken.

A group of naturalists trooped across the recently-drained Burwell Fen in 1848, and noted 'a fen beyond still undrained' where they thought the fen orchid (*Liparis loeselii*), once plentiful in Burwell, might still be found (Chapter 7). This was undoubtedly the Sedge Fen. Two years later, Frederick Bond referred to Wicken Fen as a collecting site, and he is believed to be the first entomologist who systematically worked the site. Several other naturalists mention the Fen during the 1850s, with botanical records being collated at the end of the decade in the list given by Babington in his *Flora of Cambridgeshire*.[22]

Soon the entomological literature carried many references to the abundance and diversity of insect life at Wicken, and to the ease of collection there; 'The Home of Ease for Entomologists' as one writer dubbed it. Insect collecting soon became a small local industry – sedge cutters had long known the value of the pupae of the Swallowtail

– with equipment hire, accommodation, the sale of insects, and expert guiding all
becoming sidelines in the village. One collector wrote:

'I have always had to rough it, and it was quite a new experience to find old and experienced collectors ready to wait on you, to sugar, find lanterns and attracting lamps and
all other necessaries; in fact, to wait on you hand and foot for a small consideration. A
note to Mr Albert Houghton [Fig. 59] or Mr Tom Rowlison at Wicken is all that is necessary, and a lepidopterist will find himself fixed up with almost everything, and really
when one comes to consider that these men take us into their best localities, and fix us up
as if they had known us a lifetime, we have certainly much to be thankful for. Mr
Solomon Bailey is another good local collector .... My own special henchman was Mr
John Clark, of the Black Horse, Wicken ... There is good accommodation to be obtained
in Wicken, at the Red Lion, Maid's Head, or if any one prefers it, at Mrs. Phillips' house
(The Sycamores).'[23]

We are lucky that the Fen was so popular at this time. Not only did its popularity lay
the foundation for conservation, but it also ensured that many descriptions of the Fen
have survived. The most vivid is the painting of the sedge harvest painted by R. W.
Macbeth and exhibited at the Royal Academy in 1878 (Plate 10). There is also an excellent description of sedge harvesting, more or less contemporary with the painting.

Figure 59 Mr Albert Houghton (right) and companion trapping moths at an 'Eddystone Lighthouse',
Wicken Fen, c.1894. Apart from illustrating the open nature of the vegetation at the time, this appears
also to be one of the first photographic records of an entomological light source. The oil lamp depicted
was superseded at the turn of the century by acetylene, which was used until the use of lights was
suspended in 1939 at the outbreak of war.[24]

William Farren collected insects on the Fen with his father at the same time, staying in one of the cottages at the entrance to the Fen on Sedge Fen Drove. Macbeth stayed with them, covering the walls with caricatures of local characters. Farren gives us interesting insights into the character of the Fen in about 1880 and then again in about 1920, in his writings in *The Natural History of Wicken Fen*:[25]

> 'I am not sure what were the arrangements between owners and sedge cutters, but I believe they involved keeping the land comparatively clear of bushes, buckthorn and sallow especially. All the time I have known the fen there were several large permanent patches of mixed bushes and, especially in certain parts, many small clumps and scattered single bushes. Since then bushes have increased, obviously not having been kept in check as they were when sedge paid to cut...

> 'The change in the general aspect of the fen in 40 years, conspicuous to one who was very familiar with it in those days, is yet of a subtle nature and might not be noticed by a casual visitor. It is chiefly due to an increase of bushes and old sedge, together with a general air of wildness and neglect, all no doubt the result of the decrease in sedge cutting, and possibly the very effect desired. The dykes, however, are larger and kept clearer of vegetation. In my time they were allowed to grow up, and could be crossed with a bundle or two of cut sedge as a bridge. Now they are broad and deep and must tend to keep the fen drier. But the Sedge Fen always was dry except in very low places.

> 'Even the drove appears less frequented and more overgrown. It used to be regularly cut; swampy hollows were filled and made good, and there was a general feeling of occupation. There were always stacks of sedge and fodder along the sides, which we used to beat for many species of small moths which lurk in such places...'

The rise of interest in the natural history of the Sedge Fen was paralleled by a decline in the demand for sedge which, in turn, was manifested in increasing neglect of the sedge fields and ditches. Furthermore, rumours abounded of the imminent drainage of the Sedge Fen,[26] and it was this perhaps that prompted entomologists to start to buy portions of the site. J. C. Moberley appears to have started this off by purchasing two acres (0.8ha) in 1893. Six years later, in 1899, he sold this piece to the National Trust for £10, marking the beginnings of the reserve. Meanwhile, G.H. Verrall, the dipterist, was amassing whatever parts of the Sedge Fen he could. By the time of his death in 1910, he owned 220 acres (89ha) all of which he bequeathed to the National Trust (see Fig. 81, Chapter 13). The basis for future conservation of Wicken Fen was laid.

ADVENTURERS' FEN

The Adventurers' Fen portion of the reserve is in Burwell parish, the division between this and Wicken parish being along the line of Wicken and Monks Lodes. Indeed, Adventurers' Fen is part of Burwell Fen, and gained its name when it was taken by the Adventurers as part of their share of the drained Fenland following the great drainage scheme of the 17th century, as described above.

Like the Sedge Fen, Burwell Fen was common land at the beginning of the 18th century and was used mainly for the production of sedge and peat. Following the second phase of the 17th-century drainage, part of Burwell Fen was cultivated, the area nearest to Wicken Sedge Fen was dug for peat (Fig. 60), and the remainder was grazed. By the end of the 18th century, the Fen was regarded as 'greatly injured by the digging of turf'. This had encouraged the spread of reed and sedge which were being cropped.

The taking of fen crops, peat, sedge, reeds and litter, continued until 1840 when a temporary respite resulted from a new attempt to drain Burwell Fen. By 1856, a few areas of Adventurers' Fen were being cultivated, and within twelve years the whole of Burwell Fen was bearing agricultural crops. This did not last. From the 1870s until about 1920 extraction of peat and coprolites, supported by much small-scale drainage activity, reduced the level of Burwell Fen drastically.[27] Once these industries had died,

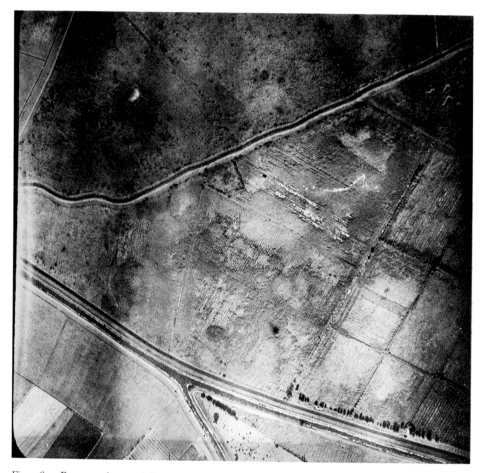

Figure 60 Peat trenches on Adventurers' Fen, *c.*1929. The area between Wicken Lode and Burwell Lode, which run across the field of view from top right and bottom right respectively, is covered by the long parallel lines of recent turf-diggings. Faint traces of old diggings are also visible to the north of Wicken Lode, on the Sedge Fen. (cf. Fig. 55)

wetland vegetation reclaimed the area, much of which was, by then, part of the National Trust reserve. The land was, however, commandeered during World War II, successfully drained, and converted to arable. The story of this endeavour is told in Alan Bloom's book, *The Farm in the Fen*.[28] After the war, Adventurers' Fen was handed back to the Trust and reed-beds and open water have been re-created (Chapter 11).

LITTLE BREED FEN

Little Breed Fen lies on the eastern boundary of the Sedge Fen, and is divided from it by a sinuous ditch (see map, Appendix A). It is bounded to the north by Spinney Bank, to the east by Breed Fen Drove, and to the south by Lode Lane. Sedge Fen Drove runs east–west across the area. Today, Little Breed Fen is part arable and part meadow; being on the fen edge it is also part peat and part clay. Within its bounds are the main complex of the Wicken brickpits, remnants of an earlier land use.

Little Breed Fen existed as a distinct unit of land as early as 1636. It was then common land called 'Broad Fen .... extending east a little beyond the Lodes end'.[16] During the period 1656–59, the records of the manor court at Wicken refer to peat digging in the common land on Broad or 'Bread' Fen. Relict peat-trenches can be identified on aerial photographs of the northern section of this fen.

In 1666, Little Breed Fen was enclosed in the same way as Edmund's and Sedge Fens. It was divided into two, and allotted to two commoners. The northern section was further subdivided by Sedge Fen Drove to create the distinctive triangular area now occupied by the Brickpits.

Once Little Breed Fen had been allotted, passing into private ownership, we lose sight of it for a period of 180 years. In 1842, the site was part grass, part arable, and part wood according to the Tithe Award. The record of woodland so close to the Sedge Fen, albeit only 0.8 ha in extent, is of interest. Only about 2.2ha were recorded for the entire parish in the Award.

This area of wood covered the present site of the Brickpits. The earliest suggestion of brick-making here is in 1869 when the plot was bought by John Owers, a builder and brick-maker from Soham. The brickyard was in full operation by 1880, having a kiln and a windpump to keep the pits dry. The yard was still in a functioning state in 1894,[25] but was disused by 1901 and has remained so ever since,[29] though the remains of the kiln still stand. The water-filled pits were colonized by wildlife, and have become an important freshwater haven on the edge of the reserve (Chapter 3).

Apart from the Brickpits, there is scant information about the remainder of Little Breed Fen in the 19th century. However, the Tithe Award map indicates that the original enclosures of 1666 had become further sub-divided. Active drainage of the northern area had begun by 1886. The pump was still functioning and in good condition in 1901, but was abandoned during the following twenty years (see Fig. 7a, Chapter 3); its post-hole alongside Sedge Fen Drove can still be found by careful search. The field was used for hay and grazing for some time prior to 1929. The area of grassland south of the Brickpits was meadow in 1929, as it is today. The presence of a population of the narrow-leaved marsh-dandelion (*Taraxacum palustre*), not found elsewhere on the reserve, suggests a long history of annual cutting (Chapter 7).

SPINNEY FARM

To the north of the Sedge Fen lies the farmland of Spinney Farm. This property has a long history, originating as a priory during the early 13th century, and becoming a private estate following the dissolution of the monasteries during the 16th century.

From the earliest times, as we have seen, the priory was associated with a marsh in Upware called Frith Fen. 'Frith' persisted for many centuries as an element of the field names at Spinney, and suggests that the Fen of the same name was probably to the north of the present Sedge Fen, and contiguous with it. By the 17th century, there was still an area of about 57 acres, north of the bank which divided the Spinney lands from the Sedge Fen, which was regarded as sedge land (i.e. bearing *Cladium*). There was, however, an element of active drainage, as a windpump is represented at the western end of Spinney Bank in Byrd's map drawn in 1666. Towards the end of the same century, the sedge land remained as part of a total of some 200 acres of peat land on the estate. Poor quality fenland survived as a part of the farm until the 19th century when drainage was improved. By 1857, virtually the whole of the peat land had become arable, with only a narrow strip of grass intervening between the Sedge Fen and the cultivated area. This situation persists to the present day.

EDMUND'S FEN AND WICKEN POOR'S FEN

When William Hayward recorded, in his survey of 1635–36,[16] 'a litle comon' of 61 acres with Wicken Lode to the south, east and west, this was clearly Edmund's Fen. He does not mention the Poor's Fen, a ten-acre patch of scrub and wet hollows.

Following the history of this Fen, we find it reserved for the mangey beasts of the parish in the 1650s, then divided permanently amongst the commoners in 1666, as also happened to the Sedge Fen, and other areas of common land in Wicken. The process of subdivision is recorded in excellent detail for Edmund's Fen due to the survival of a manuscript map by Theophilus Byrd (Fig. 61); no doubt the Sedge Fen was similarly mapped, but the map has not come to light. Byrd's map shows the Poor's Fen as a separate area of ten acres, and distinct from the rest which is divided into thirteen 'dolls', doles or shares. Each dole is marked with several names with the number of freehold or copyhold shares allotted to each, with four shares per dole, 52 in all. These parts survived, like those on the Sedge Fen, until they began to be bought up for conservation purposes, eventually to be amalgamated under the National Trust.

No direct evidence has been found for the use to which Edmund's Fen was put after the subdivision, until the Tithe files record the harvesting of sedge in the early 19th century. However, field observations and aerial photographs indicate that peat digging has occurred over much of the site and, as the trenches are all aligned with the strips formed in 1666, it is reasonable to conclude that they were dug after that date.

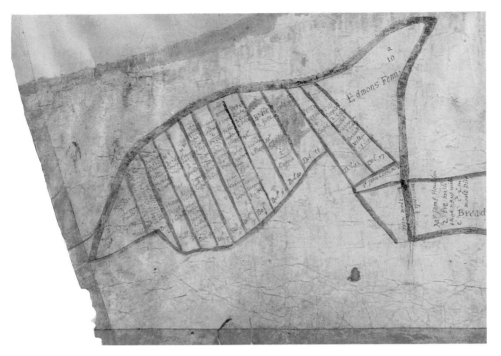

Figure 61 Theophilus Byrd's map of Edmund's Fen, showing the strips set out for the commoners in 1666.[20] The original map is in colour, with Monk's Lode and Wicken Lode shown as sinuous broad blue lines meeting at the top of the map (NB, north is at the bottom). The present Poor's Fen is the triangular area labelled 'Edmons Fenn', and part of Breed Fen – 'Bread Fenn' – is at bottom right.

Edmund's Fen became the property of the National Trust in the early part of the 20th century; at about this time, the name was modified to become 'St Edmund's Fen'. Unlike the Sedge Fen, where cutting was maintained in places, there has been little management of the vegetation. Consequently, the whole area is now scrub or woodland.

The history of the Poor's Fen is quite distinct from that of the rest of Edmund's Fen.[30] It appears to have been created in 1666 for the use of those without common rights and, therefore, without use of the allotted fens in Wicken. For most of its life the Poor's Fen appears to have been used to provide fuel peat for the poor of the parish. In 1686, for instance, the manor court ordered that:

'.....the fen reeves doe appoint one common days work to bee done by the inhabitants in Sedge fenn way and bred fenn way and Edmund's fenn way with labourers and carts to mend the ways there for the fetching up of the poors turfs and other carriages.....'

In 1720, the court defined the quantity of turf that could be dug:

'.....no man shall Digg in the Poors Ground above the quantity of Four thousand Turfe.....'

The digging of fuel in the Poor's Fen continued until the 1830s when the Charity Commissioners recorded that it was 'used by the poor indiscriminately for digging turf for firing'. By then the peat was nearly exhausted, but some fuel could still be obtained in dry seasons. Indiscriminate digging explains the pock-marked nature of the Poor's Fen, so different from the careful linear trenching wherever peat has been taken elsewhere on these fens.

By the early 20th century, it was sedge rather than peat that was being harvested from the Poor's Fen.[1,31] This grew where the peat had not been dug too deeply. Sedge cutting was governed by regulation and still is, though no-one has harvested from the Poor's Fen since about the time of World War I. Much confusion exists over the exact nature of the regulation. The earliest version dates from 1908:

> 'On the third Monday in July the poor of Wicken village are entitled to cut as much sedge &c., on..... [Wicken Poor's Fen]..... as they can. But each man must work unaided: no one can employ others to help him in the cutting.'[31]

This seemingly simple rule is clouded by subsequent writers who gave various other periods during which the sedge could be cut:

on or after the third Monday in July;[32]
after the third Monday in July;[33]
from sunrise to sunset on the longest day of the year;
from the third Monday in July until Christmas Day.

General consensus in the village in the 1950s suggested the third Monday in July as the only day on which sedge could be cut. On this day, the men of Wicken lined up on the bank of Wicken Lode with their scythes in the early morning. At six o'clock, signalled by the hooters of Soham Mill and Burwell Brickworks, they began and cut as much as they could by sunset. The area each man worked in was decided by mutual agreement. Carting away of the cut sedge could be done on subsequent days.

Lack of attention over many years means that the Poor's Fen is now overgrown with scrub. Access is made even more difficult by the treacherous nature of the old turf pits. Future management for conservation purposes seems unlikely as the Fen is still common land.

WICKEN LODE AND UPWARE SLUICE

Wicken Lode and, at its junction with the River Cam, the sluice at Upware are essential elements in the history of the Sedge Fen and Edmund's Fen. Together, they are major controlling influences on the hydrology of these peatlands (see Fig. 4, Chapter 2).

The Lode is taken to be, in common with the other lodes in the area, a canal of probably Roman origin.[34] However, both Wicken Lode and Monks Lode differ from the lodes of Burwell and Reach in being sinuous rather than straight and Fowler, in his pioneering work on past Fenland waterways, considered them to be natural at least in some places.[35]

The Lode needs to be cleaned out at regular intervals to maintain the flow of water and permit navigation. This has always been the case, but the work was not always done promptly. The inhabitants of Wicken frequently petitioned the BLC for this work, claiming in 1686 that, even in high water, boats could not pass, and in the summer the lode was dry so that cattle wandered across. In 1705 again, it was well overgrown, and again in 1723 and 1755. This overgrowth prevented water from draining away properly at Upware, and must have caused the Fen to be wetter than usual.

Once Burwell Fen was drained in 1840, other problems arose. Peat digging and wastage caused the land surface to fall, some two to three metres in the first thirty years following drainage, and put pressures on the southern bank of Wicken Lode. It continually leaked and collapsed and, despite major rebuilding in 1900, it continued to leak seriously and collapsed in both 1916 and 1919. Loss of water from the Wicken side may well have affected the water-table in the Sedge Fen.

The importance of the sluice at Upware was summarized during the 19th century:

'The sluice in question is doubtless of great importance to the Proprietry of Lands which are protected by it inasmuch as its destruction would leave their lands open to all the Floods coming from the Uplands down the Rivers Grant or Cam.'[36]

A pair of sluices appears to have been erected at Upware sometime after 1628. Before this, the low land bordering the lodes was presumably open to flooding when the Cam was high. The Adventurers and the BLC were both involved in sluice installation and maintenance in the vicinity of Upware during the 17th century, but it is unclear how the Upware Sluice was affected. During the 18th century, however, there were constant problems with the sluice and, by 1758, it was described as 'ruinous, and greatly decayed'. By 1786, it was 'so gone to decay that it will not answer the Purposes for which it was erected'; the following year, it had no doors. Although repairs were carried out, legal wrangles over responsibility for the sluice allowed it once again to fall into disrepair in the 1820s.[37]

This sad catalogue of events suggests that, intermittently at least, control over the water in Wicken Lode was lost. As a consequence, the Sedge Fen was undoubtedly subjected to a wildly fluctuating water-table until reliable pumping equipment was installed at Upware during the 1940s and the whole area came under a single integrated drainage system.

PROBLEM SOLVING WITH HISTORY

As a result of studying the history of the Sedge Fen, it is possible to answer some, at least, of the questions posed in this chapter.

Many of the obvious physical features on the Fen, such as the ditches and embankments, can now be dated. We know, for instance, that Thomas Swale built Howe's Bank in 1742–43, and that Spinney Bank is older, probably pre-17th century. Drainers' Dyke was probably constructed during the 17th-century drainage of the Fenland, serving to channel drainage waters from the land to the north, and to divide the

Adventurers' portion of the Sedge Fen from the remaining common land. Other ditches can also be dated (Table XIV), and served as boundaries to properties as well as allowing access by water.

Sedge Fen Drove originated in 1666 to divide the north and south sets of commoners' strips, and to provide access to them. All the other droves are much later, having been driven through the Fen during the present century to improve access for fen workers and visitors (Chapter 11).

The Brickpits, as we have seen, were excavated in the late 19th century, and were abandoned between 1894 and 1901. The rich variety of freshwater life that has developed there since is described in Chapter 3.

Most of the peat diggings we can see from the air are 18th-century excavations. A small amount of digging occurred during the 19th century, rather than the massive and rapid amount of extraction that has been suggested. The ecological influence of peat digging is, however, still apparent in the survival of species like the fen violet (*Viola persicifolia*) (see Chapter 7) which appear to thrive on disturbance and cannot withstand much competition from taller-growing species. Fairly harsh disturbance or, possibly, some peat digging may have its place amongst the techniques needed to manage the Fen properly.

Sedge has been harvested from the Sedge Fen for at least the past 600 years or so and, possibly, much longer. From some areas, where there is no sign of peat digging and no disturbance of the layer of shell marl, it is clear that sedge harvesting was continuous from at least the first half of the 17th century until the late 19th century. This is a considerable period for a hydrologically-sensitive crop to have been maintained in one place, suggesting that cutting may be more important to *Cladium* than short term fluctuations in water-level.

More detailed information on *Cladium* has been obtained through a study of the history of its management at Wicken. A little of this information has been given above. It brought about a realization that the earlier management of *Cladium* might have been

Table XIV. Dates of origin of the main internal ditches of the Sedge Fen

For the locations of the ditches, see map in Appendix A

Data from Rowell (1986a)[37]

Drainers' Dyke	1630s–1655
Gardiner's Ditch –	
section east of Verrall's Drove	?pre 1608
section west of Verrall's Drove	1981
Cross Dyke	? (line fixed pre-1722)*
Malcarse Drain	by 1740s (line pre-1722)
New Dyke	1849–1886
Thomson's Ditch	pre-1886 (?post-1858)

*Where the 'line' of the ditch has been dated, a boundary is known to have existed at that date, but the origin of the ditch itself is later or unknown

incorrect and, rather than conserving the plant and associated species, might actually have been damaging them (Chapters 5 & 11). Now, management is much more in line with historic practices, and with practices in Norfolk. Here, then, is an example of history influencing conservation management.

The changes in management that occurred when conservation began to be the major land use at Wicken may have been the most significant and damaging in the history of the Sedge Fen. Cropping more or less ceased, and sedge was lost to scrub over most of the site (Fig. 62) (see Chapter 6). There should also be concern over the loss of the relatively small-scale heterogeneity imposed on the Sedge Fen by ownership and the system of small strips. The previous owners were unlikely to have taken out all the sedge in their plot in any one year, as it needs three or four years to recover after cutting. More likely, they took a portion each year, with each holding or strip having a pattern of sedge of differing ages within it, a situation which must have maximized the potential for wildlife in an essentially destructive management regime. Today, with a single owner and extensive mechanization, large blocks are mown and, in most cases, all the sedge in an area is taken out in one go (see Fig. 69, p. 233). While it is impossible to claim that this has definitely had a detrimental effect on the wildlife of the Fen, it would be a relatively simple task to instigate management experiments to investigate the consequences of small- and large-scale management. Indeed, this has begun, with the management of small areas of sedge, cut out of phase, to encourage milk parsley (*Peucedanum palustre*), the food plant of the swallowtail butterfly (Chapters 8 & 11).

The question of why the Sedge Fen survived when all around it was drained is easily answered. It was the stubbornness of its owners that ensured its preservation. They continued to believe in the value of the Fen's natural crops right up to the point where

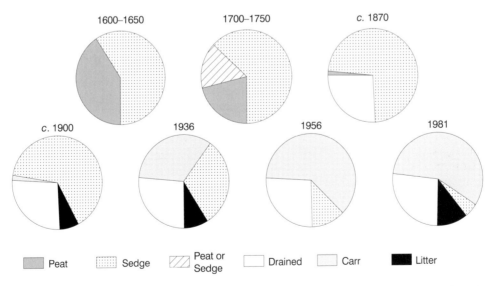

Figure 62   Changes in land-use from the 17th century to the present.[19] All the charts are based on the original area of the Fen as it was in the 17th century.

they ceased to have a value. The Sedge Fen could so easily have disappeared at the same time as Burwell Fen, or even earlier when the Swaffham Fens were drained. That the disastrous fall in value of the fen crops should coincide so neatly with the rise of interest in conservation was similarly fortuitous. Since then, of course, survival of the Fen has been a matter of a great deal of hard work by many dedicated people.

References

1 Evans (1923a)
2 Godwin & Tansley (1929)
3 Godwin (1978)
4 Rowell (1983a)
5 *Cantabrigia Depicta* (1763), pp. 15–16
6 Foster (1905)
7 Gooch (1813)
8 Rowell (1986b)
9 Rowell (1983a), p. 105
10 Evans (1925)
11 Sheldon (1916)
12 Gardiner (1932b)
13 Godwin (1941a)
14 Marr (1928)
15 Hayward (1635–6) *in* Wells (1828), vol. 2, p. 171
16 Moore (?1706)
17 St Ives Law (1658) *in* Wells (1828), pp. 264–265
18 Lindley (1982)
19 Rowell & Harvey (1988)
20 Byrd (1666), Cambridge University Library, ms. plans 647.
21 Miller (1889)
22 Babington (1860)
23 Tutt (1891)
24 Chalmers-Hunt (1966)
25 Farren (1926a)
26 Mitchell (1894)
27 Friday & Ballard (in press)
28 Bloom (1944)
29 Rowell (1982a)
30 Rowell (1982b)
31 Yapp (1908)
32 Evans (1923a), p. 26
33 Godwin (1978), p. 115
34 Royal Commission on Historic Monuments (1972)
35 Fowler (1933)
36 Bedford Level Corporation in Rowell (1983a), p. 32
37 Rowell (1986a)

II

The Management of the Fen

J. M. LOCK, L. E. FRIDAY AND T. J. BENNETT

WICKEN FEN has been owned and managed by the National Trust for nearly a century. The Fen's archive contains remarkably complete documentation of this long period of intervention devoted specifically to the conservation of the dwindling areas of fenland habitat; in this chapter we make extensive use of this material, first to examine how ideas and arrangements for management have changed over this time, and secondly to describe the evolution of our current management practices. Unless otherwise stated, the material quoted is taken from the Committee Minute Books.

FENMEN, PROFESSORS AND THE EVOLUTION OF THE MANAGEMENT PLAN

In the earliest days of the Trust's ownership, the Fen was looked after by a 'watchdog', Solomon Bailey, who owned land on St Edmund's Fen and was a 'sedge cutter and professional moth collector'.[1] In 1911, a Local Committee for Management was appointed, comprising at first A. H. Evans, Sir Francis Darwin, J. E. Collin, F. G. D.

Drewitt, J. S. Gardiner, C. E. Moss and the Hon. N. C. Rothschild. This committee's function was to manage the Fen 'to the best interests of the naturalists and others and to the best financial advantage consistent with such interests'. One of the first priorities seemed to be to raise funds by an appeal to endow the post of 'watcher', to which G. W. Barnes was appointed in 1914 (Fig. 63). The Committee also introduced a system of permits for collecting and began the first remedial bush clearance.

The Local Committee rapidly established itself as a body of up to 40 local naturalists and others who met annually to discuss points of management and to walk on the Fen. This was clearly not the best arrangement for achieving a well-planned and supervised approach to management and an Executive Committee was constituted to meet at least once a quarter to 'attend to the business aspects of the Fen'. This Executive Committee, comprising Chairman, Secretary, Botanical and Zoological Secretaries and about six elected members, was drawn from leading Cambridge academics who were associated with the Fen but probably had little direct experience in practical aspects of fen management. The Executive Committee met for the first time on 6 October 1925, in the Newton Room of the Department of Zoology.[2] In the early days, this Committee was virtually in sole charge of the Fen; the National Trust had no regional offices, and control, in so far as it existed at all, was from Head Office in Queen Anne's Gate, although the Trust was represented on the Committee from 1926. The Secretary of the Executive Committee took the lead in virtually all aspects of Fen management, including the hiring, firing, and supervision of staff.

Figure 63   G. W. Barnes, bringing the sedge crop down the Lode by fen boat, 1929

For most of the reserve's history, the manual labour has been in the hands of the Barnes family. G. W. Barnes's employment by the Trust continued through the First World War, and, in 1920, a watcher's cottage was built on the approach to the Fen to accommodate him and his family. By 1925, Barnes's position was upgraded to 'Keeper' of the Fen. His son, Henry, was also employed by the Trust and his younger sons too, William and Wilfred, joined the Fen staff (Henry achieved 50 years of continuous service in 1966, and Wilfred worked on the Fen for 51 years until his retirement in 1987) (Fig. 64). By 1932, the finances were in such a poor state that the Committee momentarily considered dismissing Bill Barnes but it was deemed necessary to retain three permanent workers to maintain the Fen. Casual labour was also employed, at a rate of 6s. 6d. (32.5p) per day in 1938.

At the beginning, the Executive Committee's main concerns seem to have been financial: the acquisition of land to complete the reserve, and paying wages. In 1933, the National Trust took the step of placing the responsibility 'for all payments and receipts with regard to Wicken Fen' with the Local Committee, and auditors were appointed from within the tight circle of academics, an arrangement which continued till 1948, when, 'in view of the large increase...in the amount of money involved' professional auditors were appointed.

Figure 64   Wilfred and Henry Barnes cutting sedge, *c.*1960. Wilfred is sharpening the scythe with a 'rub', while Henry holds the fork and strings. The brothers remember working from west to east, taking turns to scythe while the other forked off the sedge and tied it into bundles.

The Committee's approach to active conservation of the Fen's habitats during these early years appears largely to have been one of *laissez faire*. This led to rapid changes in the vegetation (Chapter 6) and provoked considerable concern among local naturalists. W. S. Farren articulated the problem very accurately:

> 'When parts of Wicken Fen first came under control of the National Trust, there was a general idea – perhaps a natural one – that it should be allowed to run wild and, to quote an expression often used, to return to its original state. This entirely ignored the question, what is the state most suitable to the economy of the species of insects of all orders for which the Sedge Fen is famous?'[3]

Indeed, it seems that the Committee may have been unclear as to the 'original state' it was aiming to achieve. From the start, Verrall's Fen had been 'set aside' as a 'sanctuary for insects and migratory birds'[4] with the result that some large areas were never cut. In the case of 'the Harrier Reserve', access was prohibited in order to protect the two breeding pairs of Montagu's harriers (see p. 145). Given the very limited money and manpower available to manage the Fen at the time, this was probably the only reasonable approach, but the resulting lack of active management inevitably led to a deterioration in the birds' preferred open, grassy nesting habitat. So it seems that some carr encroachment may have occurred as an unfortunate by-product of deliberate policy, rather than simple neglect.

During 1927, the Executive Committee began to engage fully in establishing cutting regimes. However, concern was soon being expressed by entomologists about an apparent deterioration in the habitat available for insects on the Sedge Fen. Matters came to a head in 1931 when the Entomological Society of London took the initiative, persuading the Committee to cut some of the litter fields in summer rather than, as had become the practice, in autumn (see Chapter 5).

Other major projects, such as the excavation of part of Gardiner's Ditch, the clearance of 20 acres of scrub and the cutting of a cross drove are recorded in the Minutes for 1929. By 1936, the Committee was beginning to feel more confident in dealing with the practical side of the Fen's management. The Minutes of 2 June 1936 record that 'the work of the last 10 or 15 years makes possible the formulation of a policy and programme for the conservation and for the further development of the Fen'. This had included the research on cutting regimes carried out by Godwin from 1927.[5] The new Secretary, W. H. Thorpe, prepared the first management plan (*Wicken Fen Management Scheme*)[2] which dealt with the different areas of the Fen, the dominant vegetation types and cropping activities: marsh/grazing land; litter; bush clearing; peat cutting. Extra funding was secured from the National Trust to support this new programme, particularly the cutting and clearing. On receipt of this £300, 'four additional men had been engaged and had commenced work on the clearing of bush' but heavy rain brought this work to an end within a fortnight, and the men were dismissed.

In 1938, the Barnes family was hard at work, excavating the mere which is named after them and which earned them a bonus of £14 (see Fig. 39, Chapter 9.1). When the Second World War broke out, the concerns of the Committee and the staff obviously changed. An emergency meeting of the Committee on 13 July 1940 considered the staffs' wages in the light of an increase in the minimum agricultural labourer's wage, which had gone up by 11s. per week at the outbreak of War. Mr Barnes' wage went up to 52s. 6d. per week and his sons' wages to 50s., 48s. and 42s. respectively. All three young men were likely to be called up for war service; Wilfred was the first to be called up in 1943. The Committee conceded that the Fen might just be kept by Henry and his father, but Mr Barnes alone 'could not possibly keep the Fen in a safe condition'. In spite of representations arguing that Bill and Henry Barnes were both needed to keep open the drains and ditches, (indeed the whole family had been engaged in a 'very thorough' excavation of Drainers' Dyke and Wicken Lode in 1941 and Howe's Dyke in 1942), Bill was called up later in 1943. Henry Barnes remained on the Fen throughout the War.

The major effort of the war years appears to have been carried out by outside labour: 25 men and women were brought in to cut alder buckthorn for the Forestry Commission. With the absence of two regular staff members, a reduction in the projects carried out on the Fen was inevitable and led to a 'very considerable arrears of work' by the end of the War. Finances were not, however, considered a problem (because of the reduced wage bill) and the Committee continued to plan to extend the reserve and to develop the amount of open water on the Fen.

In 1946, Bill and Wilfred Barnes were taken back into employment and Mr Barnes was finally able to 'retire', aged 68. He was presented with an inscribed 'black mahogany arch brass dial bracket clock, dated 1780, at a cost of £20' and a cheque for £15. Henry became the Keeper and Mr Barnes became 'Warden' with 'light duties and a small salary in lieu of pension'. His duties included 'the supervision and assistance of visitors... and, by arrangement with Henry Barnes, such manual and other work on the Fen as may be within his powers'. His wage was to be £1 per week with rent-free accommodation.

With four salaries to pay and a great deal of work to be done, the Committee suddenly found itself in financial difficulties again. Salvation came from a number of sources. In 1948, a bequest of £1,000 was received from Mr Ackroyd, for the Wicken Fen Endowment Fund. The National Trust's annual contributions, which had lapsed during the War, were now renewed, as was an annual grant of £100 from the University of Cambridge. A letter was now sent to the Vice-Chancellor asking that the University 'ensure that the income of the Fen does not fall below the minimum necessary for adequate preservation and management'. The result was an annual donation of £450 and a commitment to 'accept responsibility for the reasonable costs of maintenance of the Fen so far as provision for that maintenance cannot be made from other sources of income'.[6] The special relationship with the University was further strengthened by a further increase in the donation in 1951 'in view of the value of the Wicken Fen to the University as a field station'. The University continues to contribute annually to the cost of running the Fen, and benefits in turn from the research and teaching opportunities afforded by the reserve (see Chapter 12).

The financial situation fluctuated considerably in the 1950s. The substantial bequest from Mrs A. C. Bouquet was largely absorbed by the major works on Adventurers' Fen when it was reclaimed from the Agricultural Lands Commisssion, including the construction of the Mere at a cost of £3,933. The development of this area as a wetland reserve was perhaps the major concern of the Committee in the 1950s (See Chapter 9.1). In 1955, the finances were 'not unsatisfactory', but applications for aid from both the Society for the Promotion of Nature Reserves (SPNR) and the Nature Conservancy were being actively pursued. By 1959, the deficit was again considerable, largely because wages now amounted to £1,350 per annum, and it was reluctantly decided to dismiss Bill Barnes.

In 1956, the Botanical Secretary, S. M. Walters, drew up a *Memorandum on Management of Wicken Fen*[7] as a plan for future management policy. This eight-page document identified the main plant communities of the Fen and a prescription for their management. It also set out the philosophy for management of the Fen, which is still pursued today: the preservation of the 'maximum diversity of plant communities known or reasonably inferred to have been present in the Wicken Fen area in recent historical time' and the consequent conservation of typical fenland flora and fauna. Two interlinked problems had, however, to be overcome: finance, and the supervision of work on the Fen. The latter problem was tackled in a number of ways: Henry Barnes was asked to keep a regular log of the work on the Fen and submit it to the Committee's Secretaries; volunteer work parties were organized for the first time in 1959; and, in 1961, a permanent full-time Warden, Lt.-Col. C. Mitchell, was appointed.

Charles Mitchell provided the necessary link between the academic members of the Executive Committee and the labourers on the Fen: an informed naturalist with a military background and good planning ability, his full-time presence on the Fen made it possible to draw up detailed systematic management plans and to see that they were properly executed. After six months in office, Mitchell produced a memo to the Executive[8] setting out in detail his vision for the Fen and the means by which it might be achieved. His bold ideas revolutionized the approach to management and set the pattern for the future. He concluded:

> 'I am of the opinion that to do anything other than just hold our own, with, perhaps, just a slow improvement, expenditure is required on the purchase of equipment and the construction of major works..., the clearing out of the dykes, including opening up some now completely full, and the construction of clay banks... If the Fen is to be run by two men then it is essential that maximum use is made of power-operated tools'.

The Committee immediately took action to support the plan, applying successfully to the World Wildlife Fund (now the Worldwide Fund for Nature (WWF)) for a grant towards machinery, setting aside £1,000 of the 1962 budget for equipment, and constructing sheds and workshops to house the new acquisitions. The provision of the most efficient machinery that can be obtained at reasonable cost and its upkeep are still central to the Fen's management programme.

The plan soon developed into a scheme of much greater complexity and magnitude than had previously been contemplated and a suitably ambitious appeal was launched to cover not only major works on the Fen but also the provision of visitor facilities (such as new guide books and a car park for 200 cars), and a laboratory and lecture room. This appeal to both the large foundations and the public was very successful. At the same time, an appeal in memory of a former Chairman of the Committee, Canon C. E. Raven, brought in funding for the plans to develop Adventurers' Fen as a marshland reserve (see Chapter 9.1). The combined laboratory/lecture room at the entrance to the Fen was opened in 1969 and named the William Thorpe Building, in honour of the Chairman at the time (Fig. 65). This building, which received a radical face-lift and refurbishment in 1996, currently functions primarily as a visitor reception area, housing an informative display, and also provides office accommodation for the staff.

During the 1970s, the management of the Fen became ever more active and ambitious, with increasing use of mechanization and consequent growth in financial commitment. Such schemes demand strong guidance and the management plan, drafted by H. J. Harvey in 1977 (and updated in 1986[9] and 1992[10] by successive Secretaries), became the basis for day-to-day operations. Charles Mitchell's leadership was central to the success of these developments, and his contribution was officially recognized on his retirement in 1978 by the award of the M.B.E. He was succeeded for one year by T. Clifford, and then, for the next 15 years, by T. J. Bennett.

In 1986 the National Trust brought the Wicken committees into line with its wider administrative structures by making the smaller Executive the controlling committee,

Figure 65 The William Thorpe Building

Figure 66 Members of the Wicken Committee in the Fen boat on the Annual Perambulation, 1964. Left to right: W. H. Palmer; E. J. H. Corner; S. M. Walters; H. Barnes; A. C. Bouquet; H. Gilbert Carter; C. Mitchell (Warden-Naturalist); C. Wallace (National Trust)

and renaming it the Wicken Fen Local Management Committee. The old Local Committee (Fig. 66) was reconstituted (not without some vigorous discussion and opposition) as the Wicken Fen Local Advisory Panel. The Panel meets annually to receive the Annual Report and the accounts and to walk over the Fen (Plate 11, Fig. 1). A considerable wealth of expertise and goodwill is embodied in the Panel and this is regularly tapped by holding discussion meetings on particular aspects of Fen management. With the establishment of a Regional Office of The National Trust at Blickling in Norfolk, all aspects of personnel management and administration are now carried out from there under the supervision of the Trust's Land Agents, one of whom has special responsibility for the Fen. The Secretary and the Local Management Committee can now concentrate much more on the practical management of the Fen.

The minute books of the committees and associated documents are held in the archives. It was the gift in 1967 of a quantity of papers belonging to the former Chairman of the Committee, J. T. Saunders, that prompted the Secretary, Max Walters, to call together all documents pertaining to the management of the Fen. These were eventually gathered in the William Thorpe Building and sorted and catalogued by Mrs G. Crompton to provide a remarkably full history of the management of the Fen from 1921 onwards. At the same time, a search was carried out for deeds to the National Trust's property on the Fen, in both the Cambridge Record Office and the National Trust's London headquarters. The resulting 'Terrier' shows on a map the dates of acquisition of each parcel of land with the names of previous owners and provides a record of the gradual completion of the jigsaw of the Trust's holdings on the Fen (see Chapter 13). At present, the Fen archive is housed by the University of Cambridge. A project is currently under way to conserve and computerize the entire collection and to make copies available for consultation at the William Thorpe Building, in the Cambridgeshire Collection in the Cambridge Public Library, and, ultimately, on the Internet.

Wicken Fen was designated a Site of Special Scientific Interest (SSSI) in 1981 and the Local Management Committee has a close relationship with government nature conservation bodies. This began in the late 1950s, when the lease of the Fen to the NCC was considered so that its management would become entirely their responsibility. Negotiations continued for some time, but eventually foundered on the question of control. The present situation is that the Local Management Committee produces and supervises the implementation of the management plan. Representatives of English Nature (previously the NCC) attend meetings of the Committee and the management plan must be approved by English Nature and any alterations to it submitted for approval. Wicken Fen was designated a National Nature Reserve in 1993 and a Ramsar site in 1995. This recognition of the Fen's importance as a key site for the conservation of Britain's national heritage will provide extra protection for the Fen and support for the continuing programme of management.

The Fen has benefited from having a full-time workforce since 1990 of five Wardens (including an Education Warden). They are responsible for implementing the management plan with respect to the cropping of vegetation and the maintenance of the National Trust property. In addition, the Fen currently benefits from having a regular student placement during the summer from Merrist Wood College, and trainees from the local Agricultural College and under the National Trust's 'Careership' scheme are taken as the opportunity arises (Plate 11, Fig. 2).

The task of managing the reserve has, however, become more and more complex, generating a burgeoning amount of paperwork, drawing the Head Warden increasingly away from the Fen itself and into the office. The problem is likely to be exacerbated in future by the further devolution of responsibilities from the National Trust's Regional Office to the Fen. In order to regain a desirable situation in which the Head Warden is freed to work wholly on the Fen, the post of Property Manager has been created to take overall responsibility for the running of the reserve and to act as the interface between the National Trust, the Local Management Committee, English Nature and a host of other bodies on one hand, and those who carry out the practical management of the Fen on the other. Matthew Chatfield became the first Property Manager in 1995 and Martin Lester was appointed to the new post of Reserve Warden.

As at many National Trust properties, volunteers play a part in managing the Fen. Volunteer work camps began in the 1960s and Charles Mitchell brought in gangs of young seamen to take part in the great task of clearing carr (see p. 240). The summer work camps, now known as 'Acorn Projects', are strenuous working holidays that attract young (and not so young) participants from as far afield as the USA who tackle large-scale or labour-intensive projects that might otherwise be difficult to achieve, such as keeping down agricultural weeds on the grazing land, or who work alongside the Wardens in, for example, the summer litter harvest.

THE MANAGEMENT PLAN: HOW, WHY, WHERE AND WHEN?

As in perhaps the majority of British nature reserves, one of the major objectives of management at Wicken Fen is the maintenance of diversity and, where possible and appropriate, its enhancement.[11] However, in the particular case of Wicken Fen, three essential elements shape the overall structure as well as the day-to-day detail of the management programme:

(a) protecting the Fen from the drying effects of increasing water loss from the Fen to the surrounding farmland (Chapter 2);
(b) maintaining all stages of the vegetational succession from open water to woodland by bush clearance, the continuation of traditional cropping (of sedge, litter and reed) and periodic clearing of ditches (Chapters 3, 4, 5 & 6);
(c) balancing the protection of species and habitats with the educational and recreational needs of the 30,000 visitors who come to Wicken Fen each year.

How have these three problems been approached, and how successful have the Management Committee and staff been in sustaining the legendarily rich and varied habitats inherited from the gentlemen naturalists at the turn of the century?

MAINTAINING WATER-LEVELS

There is no doubt that one of the most important factors influencing the ecology of Wicken Fen is the relationship between the level of the peat surface and the position of the water-table (Chapter 2). The relative positions of land and water are critically dependent on the rate of supply and loss of water by various routes, and alteration of the peat surface topography by natural processes (such as succession) and the extraction of turf (Chapter 2). Parts of this equation are subject to seasonal fluctuations; the pattern from the 17th century through to 1940 (when the new sluice was installed at Upware; see Chapter 10) would have been for the Fen to be wet or flooded in winter and dry or wet in summer.[12] The various accounts available from around the turn of the century perhaps indicate a certain variability in conditions: in his reminiscences of the Fen in the last decades of the 19th century, W. S. Farren comments that 'the Sedge Fen was always dry, except in very low places';[13] by contrast, Burrows' advice to entomologists wishing to visit the Fen in 1903 was 'never visit Wicken without waders'.[14] There are many other observations suggesting that the input of water has not kept pace with losses and the Fen has become drier over the past century (see Chapters 2 & 5).

Rowell, writing in 1983, considered the restoration of a high summer water-table should be a priority for the Management Committee, because of the damage that low levels can cause to specific plant communities.[12] The case for reinstating winter flooding was, he felt, less clear; on one hand, some plant communities, such as the calcifuge bryophytes (Chapter 6), would be destroyed by flooding with calcareous water, whilst, on the other, invasion by woody species would be checked.[15]

During the past decade, two approaches have been adopted to stem this seemingly fatal draining of the life-blood of the Fen: increasing the means of conducting water into the interior of the Fen by way of the ditch system; and waterproofing the boundary banks in order to retain water against the gravitational pull of the surrounding land. However, a third, even more radical solution has periodically been mooted: Godwin, writing in 1978, revealed that 'the Committee has accepted that if you cannot bring the water-level up to ground surface, then you must dig ground surface down to water-level!'[16] This, evidently, was part of the logic for creating The Mere and various 'scrapes' on Adventurers' Fen.

The northern boundary, formed by Howe's Dyke and Spinney Bank Dyke proved to be a problem during the 1970s and 1980s. Although the former was cleared in two sections in 1937 and 1949, it was overgrown by the late 1970s and it became possible to cross much of the northern boundary, if not dry-shod, then at least in boots. The problem was brought to a head in 1982, when the re-opening of New Dyke and the subsequent flooding of the north-west end of the Fen, rapidly demonstrated that Howe's Bank was far from waterproof and in danger of complete collapse.

The problem has largely been solved by waterproofing the boundaries. The entire northern boundary of the Fen was waterproofed in 1987–89 by the Anglian Water Authority (AWA) as part of a scheme for reducing water loss from the Lode system as a whole. Water from Wicken Lode, moving sideways through the peat of the Fen, was finding its way out into the farmland ditches. The northern boundary of the Fen has therefore been adopted as the effective north bank of the Lode. Because of the importance of the scheme for the ecology of the Fen, it was possible to obtain funding from both the NCC (now English Nature) and WWF. The ditches along Howe's Bank and, later, Spinney Bank were re-excavated and the spoil used to build up the banks. A vertical, 4m wall of polythene was then inserted into the middle of the banks. This was done by digging out a narrow trench with an excavator, unrolling the sheeting, and back-filling (Plate 12, Figs 1, 2).

In 1988, the AWA proposed that Adventurers' Fen south of Harrisons Drove should become an emergency flood storage reservoir. In times of excessively heavy rainfall, and failure of the lode water distribution scheme to conduct water from farmland throughout the Fens, water would be allowed to spill from Wicken Lode on to Adventurers' Fen at the lowest point in the drainage system. Flooding, over a grassed spillway from Wicken Lode, would take place only if the pumps at Upware failed for 12 hours during a flood of a height expected only once in 20 years. The works were completed by the National Rivers Authority (NRA) during 1990–91 and involved the construction of a spillway on the bank of Wicken Lode.

This proposal has a number of hydrological advantages for the Fen. A new water-proof bank was created along the eastern margin of the reserve and the banks of Wicken and Burwell Lodes were strengthened. The clay for this was won from a pit at the western end of compartment 42 (see map, Appendix A). At its deepest this Borrow Pit was 10m deep, but the sides were profiled and two islands were incorporated, so providing an additional area of potentially interesting deep-water habitat. Commissioners' Drain, along the southern margin of the Fen, was moved bodily towards the Fen (and was rapidly recolonized by a rich 'ditch' flora – see Chapter 3) and other ditching works were carried out while the machinery was on site. These works have helped to compartmentalize the National Trust's property on Adventurers' Fen, allowing a certain amount of independent control of the hydrology in different compartments. This should enable different habitats to be developed in separate areas, which possibility forms the basis of the Management Committee's plans for the future of Adventurers' Fen (Chapter 13).

Clearly, the monitoring of the effects on the water-table of these major changes in the control of water on the Fen is crucial to understanding any subsequent changes in the vegetation.

MANAGEMENT IN THE FACE OF SUCCESSION

Fens are essentially unstable vegetation systems; Wicken Fen is no exception and so must be managed to remain in its present state. The steady accumulation of peat is accompanied by a succession of plant communities that is both the cause and the result of changes in the relative heights of the surface and the water-table (see Chapter 2). The succession from open water to woodland (hydrosere) that Godwin[17] described can be summarized as:

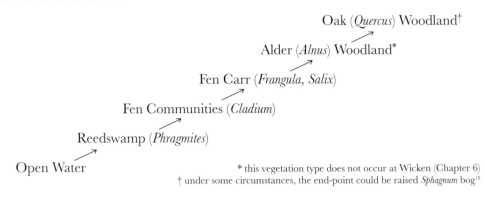

Oak (*Quercus*) Woodland[†]

Alder (*Alnus*) Woodland[*]

Fen Carr (*Frangula, Salix*)

Fen Communities (*Cladium*)

Reedswamp (*Phragmites*)

Open Water

* this vegetation type does not occur at Wicken (Chapter 6)
† under some circumstances, the end-point could be raised *Sphagnum* bog[18]

Godwin distinguished two kinds of 'fen community' and pointed out how these are associated with different management regimes: areas cut at three- or four-year intervals were dominated by sedge (*Cladium mariscus*), whilst those cut annually for 'litter' were dominated by purple moor-grass (*Molinia coerulea*) (Chapter 5). The traditional management cycles that promoted vegetational diversity lapsed in the last part of the 19th and first part of the 20th centuries, resulting in the widespread establishment of carr and a decline in diversity (Chapter 6).

The maintenance of the diversity and community structure appropriate to an East Anglian fen inevitably means that all stages in the hydrosere must be maintained simultaneously. In practice, this involves the promotion of one particular vegetation type in any one area while creating a mosaic of different types over the Fen as a whole. Which areas of the Fen are maintained as sedge or litter and which as carr are determined largely by historical patterns, but also by practical considerations, such as local variations in the height of the water-table, and, when considering the total area devoted to each vegetation type, the availability of workers and machinery.

In this section, we examine the management practices which are currently applied to maintain each stage of the hydrosere, and look at the evolution of these management regimes in the light of research and monitoring. We also consider other forms of cropping that contribute to the habitat diversity of the Fen: grazing, arable (which currently occurs on marginal land on Adventurers' Fen) and, in the past, the digging of peat ('turf').

(i) Open water

The open water habitats at Wicken fall into a number of well-defined categories: lodes, dykes and drains, meres, and ponds, all of which are artificial. The history of the Lodes and internal drainage ditches and dykes is described in Chapter 10. Of the internal waters, Drainers' Dyke alone has an important drainage function in that it carries water pumped from the lands of Spinney Abbey Farm across the Fen and into Wicken Lode. The dyke was much neglected in the early 20th century, and was said to be passable dry-shod until cleared out in 1962. The other dykes appear to have suffered a similar fate, but are now largely restored. The meres and ponds have all been created during the 20th century (Chapter 3).

The Lodes and the ditches and drains within the Fen are relatively shallow and are quickly colonized by submerged plants such as the water violet (*Hottonia palustris*) (Plate 3, Fig. 1), and by species with floating leaves such as the white and yellow water-lilies (*Nymphaea alba* and *Nuphar lutea*). These all produce material which accumulates on the bottom together with intercepted sediments and marl derived from calcium carbonate deposited on plant surfaces by photosynthesis and snail shells. Filling allows colonization by reed (*Phragmites australis*), which casts a dense shade and tends to exclude other species. Reed is very productive and material accumulates quickly beneath it; after perhaps 20 years a fen ditch will probably be passable on foot with a mat of mosses such as *Calliergon cuspidatum* beneath a sparse growth of reed.

In the early days of Trust ownership, open water does not seem to have been uppermost in the minds of those in control. The Keeper and his assistants cut the dykes and drains at least once a year and sometimes more often, but this did not prevent silting, and some of the dykes became almost dry. The River Board dredged Monks Lode in the

1920s but did not clear Wicken Lode, which was at that time too shallow for boats to pass except at times of high water – a statement which also implies that water-levels were more variable than they are now. Until the last war, clearance of the ditches and dykes on the Fen was done by hand, at times when water-levels were low, sometimes due to the Lode level being lowered by the Drainage Board to allow works to take place elsewhere.

The first mention of mechanization comes early in the Second World War; the staff had spent some time in digging out Howe's Dyke but had not finished it, and the Drainage Board was asked for the loan of a dragline, which it was unable to provide until 1949, when the work was finished in this way. Subsequently, most 'slubbing-out' (the removal of accumulated sediment) has been done mechanically, usually by an excavator with a slatted bucket, although the process of 'roding' (the cutting of vegetation at or below water-level) was done by hand. In theory, roding should check reed growth by flooding the airspaces in the submerged parts; in practice, it seems to have rather little effect. Roding has been abandoned at Wicken Fen since 1988, except in certain areas, such as the Lode at the immediate entrance to the Fen, where aesthetic considerations come into play (as a bonus, a prolonged cold spell offers the prospect of excellent fen skating on a sheet of ice uninterrupted by *Phragmites* stems).

Wicken Lode has to be kept navigable, and this has been undertaken by the NRA (now the Environment Agency). The bankside vegetation is cut in early summer, to avoid the destruction of reed warbler nests, and the submerged weeds are cut later in the season (Plate 12, Fig. 3). The vegetation in the un-navigated part of Monks Lode is also cut each summer by the NRA and the cut material piled onto Wicken Poor's Fen where it rots away. Weed cutting is justified by a need to maintain free water flow, to provide clear water for local anglers and, in navigable stretches, to allow boat passage.

There has, however, been much debate in recent years about the most desirable way of managing the reed fringing Wicken Lode. Visitors were delighted to see the reeds cut uniformly to water-level in the winter of 1993 (Plate 15, Fig. 2), and there was some feeling that this restored the vista along the Lode to its original state when a working waterway, but naturalists were alarmed at the possible effects on the aquatic fauna. The NRA agreed to co-operate in a research project in 1995, when the reeds were cut in alternate 50m stretches down both banks. The distributions of aquatic invertebrates and fish were monitored throughout the following winter and this demonstrated beyond doubt the value of standing reed as a winter refuge.[19,20] A compromise has now been reached in which reed will be cut along the southern bank, adjacent to the public footpath, but left standing on the north bank adjoining the Sedge Fen.

Wicken Lode has been dredged at intervals by the NRA and the spoil deposited on the banks where it quickly grasses over. In the past, slubbing was achieved using a drag-line, resulting in a patchy treatment that left parts of the habitat relatively undisturbed. Now it is carried out using hydraulic machinery to guidelines drawn up and agreed with the National Trust and English Nature. In October and November 1985, Wicken Lode upstream of Monks Lode was slubbed from the south bank, leaving the sediment close to the north side undisturbed. Every fifth bucket width (approximately 1.5m) of the south bank sediment was left intact. The success of this scheme in achieving improved drainage while conserving biological communities depends largely on the skill and responsiveness of the operator.

The Lode downstream of Monks Lode was dredged in the winter of 1994–95 under the watchful eye of David Aldridge, who studied the impact of the operation on the populations of mussels in the sediment (see Chapter 3). He discovered that the dredge removed at least 20 per cent of the mussels from the centre of the channel and many of those that remained were dragged across to the southern side. By marking displaced mussels, he was able to establish that they showed remarkably little tendency to redistribute themselves. It seems that the act of dredging every decade effectively fixed the pattern of mussel distribution in the Lode, even though these animals have larvae which are parasitic on fish and therefore potentially highly dispersive.[20]

Drainers' Dyke has water pumped into it from the drainage ditches of the arable lands of Spinney Abbey Farm. At some times of the year, this water is rich in nutrients (Chapter 3), and it is desirable that it should be removed from the system as soon as possible. The National Trust also has an obligation to keep up the drainage function of the Dyke. It has therefore been slubbed out about every six years since 1962, but generally only part of the length has been cut in any one year to reduce as much as possible the adverse effects on the fauna and flora.

Other dykes on the Fen have in the past been cleared at irregular intervals. To manage the entire system is extremely demanding of labour: there are more than 5km of internal waterways. It is essential to have a strategy that achieves as nearly as possible the desired effects with the expenditure of least labour and time on the part of the Wardens. It is therefore important to know exactly why ditches are managed. Open ditches conduct water into the main body of the reserve, fulfilling an important hydrological function, provide fire-breaks and sources of water for fire-fighting, and control visitor access, quite apart from maintaining the habitat, flora and fauna associated with early stages of the hydrosere. Frequent clearance may, however, reduce the habitat available for some species such as reed warblers and certain fenland invertebrates such as the beetles *Hydraena palustris* and *Dryops anglicanus*, and it is intended that some currently shallow and overgrown ditches should remain so.

How can all these, sometimes conflicting, aims be reconciled? The 1986 management plan[9] set out a scheme for ditch maintenance on a six-year cycle. Following discussions with NCC, this was increased to 10 years, as some species which had been lost from the Fen, such as frog-bit (*Hydrocharis morsus-ranae*) might return under a regime with longer maintenance intervals. It was also planned to alter the cross-sectional profile of some of the ditches. Most have almost vertical sides and a flat bottom, giving minimal area for the establishment of shallow-water rooted vegetation. An alternative shape, with a marginal step close to mean water-level and then a slope to a central deep area has been tried for the new ditches in the commercial reed-bed.

The 1992 management plan goes much further, prescribing a programme for the ditches on the reserve.[10] Some, such as parts of the old ditches along both sides of Sedge Fen Drove and the recently re-excavated North Dyke, will be left untouched to undergo succession to dryness. All the other ditches will be slubbed in short sections of no more than 50 m length, with the number of 50 m sections cleared in any one year being dictated by the length of rotation cycle and the length of the ditch. Thus, for Drainers' Dyke, which is approximately 880 m long and now on a 4-year cycle, every fourth 50m-stretch (16 in all) will be cleared every year, starting one section further along each year. Such a pattern should encourage the maximum diversity of flora and fauna while maintaining the drainage function of the dykes (Figs 67 & 68).

This scheme has two practical draw-backs. First, the healthy regrowth that this procedure promotes is the reason for clearing the channel in the first place; leaving 'islands' from which the flora and fauna can recolonize increases the frequency of treatment needed. Secondly, it is expensive to bring in the necessary machinery on an annual basis to slub a few short sections; it makes far better economic sense to hire plant opportunistically, whenever money is available, and then do as much as possible at a time.

However, these economic objections were outweighed by ecological considerations and the ditching programme began in earnest in the winter of 1991–92. The work is now contracted out locally, funded by grant aid, which frees the wardening staff from this difficult task and avoids the need for the Fen to invest in the very expensive machinery required. The programme will be reviewed for the 1998 management plan in the light of recent research on ditch recolonization (see Chapter 3).

Reed encroachment is also a major problem on the Mere. Here, this has been dealt with by spraying with Dalapon in July, followed by roding out the dead material, or

Figure 67 Cross Dyke, from the east, slubbed out in alternate 50m stretches, January 1993

Figure 68   Malcarse Drain, looking north from its junction with Cross Dyke,
before and after reed-cutting, autumn 1993

cutting it when the Mere is frozen. Dalapon has very low toxicity to animals of all kinds and no problems have been experienced with its use. Where pond margins are accessible to cattle, their grazing seems to control reed.

The ponds in the disused brickpits are, because of their deep, steep-sided construction, less prone to reed invasion. They are also cut off from potential sources of pollution and enrichment (Chapter 3). Little practical management has therefore proved necessary. Indeed, the appearance of the Main Brickpit has changed rather little over sixty years (see Fig. 7, Chapter 3). The smaller ponds by the windpump, however, rapidly fill with *Phragmites* and sediment and are slubbed out as necessary, returning some of the dredged material to provide a nucleus for re-establishment of plant and animal populations.

The present programme of slubbing would seem to be adequate to maintain the drainage and navigation functions of the ditches, drains and lodes. Active ditch-management has led to a considerable increase in the amount of open-water habitat on the Fen in recent years. The planned rotation cycle should allow both early and late stages of the hydrosere, and every transitional phase in-between, to persist simultaneously on the Fen.

It is now easier to bring water into, and distribute it around, the Fen. Open water in a ditch will stabilize the water-table in the surrounding peat (Chapter 2), and so the conduction of water into the Fen is hydrologically a good thing. But the biological implications are more complex. The case of Gardiner's Ditch, which penetrates the very heart of the Sedge Fen, has been the subject of intense debate by the Management Committee and the source of tension between members whose sympathies lie with terrestrial habitats on one hand and freshwater communities on the other. If left unmanaged, the water-level in Gardiner's Ditch fluctuates seasonally by over a metre, from over-brimming in a wet winter to almost complete dryness in a long, hot summer. Those concerned with the maintenance of wet fen vegetation, and therefore high water-tables, would argue that water should be let into Gardiner's Ditch from either Drainers' Dyke or the Windpump Ditch in periods of drought. Freshwater biologists have generally opposed such action. Although letting in water undoubtedly would save the least drought-tolerant of the ditch's aquatic species, it appears that fluctuating water-levels may be partly responsible for the luxuriant growth of certain notable elements of the ditch flora, the charophytes and the genetically diverse population of fen pondweed (*Potamogeton coloratus*).[21] Furthermore, it is inevitable that the transfer of water will be accompanied by the transfer of dissolved organic and inorganic substances, small animals and plants. The aquatic communities of Gardiner's Ditch are distinctly different from those of both Drainers' Dyke and the Windpump Ditch, and the latter two ditches are known to be vulnerable to pollution from outside the Fen (Chapter 3), so adulteration from either source would appear to be undesirable. Such an apparently simple matter as opening the sluice between two ditches can produce the most difficult management dilemma.

(ii) Reed-beds

Reed was not cut on a large scale at Wicken Fen until the 1950s, but is now harvested commercially over a large part of Adventurers' Fen. The history of the changes in attitudes towards reed cropping and changes in practice at Wicken are discussed in Chapter 4. In summary, the transition from small-scale cutting along the dykes (which was principally aimed at dyke management) to large-scale harvesting of the Adventurers' Fen reedswamp was stimulated by financial considerations: the reed crop generated much-needed income for the reserve. Since then, the conflict between commercial cropping and the conservation of the reedswamp fauna has become a major concern. This has largely been resolved since 1963 by the setting aside of the area around the Mere and, more recently, of a large block of the commercial field as 'conservation' reed-bed (see Fig. 14, Chapter 4).

The timing of the harvest is constrained by a combination of biological and commercial considerations (Chapter 4). Thatchers require a clean and uniform product. The culms must be dead and dry, and the leaves must have fallen. This combination is produced by hard frost in autumn, followed by gales to detach the leaves. The crop is then ready for cutting between January and March. After this, growth will begin in warm springs, and the field must be flooded to protect the shoots from frost, and water must continue to be run on to the field during the summer to satisfy the considerable water requirement of the crop.

The demand for a uniform crop also means that an annual cut is desirable to give a crop of a single age. The depth and duration of flooding is also critical to the quality of the reed. Plants standing in permanent water tend to root and develop algal coatings above soil-level and may rot at the base of the stem, none of which is popular with thatchers. On the other hand, flooding helps to suppress weedy herbs and shrubs.

Flooding of the main reed-beds is achieved by allowing winter water-levels to build up on the Mere side of Harrison's Drove and then allowing this to spill across on to the reed-beds immediately after the harvest. In the 1970s, larger pipes were installed under Harrison's Drove to speed up this operation. More recently, there have been some difficulties in guaranteeing a high enough water-table. The dry summers of 1989, 1990 and 1995 have demonstrated clear shortcomings in the degree of control, despite major earthworks carried out by the AWA as part of the emergency flood reservoir scheme. Part of the project involved the excavation of a new waterproof bank and sluice control immediately downstream of the conservation reed-bed, which means that in theory the whole area can be surrounded by water, thus raising the water-table upstream. Further downstream, this part of the nature reserve has been isolated from local Internal Drainage Board dykes by the installation of a heavy duty control valve. The problem is no longer one of losing water out of the system by drainage or seepage, but rather one of not being able to get enough in the first place. A more direct and larger inflow is necessary to complete the system. This is likely to be achieved as part of the development of Adventurers' Fen and Priory Farm (see Chapter 13): a new inlet is planned from the Lode directly on to the area adjacent to the reed-beds where it will be stored for controlled release. The area around the Mere would then become an independent hydrological unit which could also be used for storing winter water.

The past ten years have seen a number of innovations in reed harvesting methods employed at Wicken. These were initially intended to increase the profitability of the operation by speeding up the cutting and handling of the crop, or adjusting the size of the bundles produced. Each modification has subsequently proved successful, and even though it may have involved investment in new equipment, this was quickly shown to have been worthwhile.

Perhaps the most significant change has been the reduction of the time and physical effort expended by the wardening staff on the harvest. This has partly come about through mechanization, but also because parts of the task are now carried out by employees of a firm of thatchers who work alongside the Fen staff.

The crop is currently cut using an Olympia rice harvester, which is easily operated by one person who walks behind (Plate 13, Fig. 1). The machine has a relatively long cutter-bar and bundles and ties the cut reed automatically. Once cut, the reeds are loaded on to a tracked low ground-pressure vehicle, and moved off the reed-beds to the bank of Wicken Lode for cleaning and tying. This is done mechanically and is carried out by the thatchers. It involves the combing out of short, broken reeds and other undesirable plant material, followed by tying up the cleaned reeds to form a standard-sized bundle. The reed bundles can then be transported by fen boat to the village end of Wicken Lode (Plate 13, Fig. 2) where they are built into a traditional reedstack to await collection by the thatcher.

The reed harvest is now a fairly minor part of the Wardens' working year (see Appendix B) and, whereas previously it had dominated nearly a quarter of the year, a number of different tasks can now been accommodated between January and March. However, the cutting operation itself remains entirely in the hands of the National Trust staff, so that it can be controlled in such a way as to diminish any possible conflict between conservation and commercial considerations.

The resolution of the conservation versus cropping problem has largely come from another change in policy: the introduction of entry fees for visitors and additional financial support from the National Trust resulting from the rise in visitor numbers (see p. 249) have removed the need to raise funds through the sale of crops. It is therefore now possible to concentrate more on the conservation potential of Adventurers' Fen, and to make plans for its further development as a wetland reserve.

The distinctive fauna of the reed-beds is of considerable interest. The special birds of the reed-fields are described in detail in Chapter 9.4 and some of the reed invertebrates in Chapter 4. Some features of the management of the reed-beds are designed specifically with birds in mind and the planned expansion of this habitat type across the low-lying southern fringe of the reserve (Chapter 13) is likely greatly to increase the area of uncropped and relatively undisturbed habitat available to reedswamp species.

(iii) Sedge

Sedge (*Cladium mariscus*) harvested from the Fen is now sold exclusively for thatching, where its flexibility allows it to be used for roof ridges; in the past it was extensively used as fuel and animal bedding (Chapter 10). Formerly it was also used to thatch entire roofs, and the outhouses of the fen cottage have been restored in this way (Chapter 12). The area of sedge-fields at Wicken Fen had declined steadily from 1920 to a minimum of about 2.5ha before the restoration of the sedge-fields by clearance of carr began in the early 1950s. The present sedge harvest is taken from several fields on the Sedge Fen and a small part of Verrall's Fen (Fig. 69), a total of 8.7ha (see Plate 12 , Fig. 4).

The life-history of sedge, and in particular the life-expectancy of its leaves, undoubtedly shaped the evolution of the historic management regime of mowing every four years (Chapters 5 & 10). However, this was changed to a three-year cycle, probably in the 1930s, perhaps to produce a better quality crop. Thatchers require flexible material that has been cut green and dried; sedge which is already brown when cut is brittle and of little use. The restoration of the traditional four-year cropping cycle on ecological grounds in the 1980s increased the proportion of unusable material, and there have been minor grumbles about quality from the thatchers.

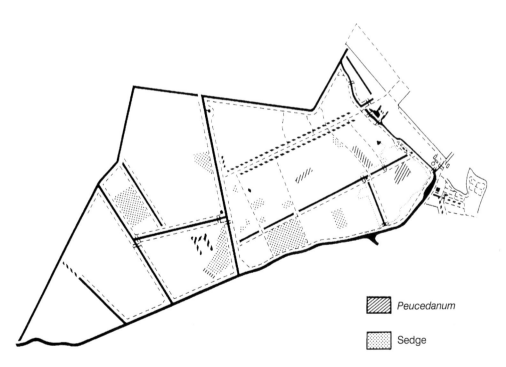

Peucedanum

Sedge

Figure 69   The sedge fields and areas cut specifically to encourage growth of milk-parsley (*Peucedanum palustre*)[10]

233

The sedge crop is cut at Wicken Fen by machine and gathered up with a long-handled four-tined fork (see Fig. 64). It is then sorted before being tied into 'yealms'. Until 1991, each yealm consisted of two halves, one with the butts to the left, the other to the right; this 'double yealm' was unique to Wicken. It has been replaced by the single yealm, which is quicker to produce, but more awkward to transport. The bundles are stacked to dry in the field before being carted off to stacks in Lode Lane. The Fen is probably the largest producer of sedge in Britain; the crop is on average worth about £3,000 per annum (Table XV). Demand for sedge for thatching has varied over the past few years, but in most years there has been a ready market; only when two bumper harvests occur in succession (as in 1995–96) do problems arise in disposing of the crop.

The timing of the cut has been a subject of considerable deliberation, but is now reasonably well established. Godwin[5] believed that the traditional time for cutting was during the winter, and this practice was followed till quite recently, in spite of Conway's work in the 1930s[22] that had shown that cutting late in the season, too close to autumnal frosts and rises in water-level, could kill or weaken the plant.

By 1948, sedge cutting was being carried out piecemeal as required: in 1950, some sedge was cut in every month except October.[12] In the 1960s, the sedge harvest tended to begin in July and continue right through to November or December.[2] At this time, the income generated by natural fen products was of great concern to the Management Committee, but *Cladium* seemed to be in decline throughout the 1960s and 1970s. This was generally attributed to a lack of water at critical periods, and much effort was expended in pumping water on to the sedge-fields. However, Rowell[12] has shown convincingly that cutting had formerly taken place early in the year, between April and July, and not, as was currently the practice, at the end of the year (Chapter 10). Plants cut in spring and summer regrow rapidly, while those cut during

Table XV. The Sedge Harvest

Year	Yealms*	Price per yealm (£)	Income (£)
1983	2,700	0.80	2,160.00
1984	2,622	0.85	2,228.70
1985	2,250	0.90	2,025.00
1986	510	0.95	484.50
1987	1,877	1.00	1,877.00
1988	1,700	1.25	2,125.00
1989	1,088	1.40	1,523.20
1990	2,591	1.50	3,886.50
1991	3,540	0.85	3,009.00
1992	3,080	0.90	2,772.00
1993	2,710	0.90	2,439.00
1994	1,684	1.00	1,684.00
1995	4,383	1.10	4,821.30
1996	4,215	1.20	5,058.00

* in 1991, the 'double yealm' was replaced by the standard 'single yealm'

the autumn and winter do so very poorly if at all. In the light of these observations and experiments, the sedge harvest is now completed by the end of July.

The early summer harvest has the disadvantage that some birds' nests are inevitably destroyed, and these may include the nests of uncommon species, such as the grasshopper warbler. However, only a very small proportion of the total nesting habitat is cut each year, as part of the strict rotational cropping scheme laid down in the management plan. Each sedge-field on the Fen is cropped every third year, and different fields are cropped each year, so that a mosaic of different-aged sedge stands is maintained.

Summer cutting has another distinct advantage in that it favours the growth of milk-parsley (*Peucedanum palustre*) among the sedge (Chapter 5). By the 1990s, milk-parsley was absent from many of the present sedge-fields and reintroduction by scattering seeds has been attempted. This experiment has proved rather successful, and young milk-parsley plants have established themselves in quite large numbers.

The growth of *Peucedanum* in some of its existing sites on the Fen also improved dramatically during the 1990s;[23] although the plant's performance appears to be correlated with the wetness of the Fen, the sedge-cutting regime has also changed and may have contributed to the initial recovery. Some areas of the Sedge Fen are now deemed to have milk-parsley in sufficient quantities to warrant the reintroduction of the swallowtail (Chapter 8). Since 1992, some areas of the sedge-fields have been managed specifically for *Peucedanum* and the butterfly: a patchwork of different-aged stands is being maintained so that milk-parsley of a suitable size will be available every year, and the cut is being timed to avoid destruction of the butterfly's eggs and larvae.

This example has several lessons. There is a tendency to assume that looking after a habitat will ensure the survival of its component species, but the reduction of the habitat below a critical area, as seems to have happened with the sedge-fields, may jeopardize species which are at the edge of their natural range. Even when we know a good deal about the ecology of the species concerned, we do not necessarily know the exact management practices needed to maintain ideal conditions. It also shows the danger of a failure to monitor critical species. Regular monitoring of *Peucedanum palustre* in the inter-war years would certainly have demonstrated its decline, but not enough was then known for any informed attempt to be made to reverse the trend.

(iv) Litter

The litter-fields are dominated by grasses with a species-rich mixture of dicotyledonous herbs (Chapter 5), which together form the traditional litter crop. The balance between sedge and litter as the dominant vegetation of the open fields at Wicken Fen is largely determined by the frequency of cutting; longer cycles of three to four years favour sedge (see above) while annual or biennial cycles favour litter. Those areas of litter which are presumed to derive from a history of annual mowing are dominated by purple moor-grass (*Molinia caerulea*), while the areas regained by clearance of carr in the last forty years tend to be dominated by other grasses, particularly *Calamagrostis* species.

In the late 1930s, about 16 acres (6.5ha) were cut for litter, and a contemporary man-agement plan suggested that the total area cut should be increased to 70–80 ha.[24] However, the War intervened and, by the 1960s, the area of litter had fallen to 2.8ha or less. The clearance of carr since then has increased the extent of litter to about 24ha, of which at least 12ha are cropped annually. In spite of the partial mechaniza-tion of the harvest, the management of litter now creates a heavy work load for the Fen staff and there are sometimes difficulties in finishing the late summer/autumn crop, especially in wet conditions. Although further clearance of carr may be desirable on ecological grounds, it has to be weighed against the extra annual litter-cutting burden it would place on the staff.

Litter was formerly cut using a scythe, but is now cut with a tractor-mounted hay cutter; it may still be carried off by hand. As a consequence of the decline in demand for litter, there is now a considerable problem of what to do with the crop. The cut material is either stacked in areas cut into the carr and left to rot, or heaped and burned (Plate 13, Fig. 3). Straw-burning legislation does not apply to the burning of small amounts of litter. However, there is a certain danger in doing this. In 1980, the standing litter in compartment 5 was burned, but the fire got out of control and spread across Cross Dyke into compartment 3; much of the northern third of compartment 5 was burned out, much carr killed and the sedge crop lost. In 1991, a still smouldering litter heap ignited hours after the fire was extinguished and set fire to the carr in com-partment 4 (see Chapter 6).

Other ways of disposing of the litter crop are being investigated. In 1985, 1,800 bales were gathered and used on the National Trust's farm at Wimpole Hall. Material cut late in the year has a low nutritional value, but litter cut earlier, while still green, may be acceptable as organic hay if it can be dried, baled and carried off. The Fen staff are also looking into the possibility of composting the cuttings.

In the first part of this century, the crop was principally taken in autumn and winter, although Ennion[25] mentions a July cut on Adventurers' Fen. However, Rowell[12] has established that much of the cutting was done much earlier in the past, and further research showed that cutting in May or July increased the proportion of dicotyledons in the sward (Chapter 5). As a result, some small patches are now cut in May and large areas are cut in July; a few patches are left to be cut in September–October.

Most of the litter at Wicken is cut annually, but some areas are now cut every other year and others in two years out of three. With the three periods of cutting, this pro-duces nine different permutations (Fig. 70). While there can be little doubt that this produces diversity, a programme of monitoring is needed to see exactly what the long-term effects of these different mowing regimes are. In the summer of 1992, the first steps were taken to establish a system to monitor the abundance of a relatively small number of species that may be sensitive to the effects of management. It should ideally be accompanied by studies of the fauna inhabiting the litter-fields; further research on the small mammals of the Fen, or on plant-feeding insects, may be partic-ularly fruitful.

(a)

(b)

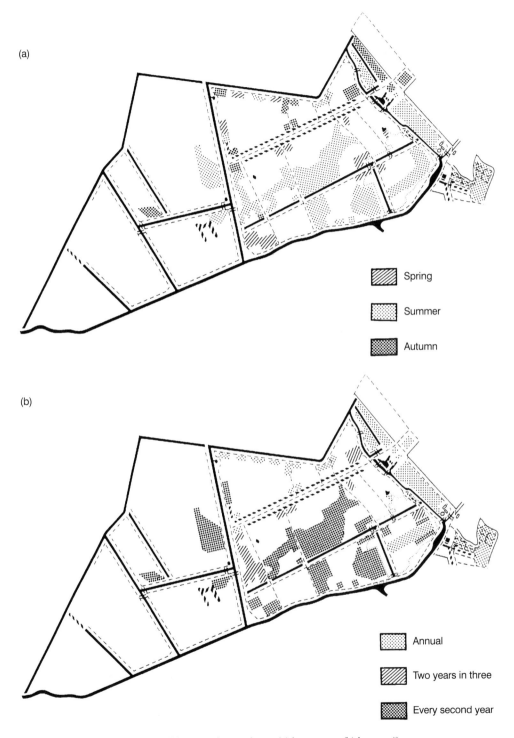

Spring

Summer

Autumn

Annual

Two years in three

Every second year

Figure 70 Litter cutting regimes: (a) by season; (b) by year[10]

(v) Droves

The droves on the Sedge Fen have two main roles: they provide access routes for the public and for Fen staff and machinery, but they also provide habitats for various plants and animals which do not occur elsewhere. Successful drove management should meet both needs; indeed, if a varied flora and fauna is maintained along the droves, visitors are content to stay on the paths rather than wandering off into the fields or the carr.

The typical Wicken drove is 5–10m wide and usually straight, passable by tractor when dry enough, and usually has a regularly-cut portion in the centre for walking, and margins that are cut less often.

The fen archive contains no detailed records of drove management before 1928. From around 1928 to 1948, two cuts were made each year with a scythe, the second cut being delayed until most flowering was finished, and the cut material was removed. By 1948 this pattern had been slightly modified to give a central strip cut in June or July, and a broader swathe, including the central strip, which was cut in the autumn and the cut material removed.

In 1949, a motorized Allen scythe replaced the traditional scything method. From this point till 1955 three cuts were made annually, in June, July, and August–October. The frequency of cutting increased still further till 1978 and the first cut was taken earlier (April–May). The frequency of cutting of the central strip depended on usage, with the most-used paths on the Sedge Fen being cut every 2–4 weeks (5–8 cuts per year) and less-used paths on Verrall's and St Edmund's Fens cut 2–4 times each year.

The frequency has now been reduced so that the pattern closely resembles the 1928–48 regime, except that the central strips of the most heavily-used routes (about 3km) are mown as required, every two to four weeks during the growing season. The reduction was made partly because of the considerable demands the work made on the staff, but also because there was a feeling that the Fen was acquiring too regimented an appearance. On most of the routes, the central strips are cut once or twice a year, and the whole width is cut in the autumn and the material carried off. The central strips are now mown using a rear-mounted Twose rotary flail cutter mounted on the Kubota mini-tractor, and with this combination the entire network of paths and droves can be cut in one day. There are about 10km of droves on the Sedge Fen (including Verrall's Fen) and at least 1.7km on St Edmund's Fen.

At certain times of the year, usually in the spring, some of the paths on the Fen become over-used and break up to give a very muddy surface. This has been largely overcome by encouraging visitors to use the peripheral nature trail in critical periods (see below), and by providing duckboards at vulnerable points. At the same time, the droves in the central part of the Sedge Fen are closed off with string barriers. The public is informed of the state of the paths and of any closures by a notice in the car-park. The closure of the centre of the Fen also lessens the disturbance of breeding birds. However, Sedge Fen Drove cannot be closed as it is a public bridleway; it becomes extremely wet and muddy and is sometimes impassable even in late May except in Wellington boots. Warning notices are placed at each end, but many visitors find themselves mired and muddied or forced to turn back (see Plate 2, Fig. 3).

At times the paths need to be repaired. This is done using materials from the Fen itself: stick walkways are laid and turves, if used to fill holes, are cut from close to the site. The opening of the boardwalk (see below) in 1987 has greatly relieved the pressure of visitor access on the droves. Indeed, the Fen staff now find that the vegetation on some of the principal droves, no longer kept in check by trampling, requires cutting more frequently than before.

(vi) Carr

The history of carr management at Wicken Fen is a story of a continuous battle against the relentless progress of succession. That sedge- and litter-fields would be colonized by carr if left uncut seems to have become obvious early in the Trust's ownership of the Fen, and clearance of scrub soon became a priority in management. In 1926, the Annual Report stated that 'The bushes have been removed and the overgrowth cleared from a considerable area', and in 1927, the Committee viewed 'with grave misgivings the overgrowth of parts of the Fen with bushes' but was 'quite unable on the funds at their disposal .... to clear further areas'. Indeed, the relentless encroachment by carr progressed to such an extent that St Edmund's Fen was 'almost waste'.[2]

At the 1927 Annual Meeting, thanks were expressed to Professor Gardiner 'for the clearances which he had undertaken in Aspland's Piece (compartment 18; see map, Appendix A) by Wicken Lode. Gardiner also paid for the clearance of the long drove parallel to Sedge Fen Drove and Wicken Lode which now bears his name. A cross ride was also cut through the carr from Sedge Fen Drove to Wicken Lode (this is the present Thomson's Drove). The other two cross droves, Verrall's and Christy's, were also cut at this time. When Milner-White's Piece (compartment 19) was bought and presented to the Trust in 1926, Milner-White also gave money for scrub clearance. All these extra payments were used to hire extra labour to assist the Barnes family with the work.

The Annual Report of 1936/37 shows that all cutting had been abandoned in St Edmund's Fen, and 'spreading ash grove' had become established in the centre. Wicken Poor's Fen was 'gradually becoming bushy', and on the Sedge Fen bushes were gaining ground. Various methods for control had been considered; raising the water-level was impractical, and it was felt that only greatly increased expenditure on hand clearance would be satisfactory. A 5-year management scheme[24] was put forward involving extra expenditure of £300 each year on bush clearance. In the following year, the Pilgrim Trust, Cambridge University and the Royal Society all made grants towards this.

Following the outbreak of war in 1939, the harvesting of alder buckthorn by the Forestry Commission for use in charcoal manufacture began – it was found to be ideal for making bomb fuses – and appeared at first sight to be doing the job of bush clearance that the Committee had always wished for. The crop would even generate cash (£10 per ton) and the labour would be free. That the harvesting of *Frangula* could be used as a political tool emerges from the Committee minutes at this time: an attempt to requisition Adventurers' Fen for bombing practice was resisted partly on the grounds that this was an area valuable for the production of charcoal, and it was even suggested that *Frangula* be planted.

This project proved to have little lasting effect on shrub cover on the Fen. The *Frangula* was only cut, and the stumps that remained in the ground were capable of rapid regrowth. The reduction of the Fen staff to just two, following the call-up of Wilfred and William Barnes, led to an even greater backlog of work and to a further increase in bush cover.

After the War, trials were carried out on clearance by controlled burning, which although successful, were not pursued. The large fire on 31 May 1951 (which burned out almost the whole area bounded by Thomson's Drove, Gardiner's Drove, Drainers' Dyke, and Wicken Lode), probably brought home to the Committee the potential danger of such practices to the Fen as a whole, although the cause of this particular fire was thought to have been a discarded cigarette.

When S. M. Walters wrote the 1956 management plan,[7] he envisaged 50–60 acres of sedge-fields, but by October 1958 he had to report that this was 'still far from being realised'. Such was the scale of the problem that he clearly felt that the only way forward was 'to negotiate an agreement with the Nature Conservancy whereby the management of the reserve became the Conservancy's responsibility'. These negotiations came to nothing. In spite of the evident despair felt by the Committee at the deteriorating state of the Fen, the next few years proved to mark an upturn in the Fen's circumstances.

In 1958, A. S. Watt suggested that the Committee should look into the possibility of using chemical methods for bush control. This was not taken up at the time, but in 1961 N. W. Moore proposed a trial of bush clearance by the herbicide Spontox (the active ingredients of which are 2,4-D and 2,4,5-T), including detailed studies of its effects on the fen flora and soil fauna.[26] The experiment appears to have been a success; there was no obvious effect on the soil fauna, and no differences in the herbaceous vegetation between areas cleared by digging and by herbicide. Chemical residues were no longer detectable in the soil after six months. However, herbicide was never used on a large scale because even if the shrubs were killed, there was still a need to dig out the stumps to allow easy cutting and to avoid damage to tractor tyres.

The use of voluntary groups to clear scrub on the Fen began in 1960 with a camp of the Conservation Corps of the Council for Nature The camp was visited by HRH the Duke of Edinburgh in July of that year (Fig. 71). The use of voluntary labour was extended greatly by an arrangement with HMS Ganges, a Naval Training Establishment in Ipswich, started in 1964 and agreed by the Committee in spite of reservations about the amount of noise likely to be made by 30 or 40 young sailors. They constructed their own accommodation hut (named in their honour the 'Ganges Hut'), which was opened in 1965. They, the Acorn Camps of the National Trust, and the Conservation Corps, have been largely responsible for carr clearance on a heroic scale (Plate 14, Fig. 1).

Figure 71 HRH The Duke of Edinburgh's visit to Wicken Fen on 8 July 1960: (above) meeting (from left to right) Wilfred, William and Henry Barnes, near the site of the Tower Hide; (below) questioning members of the Conservation Corps during the clearance of Milner White's piece. With the Duke are (from left to right) Pam Nichols and Michael Chinery (two volunteers), E. F. Lousley, a well-known botanist, and Brigadier E. F. E. Armstrong, in charge of the operation. Michael Chinery, now author of best-selling natural history field guides, returned to the Fen in 1995 as a volunteer in the education programme.

Scrub clearance continues today, but at a very much reduced rate. Clearance is labour-intensive; not only must all the scrub be cut, but the stumps must also be dug out, and all the residue stacked and burned when it is safe to do so. Some idea of the degree of difficulty presented by such a task can be gained from Alan Bloom's account of clearing Adventurers' Fen in the 1940s[27] and from the film he made of his endeavours.[28] In the last ten years, clearance of some areas has potentially become easier because of the disease which has killed large areas of *Frangula* (see Chapter 6); this dead carr burns readily, so that controlled fires may prove useful if further clearance is desired. However, even though the Fen is still far short of Walters' ideal of 50–60 acres (*c.* 28–34ha) of sedge (about 8.7ha are cropped at present), there is little enthusiasm for further large-scale scrub clearance. Once areas are cleared, they must be cropped regularly, and there is insufficient labour available to sustain this increased effort.

Now that the Management Committee is at last reconciled to the practical limitations of carr clearance, it is perhaps time to adopt a more positive attitude to this habitat on the Fen. The carr has undergone catastrophic declines in this century (Chapter 6) with the result that much of the carr consists of even-aged stands. The present management plan includes a scheme to diversify the carr by cutting, but not clearing, some areas which would be allowed to regenerate naturally, so creating a range of age among the shrubs.

(vii) Trees and woodland

Some of the trees on the Fen seem genuinely to represent a final stage in succession, but others are clearly planted (see Chapter 6). Although the general policy in recent years has tended to oppose the maturation of carr into woodland, there is a case to be made for allowing the process to run its course in some areas. The ash woodland developing on St Edmund's Fen (and its associated fern flora) was of sufficient interest to the Committee in the 1970s for a survey of the area[29] to be commissioned. On the Sedge Fen, however, the development of areas of large birch trees has been a cause for concern to successive Botanical Secretaries. The invasive nature of birch and the ecological consequences represent only one facet of the problem: the presence of clumps of large trees in an area of otherwise quite low vegetation has a considerable impact on the landscape. As a first step towards assessing the extent of this problem and its likely future course, an inventory of trees in different size classes on the Fen is needed.

A need for tree cover occasionally arises that cannot be met in the short term by natural colonization or regeneration. For example, *Salix alba* cuttings from local stock were planted to create a quick screen between visitors and the Mere in the late 1980s. Planting has also been used to create woodland on marginal land at the north-east corner of the Fen.

Any suggestion that trees should be planted on the reserve provokes a good deal of discussion in the Management Committee, even when the species involved are typical of the habitat and may already occur on the Fen. The planting of non-native species, or even British species from other types of habitat, has come to be regarded as completely unacceptable. However, suggestions for 'improving' the Fen's range of habitats for various animal groups by planting particular species of trees have arisen many times during the history of the reserve and occasionally do so today. The Committee minutes record the successful action by the botanist Harry Godwin in the 1920s to fend off proposals by entomologists to plant *Buddleia davidii* as a nectar source for butterflies (although a few bushes were later planted at the entrance to the reserve). A plan to plant poplars on Adventurers' Fen in the 1970s was averted only after the choice of species was questioned. In the 1990s, the fashion for planting poplars in East Anglia to encourage golden oriole (*Oriolus oriolus*) appealed to some of the more ornithologically-minded members of the Committee, but the introduction of the tree to the Fen was vetoed by the botanists.

As on any National Trust property, the trees on the Fen have to be managed with public safety in mind; the health of the trees themselves is a secondary concern, but this is perhaps reasonable in a wet fenland nature reserve. Many of the trees on the Fen are dying, which may be linked to a rise in the water-table and some, such as those along the boardwalk trail, have become a possible danger to the public. A number of these dead or dying trees have been felled. However, dead trees also provide valuable habitat for many insects and birds and over much of the Fen where the public never penetrates they are left standing. Dead wood is also a valuable habitat for invertebrates (Chapter 8) and a proportion of the timber cleared during tree work is left stacked and allowed to rot.

For living trees, pollarding is favoured; it is a traditional management method which prolongs the life of the tree and produces a useful crop. The large *Salix alba* specimens on and around the Fen are pollarded as necessary to conserve the trees and ensure public safety. Priority is given to trees that have been pollarded in the past and those close to paths. The line of very tall *S. alba* that forms the southern boundary of the Education Area became a safety concern when the new pond-dipping ponds were excavated in 1991 (Chapter 12). This case illustrates well the problems involved in finding the optimum management plan for a site that has many varied qualities and uses. The safety of the children using the area must be safeguarded, but the old pollards are excellent habitats for invertebrates (particularly flies), they are an important feature in the landscape, and they form part of the immediate environment of the bird-ringers' constant-effort net site in St Edmund's Fen (see Chapter 9.2). The well-being of the trees themselves must also be considered. Overhanging and patently dangerous branches have been removed, and then one tree at a time will be pollarded, possibly over a period of decades. A similar programme of rotation pollarding, removing one limb at a time, will be applied to other large and decrepit pollards on the Fen, notably those along Little Drove on Adventurers' Fen, and the bay willows (*S. pentandra*) at the north-east corner of the Fen.

(viii) Turf-digging

Peat has been an important crop at Wicken in the past (Chapter 10), but turf-digging on a large scale ceased in the early part of this century. The idea of exploiting the peat resources of Adventurers' Fen occurred to the Committee as a means of relieving the chronic shortage of funds at the end of the Second World War: enquiries were made about selling peat to Humex Products Ltd., and 'skilled labour for peat cutting' was discovered in Burwell.[2] However, as Godwin pointed out, the peat was likely to be of little commercial value and, as the Fen's financial situation improved after the War, interest in the scheme faded.

Turf-digging on the reserve has assumed a number of roles related to nature conservation. In the late 1930s, Barnes' Mere was cut to encourage birds (Chapter 9.1). In the 1950s, diggings were made in compartment 19, which rapidly produced the rare charophyte *Nitella tenuissima*.[30] In the 1970s, some turf was extracted just outside the William Thorpe Building and used to create the fen display in the Cambridge Botanic Garden.

The present management plan recognizes the importance of reinstating limited turf-diggings on the Fen. The first reason for doing so concerns the distinctive habitat created by removing the peat surface and piling the 'top' adjacent to the trench. This traditional way of working produced the characteristic ridge-and-furrow topography still to be seen as shallow surface features on the Fen. By bringing the peat surfaces in the trench and the heap far below and above the water-table respectively, the chemistry of the peat and the water will be dramatically changed (Chapter 2). Local strips of leached and acidified habitat may be created.

It is hoped that the digging of the pits may stimulate the germination of plant propagules lying dormant in the peat. Writing in 1845, Jenyns noted that the community of macrophytes typically emerging in local turf pits was rich and profuse, and included *Chara hispida*, *C. gracilis*, *Utricularia vulgaris*, *Nymphaea alba*, *Potamogeton* spp., *Sagittaria sagittifolia* and *Baldellia ranunculoides*.[31] Some plant species which have been lost from the Fen or are declining might possibly be restored by a resumption of turf-digging (see, for example, *Viola persicifolia*, Chapter 7), but the loss of certain invertebrates associated with acid waters can probably now be rectified only by reintroduction (Chapters 8 & 12).

A second reason for reinstating turf-digging would be to revive and maintain a traditional activity. In the summer of 1989, a series of small turf-diggings were made, using traditional tools, parallel with old diggings in compartment 18. However, turf-digging on a somewhat larger scale is again being contemplated by the Committee as a means of maintaining wet fen habitats in the heart of the Sedge Fen by lowering the peat surface.

(ix) Grazing and arable land

For at least the last fifty years, the area south of Wicken Lode (Adventurers' Fen) has been thought of as inferior in quality to the Sedge and Verrall's Fens. It has certainly had a much more chequered history: several attempts to drain the land had been made from 1651 onwards, and turf-digging had occurred here on a large scale (Chapter 10). Most of the National Trust holdings on Adventurers' Fen were acquired between 1920 and 1930 (see Fig. 81, p. 278); some idea of the landscape at this time can be gained from the works of Bloom[27] and Ennion,[25] although the latter actually describes 'South Adventurers' Fen', the land to the south of Burwell Lode. By 1936, it was estimated that the Trust's land on Adventurers' Fen consisted of 150 acres of litter (half of it with extensive bush); 40 acres of carr; 20 acres of reed; and 40 acres of grazing land.[24]

During the Second World War, much of this land was requisitioned by the County Agricultural Executive Committee, and was drained, cleared and cultivated. The story of this has been told from the tenant's point of view by the farmer, Alan Bloom.[27] However, on 12 November 1940, the Management Committee were informed that Bomber Command wished to take over a circular area of 155 acres, centred to the south-east of the present Mere, for bombing and machine-gun practice. This was strenuously and successfully resisted, with Professor A.V. Hill, then Secretary of the Royal Society, taking a leading role.

At first the requisition order for agriculture was resisted; the area carried some *Frangula*, and was seen as a buffer zone to the Fen. It was also (although this does not appear to have been used as an objection) the site where the large copper butterfly had been successfully reintroduced. The harvesting of *Frangula* for the war effort staved off the threat for a few years. However, in the prevailing climate of opinion, resistance was useless, and clearance and drainage began in 1941.

It was difficult work. First, the land had to be drained and, as Bloom ruefully observed 'The National Trust had done the job of making a swamp very thoroughly. Not a drop of water which could have run away into the drainage system was allowed to do so'. For Bloom, the 'reclamation' of the National Trust land held the key to the drainage of his own land to the south-east, with which he had been struggling since 1939 (Fig. 72). Secondly, reeds and carr had to be cleared: Rothschild's '30 acres' was an 'impenetrable mass of bushes' and, for Bloom, the '*pièce de resistance*, the bogey of Adventurers' Fen'. The clearance of above-ground vegetation from this one piece of land took thirty men and three women a whole month, and the grubbing out of the stumps a further four months. Perhaps the greatest hindrance, however, were the bog-oaks, some over 100 feet long that lay just below the surface of the peat and prevented ploughing. These were set about with saws and explosives and finally dragged out by tractor.[28] The scale of the problem may be judged by the results: 'by the end of the month, we had a heap over 200 yards long, five yards wide and eight feet high in places, all from eighteen acres of land'. Finally, crops could be planted, and potatoes, sugar beet and wheat were grown, but yields were low due to the difficulty of controlling the water-level (Fig. 73).

The future of the land after the war was soon under consideration; Bloom's frustration at hearing that the Trust would allow it to revert after all his effort at clearance was understandable. The attitudes and ambitions of the National Trust and scientists on one hand and the farmer on the other were diametrically opposed and irreconcilable. Encountering a botanist on Adventurers' Fen, who ventured the opinion that it was 'such a pity that such a place... should have to be destroyed' and that it would 'take years to grow up again into its natural state', Bloom was taken aback:

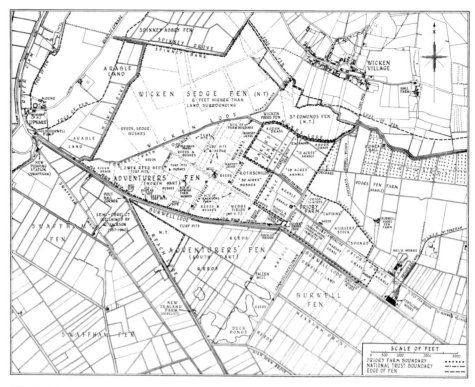

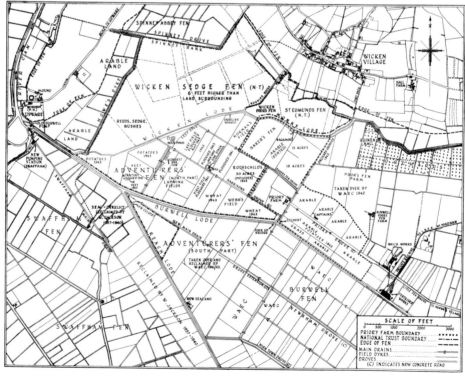

(a)

(b)

(c)

(d)

Figure 73 Reclaiming Adventurers' Fen: (a) the first job, April 1941; unstopping ditches blocked by the National Trust. This lowered the water-level by c.30cm; (b) clearing bushes with tractors; (c) tractor bogged down while trying to drag out a bog oak; (d) a bank lined with extracted oaks; there was no room to put them elsewhere.

Figure 72 (facing page) Burwell Fen, Priory Farm and Adventurers' Fen (above) in 1939, and (below) in 1943[27] 'the thought the Adventurers' Fen might ever be allowed to revert had scarcely entered my head. ...land, good land, now that it has been so hardly won back from dereliction, should never again be neglected or diverted from its true purpose.'[27]

Bloom's own land on the Fen remained in production till 1994 (Chapter 13), but the rest was returned to the National Trust and allowed to 'revert'.

When the National Trust land was finally returned, the Ministry of Agriculture made a substantial betterment claim against the Trust in respect of the drainage works and the improvement of access along Harrison's Drove. This gave rise to a great deal of discussion and negotiation, finally settled by granting the Ministry a 99-year lease of the 25 acres of Trust land on Pout Hall Fen, at the junction of Reach and Burwell Lodes, at a peppercorn rent (see map, Appendix A).

Much of Adventurers' Fen now lies within the waterproof banks that enclose the flood relief area and is therefore hydrologically isolated from arable land. Since the 1950s, it has been allowed to become much wetter and revert towards fen. Major excavations have also been carried out to provide open-water habitats for wildfowl and develop the area as a marshland reserve (Chapters 9.1 & 13). The area now contains a variety of habitats: open water (the Mere), reed-beds and grazing marsh (Plate 14, Fig. 2).

About 39ha of wet pasture around the Mere is let on an annual grazing licence. Since the area lies within the SSSI, the use of artificial sprays or fertilizers is not allowed. The cattle have succeeded in producing a rough, poached area which is ideal habitat for a large number of interesting dipteran species[32] and a distinctive flora (Chapter 7). However, these areas became much wetter after the banks around the reserve were waterproofed and encroachment by rushes (mainly *Juncus effusus*) became a problem. Rushes have since been controlled to some extent by cutting in the summer, but they are still apparently increasing. The drier areas tend to become infested with thistles (mainly *Cirsium arvense*) and ragwort (*Senecio jacobaea*), and these have been controlled by hand-pulling by work parties of volunteers in the summer. These problems are now being tackled by creating scrapes, improving control over the hydrology of the area and imposing a more systematic grazing regime.

The National Trust also owns some land outside the SSSI, beyond the waterproof banks. Seven fields at the eastern end of Adventurers' Fen (30ha) have until very recently been let under normal agricultural tenancies for arable cultivation. There has been no control on the application of either pesticides or fertilizer, and wheat, carrots, potatoes and sugar beet have been the main crops. The arable fields south of Harrison's Drove will continue in cultivation, but those to the north are being reclaimed as grazing meadows (see Chapter 13).

The fields at the northern end of Little Breed Fen have also been let as arable in the past but have been brought out of production and are now valuable parts of the mosaic of habitats at Wicken. Compartment 68 was cultivated until 1986 but has since been planted with native trees and shrubs (Chapter 6). The southern end of the adjacent field (compartment 21) was arable until just after the Second World War and the northern end may also have been cultivated at some time. This field was left to colonize naturally and has become a most attractive area of rough grass and scrub in which hawthorn, sallow and alder buckthorn are prominent and occasional young oaks occur. The grass here is dotted with adder's-tongue fern (*Ophioglossum vulgare*) and a population of bee orchid (*Ophrys apifera*) has recently been discovered. It is an excellent place for birds and butterflies. The herbaceous vegetation is cut in late summer and the willow scrub at the wetter northern end is coppiced at suitable intervals. Compartment 69 was abandoned in about 1980 and now has a rich and colourful herbaceous vegetation, which is cut in autumn. Parsley water-dropwort (*Oenanthe lachenalii*), common fleabane (*Pulicaria dysenterica*) and yellow flag (*Iris pseudacorus*) are abundant here.

It has recently been recognized that there has been no consistent policy for the management of the Fen's marginal land; each field has been dealt with in a piecemeal manner when its future has been in question. However, these areas clearly offer opportunities for the diversification of habitats within the area owned by the National Trust, whether by natural colonization or by planting, and they also provide a buffer between the SSSI and the arable farmland beyond. As the future viability of arable farming in the immediate vicinity becomes more uncertain, the value of these buffer zones increases. It seems important, therefore, to aim to bring these areas within the management objectives of the reserve as a whole, and this is part of the Management Committee's plans for the next decade.

(x) Management of Visitors

The number of visitors to the Fen increased steadily during the 1960s and 1970s (Fig. 74). It is difficult to be sure just how many people came towards the end of this period; all visitors were supposed to sign the book in the Keeper's House, and the totals were obtained from these signatures (the Visitors' Books are conserved in the archive). Undoubtedly many never bothered to sign, and by the late 1970s it was suggested that as many as 50,000 could be coming each year, though this was probably a considerable over-estimate.

The increasing numbers produced more damage to the tracks and paths on the Fen, particularly to Sedge Fen Drove, with patches becoming knee-deep in liquid peat and water. In 1980, it was decided to introduce an entrance fee, partly in response to the perceived damage and the undoubted increase in disturbance, but also to raise revenue. This had the effect of reducing and stabilizing the numbers visiting the Fen. It has also probably encouraged regular visitors to join the National Trust and this, by reason of the structure of the subsidy given to the Fen by the Trust, has benefited the Fen's finances over and above the entrance fees collected (Fig. 75). At the same time, the numbers of young children visiting the Fen in educational parties has increased enormously (Chapter 12). Many visitors bring dogs; these are allowed on the Fen under strict control, but the situation is kept under review.

Facilities for visitors have been maintained at a level conducive to the quiet enjoyment of an area of beautiful countryside. The car park and picnic site are set apart on National Trust land in Lode Lane, and public lavatories are also situated here, pro-

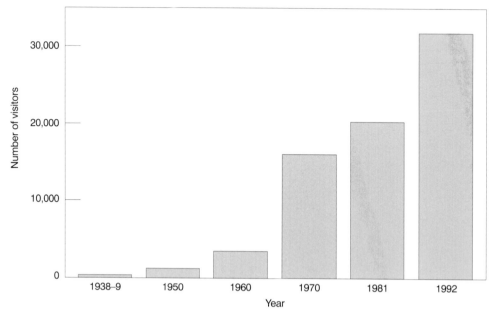

Figure 74   Numbers of visitors to Wicken Fen, 1938–92

vided and maintained by East Cambridgeshire District Council. The William Thorpe Building provides a reception area for visitors which is manned every day for most of the year and in which drinks and a variety of merchandise in keeping with the nature of the property may be purchased.

Notices on the Fen itself have been kept to a bare minimum. The first Guide to Wicken Fen appeared in 1932.[33] Today, the Fen is well-served with a colour guide to the reserve and guides for the Nature Trail and Boardwalk, all of which may be purchased at the William Thorpe Building. Checklists of the Fen's flora and fauna, and other interpretative material, including a booklet on the history of turf-digging on the Fen,[34] are also for sale. A wheelchair is available for use on the boardwalk. The interpretative display in the building, which was totally renovated in 1996, gives a brief history of Fenland and draws attention to some of the characteristic organisms of Wicken Fen as well as the traditional crops and their harvesting.

The problem of conserving the fragile habitats of the Fen, yet allowing access to tens of thousands of visitors of varying ages and interests, has been approached largely by 'zoning': some parts of the Fen near the entrance have been developed and managed with the specific aim of encouraging visitors to use these areas preferentially, leaving the more remote parts of the Fen relatively undisturbed.

Perhaps 70 per cent of the general public keep to the boarded walkway, the nature trail via Spinney Bank, Sedge Fen Drove, and the path to the Tower Hide.[35] Very few penetrate any further into the Fen. Verrall's Fen is used by a few people on busy days, but the area west of Malcarse Dyke is hardly ever visited, and that west of New Dyke, not at all. Much of the Fen, therefore, remains relatively undisturbed.

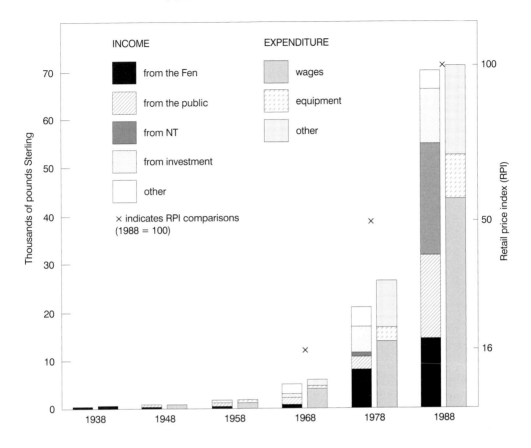

Figure 75 Income and expenditure from the accounts of Wicken Fen, 1938–88

The paths across the central portion of the Sedge Fen east of Drainers' Dyke are closed until June, or even July, partly to preserve the paths from trampling when they are still wet, and partly to prevent disturbance of nesting birds. Adventurers' Fen has not generally been open to visitors, but some walkers do venture beyond Monks Lode along the south bank of Wicken Lode. Judicious planting of willows means that this path is now largely screened from the Mere. However, the first steps towards opening up Adventurers' Fen to bird-watchers, at least in the winter, have been taken by renovating the Mere hide. Three more hides around the Mere have been constructed and access is being carefully planned to maintain some degree of control and minimize disturbance.

The idea of a boarded walkway for the Sedge Fen arose in the mid-1980s and was conceived primarily as a means whereby wheelchair-bound visitors could see at least part of the Fen. A substantial sum of money was raised by a special National Trust appeal, which sufficed to buy the materials. Construction was supervised by the Fen staff, but largely carried out by a team recruited through the government's employment scheme of the time, the Manpower Services Commission.

The boardwalk was opened in 1987 and now provides the preferred route for visitors (Fig. 76). It runs through sedge and litter fields, through carr (where there is a hide for bird-watching), alongside ditches, past the demonstration turf-diggings and along the Lode in a circular route of just over one kilometre (see map, Appendix A). Points of interest are described in a trail guide, and there are numbered marker posts along the way to show the visitor where to stop. Not the least of the attractions of the boardwalk is that it is passable in ordinary shoes in all weathers (Plate 15, Fig. 1), even when the rest of the Fen is closed, and it has proved particularly popular with families bringing small children in push-chairs.

The boardwalk has also proved to be an interesting habitat in its own right. The warm surface created by the wood when the sun shines is a preferred basking site for common lizards (*Lacerta vivipara*). In late summer, the walkway swarms with winged ants as they disperse; dragonflies swoop in to pick off the ants as they take to the air. The cool, long vegetation below the slats seems to be much favoured by small mammals, and weasels (*Mustela vulgaris*) are sometimes seen disappearing into the shade.

The question of the materials to be used for construction of the boardwalk caused much discussion in the Management Committee, and well illustrates the variety of factors that must be taken into consideration in making major management decisions. The Committee's first instinct was to choose a reasonably durable and widely available material – treated softwood. The pressure treatment of softwood impregnates it with

Figure 76   The Boardwalk

a mixture which contains, among other substances, copper, chromium and arsenic. Various studies have demonstrated that these substances are strongly bound within the wood so that once any surface residues have been washed off, there is virtually no release of metallic ions. The Committee was, however, still worried about possible side-effects, particularly to water-bodies. Copper, for example, is extremely toxic to algae. Some material would inevitably be released in dust worn from the walking surface. Additionally, there was some evidence from a walkway laid across Borth Bog in West Wales that enough metallic ions were leached out to cause damage to *Sphagnum*.[36]

The Committee then considered other more durable materials that would resist insect and fungal attack without treatment. Oak was found to be very expensive in the quality required; the sapwood of oak is not durable and it would have been necessary to use heartwood only. Elm, although durable when permanently wet, is not so when alternately wetted and dried. In the end the choice, based on cost and likely durability, fell on two tropical hardwoods. Opepe (*Mitragyna stipulosa*), from West Africa, was used for the uprights, and keruing (*Dipterocarpus* sp.) for the framework and walking surface. Opepe is very durable in wet conditions, and the high resin content of keruing both preserves it and also helps to maintain a good walking surface. By 1994, the first signs of heavy wear were becoming apparent on the main boardwalk and a few slats had broken through use. In the winter of 1995, parts of the walk, where it runs through scrub and the slats never dry out, had to be closed because of the slipperiness of the walking surface. A satisfactory solution has been found by applying 'chicken wire' mesh to the surface, which produces a good grip, is surprisingly durable, and is easy to replace. A far greater problem of rot has emerged in the supporting structure where the boardwalk lies particularly close to the ground; here air circulation is poor and the wood experiences alternate drying and wetting. Regular inspection and a rolling programme of replacement has begun to safeguard the structure for its next decade of active service.

The conservation implications of the use of tropical hardwoods were discussed, but at the time it was felt that cost and durability outweighed concerns about rain-forest conservation. The decision was questioned by Friends of the Earth, and led to careful consideration of the use of tropical timbers throughout the National Trust. There is little doubt that in the climate of opinion that now prevails, a different conclusion would be reached. Indeed, a short spur to a hide beside the walkway has been constructed in oak, and after some initial warping and shrinkage, this is now perfectly adequate.

The Fen's zoning policy has also made it possible to accommodate a full education programme which forms a vital part of the work of the Fen (Chapter 12). Most of the educational parties are of primary school children and for them practical work is the main attraction. In the mid-1980s, some concern was expressed that pond-dipping in the Brickpits might be leading to exchange of organisms between these highly individual ponds (see Chapter 3). It was decided to provide an alternative site for schools, where pond-dipping and other activities could be carried on without danger of disrupting the Sedge Fen's delicate communities. In 1986, a long trench was dug in the field opposite the entrance to the Fen (compartment 30) and boarded work-stations were constructed along each side; this trench quickly filled with water and organisms and has been a great success. Compartment 30 has been further developed over the past few years as an Education Area. This has proved to be an invaluable asset; it is used to the full, absorbing the attention of 6,000 or more young visitors each year.

References

1 Farren (1926a), p. 173
2 Wicken Fen Executive Committee Minute Books
3 Farren (1926a), p. 178
4 Evans (1925), p. 90
5 Godwin (1941b)
6 The Reporter (25 May 1948)
7 Wicken Fen Executive Committee (1956)
8 Wicken Fen Executive Committee Minutes (21 November 1961)
9 Wicken Fen Local Management Committee (1986)
10 Wicken Fen Local Management Committee (1992)
11 Friday (1994)
12 Rowell (1983a)
13 Farren (1926a), p. 181
14 Burrows (1902)
15 Godwin & Bharucha (1932)
16 Godwin (1978), p. 179
17 Godwin (1929)
18 Rodwell (1991a)
19 Atkinson (1996)
20 Aldridge (thesis in prep.)
21 Hollingsworth et al. (1995)
22 Conway (1938b)
23 Dempster (1995)
24 Wicken Fen Executive Committee (1936)
25 Ennion (1949)
26 Way & Davis (1965)
27 Bloom (1944)
28 'Reclaimation 1941', East Anglian Film Archive, University of East Anglia
29 Lock (1972)
30 Walters (1958)
31 Jenyns (1845)
32 Perry (17 January 1993), letter in archive
33 Gardiner (1932c)
34 Lohoar & Ballard (1992)
35 National Trust (1996)
36 Cripps (1984)

12

Ecology, Research and Education at Wicken Fen

L. E. FRIDAY, N. W. MOORE AND S. M. BALLARD

W ICKEN FEN is well situated as a centre for scientific research and education: seventeen miles by road from the University of Cambridge (an eleven-mile cycle ride for the earlier visitors to whom the Upware ferry was available), accessible to country- and city-dwellers alike and within easy reach of schools and colleges throughout the county. The Fen's history is as important as its geography in contributing to its special value: few nature reserves have been studied for so long and so intensively and possess such extensive botanical, zoological and historical records.

Other special features of the Fen enhance its potential for education and research. First, its size and diversity afford many interesting habitats for study, from reed-beds, sedge-fields and brickpits to small-scale habitats like temporary litter piles and tree holes. Because the management programmes generally involve a rotation of sites, a habitat such as a reed-bed will, at any given time, be found in all stages of development; this affords plenty of scope for comparative studies. Secondly, the management regime incorporates a certain amount of flexibility, and the Management Committee is sufficiently sympathetic to the needs of ecologists to accommodate a variety of types of study. Indeed, specific management activities may be scheduled in order to create the conditions needed for an experiment or to allow access to particular habitats. Thirdly, laboratory space, a library of identification guides and natural history books, and accommodation are all available on site. Finally, and perhaps most importantly, the Fen has proved to be a particularly safe place in which to carry out research that would be hazardous in the wider countryside. Many of the most informative of the projects carried out on the Fen have involved long-term studies of fixed plots, 24-hour monitoring, or repeated observations of individually-marked organisms (see Chapters 3, 8, 9.2 & 9.3 for examples); all such enterprises are extremely vulnerable to disturbance.

Wicken Fen's influence has spread far beyond Cambridgeshire. The ecology of the Sedge Fen has become known world-wide, through the publications and teaching of members of the University of Cambridge, principally the fruits of their own research. A visiting professor recently confided that he knew more about Wicken Fen by the time he graduated from the University of Auckland than he did about the ecology of his native New Zealand. Some of the academics and students associated with the reserve in its early days might justly lay claim to be among the founding fathers of ecology; their writings and ideas have done much to shape the science in its formative years.

Throughout the history of the reserve, naturalists have flocked to Wicken Fen to record its rich flora and fauna. There is, of course, no hard and fast division between naturalists and ecologists, but while the former may record the diversity, distribution and habits of organisms, the latter would seek also the controlling factors underlying these patterns. Wicken's naturalists include people from all walks of life who love the Fen and contribute to its conservation through the generous sharing of knowledge (often as members of the Local Advisory Panel (Chapter 11, p. 220)), by gifts of land, money or time, and by recording its flora and fauna.

In recent years, the Fen has found a new role in environmental education. Equipment, artefacts and, not least, knowledge have been built up to share with schoolchildren and the general public both the natural and social history of the Fen. The Fen staff and the National Trust have steadily improved the interpretative material available to visitors of all ages. These new projects have also required a great deal of deliberation on the part of the Management Committee and Wardens, to reconcile the needs of visitors with the primary task of protecting the Fen and its biological communities.

ECOLOGICAL RESEARCH AT WICKEN FEN

Ecology first began to emerge as a science in the last decades of the 19th century. The earliest published ecological studies of Wicken Fen are those of R. H. Yapp (1871–1928) who graduated in botany at Cambridge in 1895. While on an expedition to Malaya in 1900, Yapp became interested in the influence of the environment on individual species and he developed this interest on his return, working at Wicken Fen. He described in detail the spatial distribution of fen plant species in relation to water-level (Fig. 6, Chapter 2), but perhaps his most original contribution involved the way in which the three-dimensional structure of vegetation influences the conditions to which individual plants are subject (Fig. 16, Chapter 5).

Few people have done more to further vegetation studies in this country than A. G. (Sir Arthur) Tansley (1871–1955). He was among the founders of the first ecological society in the world, the British Ecological Society, in 1913. Tansley's aim was to transform ecology from the imprecise pursuit it was at first perceived to be, identifying specific problems that could be tackled in a scientific manner.[1] His introduction of the concept of the 'ecosystem' in 1935[2] prepared the ground for much fruitful ecological development. His interest in Wicken Fen ensured that it became known as a 'classic' fen site.

While Tansley did little fieldwork at Wicken Fen himself, during his time in the Cambridge Botany School he was responsible for introducing many excellent students to the Fen as a promising site for their ecological research. Among the botany undergraduates to cycle out to Wicken in 1921, on an outing of the newly-formed Ecology Club, was Harry (later Sir Harry) Godwin (1901–85) (Fig. 77). In 1923, Godwin began to record the vegetation of marked localities on the Fen, the areas now known as the Godwin Triangle and Godwin Plots. These long-term studies provided field data to support Godwin's ideas on fenland succession (see Chapters 5 & 6). Succession was not a new idea in 1923, but, as Godwin commented in introductory notes to a fen exhibit, 'In the 1920s, ecologists were mainly concerned to shew the reality and character of fenland succession'.[3] Using data from the permanent sites on Wicken Fen, Godwin argued that sedge cutting 'deflected' the normal course of succession producing other types of vegetation. Godwin's research into the fen vegetation and its relation to soil

Figure 77　Harry Godwin, examining a 'mouse-hole' on the Fen, 1934. This is the only known photograph of Godwin at Wicken.

water and other factors continued through his research students. These studies formed the basis of sedge, litter and carr management regimes on the Fen for over six decades.

Godwin's interest extended to all aspects of the Fenland. In 1932, he joined the Fenland Research Committee, a body of amateurs and professionals working to survey the Fens and bring to bear the interests of many disciplines upon the problems of Fenland history. The work of the Committee is summarized in Godwin's book, *Fenland: its ancient past and uncertain future*.[4] Meanwhile, Godwin's wife Margaret began the research on pollen found in Fenland peat that soon occupied them both; this work was done mostly at sites other than Wicken Fen, although a pollen diagram from the Fen was published (see Fig. 53, Chapter 10). In 1948, the University of Cambridge established a Sub-Department of Quaternary Research as part of the Botany Department, of which Godwin was the first Director. The group possessed one of the first radiocarbon-dating laboratories in Britain.

Another Cambridge student who visited Wicken on Botany School excursions was Paul Richards (1908–95). Shortly after graduating Richards contributed a short account of the Bryophyta to *The Natural History of Wicken Fen*[5] and maintained a strong interest in the Fen, being a member of the Executive Committee in the 1940s and remaining active on the Local Advisory Panel until his death. However, it is for his contributions to the study of tropical rain forests that he is best known. Richards, like Yapp, was struck by the three-dimensional structure of the vegetation he studied. His book, *The Tropical Rain Forest*,[6] first published in 1952 with a second edition in 1995, represents the fruits of intensive studies on three continents.

Animal ecology seems to have lagged behind plant ecology in becoming a rigorous scientific discipline. One of the most influential figures in its development was undoubtedly G. Evelyn Hutchinson (1903–91). Hutchinson knew Wicken Fen from childhood, and it evidently played a formative role in his early research:

'In my childhood, Wicken Fen was best reached from Cambridge by bicycle. In some ways the landscape was superficially rather ordinary if one did not find the details of natural history exciting, but some very curious things could turn up... After about a ten mile ride to the north, one crossed the River Cam at Upware by hiring a rowing boat large enough to carry a few bicycles, rented from the Upware Inn, "Five Miles from Anywhere, No Hurry".

'Once when riding my bicycle along the lode or boundary of Wicken Fen, a swallowtail approached from the opposite direction. I stumbled and dropped the net over the insect, the identity of which did not occur to me. I fell off the machine and saw something fluttering. As I lifted the net, a swallowtail flew out. I had therefore been one of the few British naturalists to have captured *Papilio machaon britannicus* while riding a bicycle. Of course I was bitterly disappointed not to have retained the specimen, but now I can tell the story, adding "without reducing the number of an endangered subspecies".

'Sometimes we would turn paleontologist and visit the quarry a little up the river, where late Jurassic corals were often left by the quarrymen. Grappling with the geography of Cambridgeshire soon became an obsession.

'By this time, I had ceased to be a serious lepidopterist, until a later evolutionary interest in certain curious kinds of variation led me to *Abraxas*. Though the lepidopterous fauna of Wicken Fen is quite rich, a rather gaudy appearance led to a feeling of ostentation; something having subtler characteristics began to be desired. It seemed reasonable that in groups in which many common species occurred, a few rare ones would be found, perhaps small but modestly beautiful. Actually my later scientific work has been much concerned with this kind of distribution. This grew out of the fact that while the Lepidoptera at Wicken boasted a few rare species and many less rare, little explanation of this kind of distribution was sought, either within the group, or indeed in other orders.

'Search soon provided examples. I was particularly drawn to the Heteroptera in which suborder there were many Capsidae but only a few Saldidae, a semiaquatic form in which *Chartoscirta elegantula* attracted my attention.[7] This very small but pretty insect lives on the wet ground in the sedge fen and has a curious sexual dimorphism in the coloration of the last antennal joint of the male. Like *Papilio* this little insect was apparently becoming endangered and I could not find it on the Fen in 1984.

'There are undoubtedly many more interesting problems to be solved about the original fenland biota. There is still plenty to do at Wicken.'[8]

Hutchinson's professional career was principally as Professor of Zoology at the University of Yale and it embraced many branches of ecology. His comprehensive treatise on lakes and their organisms[9,10,11,12] are regarded with reverence by freshwater biologists. Hutchinson's name will always also be associated with the concept of the 'niche' based on the principle of competitive exclusion. He was, through his student Robert MacArthur, a key figure in the revolution of the 1960s and '70s that transformed the study of communities and ecosystems into a structured, predictive science. That this movement was successful is in no small part due to Hutchinson's insistence that mathematical abstraction be tempered with a sound knowledge of animals in the field. Hutchinson's love of Wicken Fen and his deep commitment to freshwater research and to education have been brought together in the creation in 1992 of four new pond-dipping ponds in the Education Area, paid for by his family and Cambridge friends.

Wicken Fen continues to provide a site for the research projects of lecturers in the University of Cambridge and of their students. More than a dozen students of the University have used Wicken Fen as the main field site for their PhD research. These studies have been of considerable importance in shaping the management programme for the Fen, since they include ecological studies both of individual species of particular interest at Wicken, and of species assemblages in the different fen communities.

The botanical tradition begun by Yapp has been sustained for over 90 years. Our understanding of the Sedge Fen and its management have benefited greatly from the research of V. M. Conway on *Cladium mariscus*,[13] T. C. Meredith on *Peucedanum palustre*,[14] and H. J. Harvey and his students on the vegetation of the litter fields[15,16] (see Chapter 5). Autecological studies of the *Eleocharis palustris* species group by S. M. Walters,[17] of *Calamagrostis* species by K. E. Luck,[18] of *Urtica dioica* by D. Briggs, A. J. Pollard[19,20] and

S. Lahav[21], and of *Potamogeton* spp. by C. D. Preston and co-workers[22] have addressed a number of problems of taxonomic and genetic interest (see Chapter 7).

Zoological research projects were relatively few at first but have increased in frequency since the Wicken Fen Group initiated long-term studies of the Fen's bird populations in the late 1960s (Chapter 9.2). Field studies by N. Dawson on ground beetles,[23] J. C. Brown and J. R. Flowerdew on small mammals,[24] O. Prŷs-Jones on bumblebees,[25] P. Convey on dragonflies,[26] D. Eagle on whirligig beetles,[27] N. B. Davies and M. de L. Brooke on cuckoos (Chapter 9.3), and W. Duckworth on reed warblers[28] have contributed to our understanding of the behaviour and general ecology of these animals.

Aquatic community studies at Wicken Fen seem to have begun with P. M. Jenkin in the 1920s[29,30] and have been championed in more recent years by S. A. Corbet, who has initiated many cohorts of undergraduates in the delights of 24-hour sampling from small inflatable dinghies (Fig. 78). Research projects by N. V. C. Polunin,[31] D. G. Lee,[32] L. E. Friday[33], D. J. Painter[34] and D. C. Aldridge [35] illuminate the ecological processes at work beneath the surfaces of the Fen's lodes, ditches and ponds and have influenced the management of these water-bodies (Chapter 3).

Research on the history and management of the Fen carried out by T. A. Rowell[36] has been particularly valuable to the managers of the Fen in critically examining (and challenging) the generally accepted view of the Fen (Chapter 10) and providing a firm basis of well-documented information from which clear management guidelines may be drawn. A complete (up to 1988) list of theses and other works associated with the Fen may be found in Rowell's bibliography.[37]

RESTORING LOST SPECIES

Perhaps the most telling test of our understanding of the ecology of the Fen arises when an attempt is made to reintroduce a species that was previously found on the Fen but has since disappeared. Proposals for reintroductions are now assessed by the Local Management Committee and the National Trust's Nature Conservation Panel against a number of key criteria, namely that there is good evidence for the former natural occurrence of the species at the site; the reasons why the species was lost are known; the chances of natural recolonization are low; the site now offers sufficient area of suitable habitat; a source of individuals for introduction of appropriate genetic form can be found; and individuals can be taken from the source population without risk to that population.

The earliest reintroduction at Wicken Fen was in 1909, when G. H. Verrall attempted to return the large copper butterfly to the Fen. The British race of the species, *Lycaena dispar dispar*, had a rather restricted distribution in East Anglia, mainly in the Cambridgeshire Fens, in the early 19th century. It was particularly abundant at the now-drained Whittlesey Mere, and was last taken at Holme Fen in 1847/48. This large and conspicuous insect was almost certainly over-collected, but also suffered from the draining of open marshy habitat in which its larval foodplant, water dock (*Rumex hydrolapathum*) grew in abundance.

Figure 78   Sampling plankton in the Main Brickpit; Greg Hurst and
Nicola Muggeridge, August 1989

Because the English race was extinct, Verrall was compelled to introduce *Lycaena dispar rutilus*, the common European race, to Wicken. This attempt failed, but a further attempt was made in 1930, this time using the Dutch race, *L. d. batavus* (Plate 5, Fig. 7), which is almost indistinguishable from the extinct *dispar*. Three hectares of Adventurers' Fen were cleared and planted with *Rumex hydrolapathum* and the introduced butterflies bred and survived there until the area was drained for agriculture in 1942.

However, with continuous management, the Dutch race has been maintained at Woodwalton Fen in Huntingdonshire, but there the fen is too dry to produce ideal oviposition sites and the limited habitat supports a population that is too small to withstand setbacks due to predation, parasitism and flooding. Adventurers' Fen would seem to offer a good site for reintroduction of the large copper; the biology of the butterfly is much better understood as a result of the earlier reintroductions and the experience gained at Woodwalton Fen, and the land is now probably as wet as it was before, protected by the new waterproof banks. It is hoped that a new attempt can be made in the near future.

Two recent reintroduction attempts began at Wicken in 1992: of the swallowtail butterfly and the fen ragwort (*Senecio paludosus*). The story of the swallowtail has been recounted elsewhere (Chapter 8); in this case, a very large body of research supports the reintroduction. Financial support has been provided by English Nature and the British Butterfly Conservation Society. In the summer of 1993, some adults and large larvae were released on to *Peucedanum* plants in four sedge-field sites which are being managed specifically to encourage the larval foodplant. Adult swallowtails have been seen flying on the Fen each summer since 1994, albeit in very small numbers. The fortunes of the butterfly are being monitored closely by the same scientists (Dr J. P. Dempster and Mrs M. Hall) who carried out most of the preparatory studies.

The reintroduction of *Senecio paludosus* is a little more problematic. The reasons for the disappearance of this species from the Cambridgeshire Fens (Chapter 7), and the present suitability of the habitat at Wicken Fen are less clear; drainage and agricultural intensification can hardly have been the cause of the demise of the plant at Wicken Fen. The reintroduction has therefore proceeded in an experimental fashion, sowing seeds in small plots which are managed in a variety of ways to provide different conditions for establishment and planting individuals raised from seed in an area with a range of water-table depths. The success of the plants is being monitored as part of English Nature's Species Recovery Programme. This experiment offers an excellent opportunity to learn a great deal about the requirements of the plant and so, it is hoped, retrospectively to satisfy the criteria for reintroduction.

RECORDING THE FEN'S SPECIES

We cannot know how best to manage a nature reserve unless we first discover which organisms the area contains. Wicken Fen has been particularly blessed in this respect by the keen interest shown in its insects, plants and birds over more than a century. Wicken Fen appears to have become the focus for collectors and recorders of the

Fenland flora and fauna following the drainage of Burwell Fen and Whittlesey Mere (Chapter 1) in the 1950s.[36] Once the botanical riches of the Sedge Fen had been discovered, records accumulated rapidly (Fig. 79).

Cambridge academics and local people, including teachers, doctors and clerics, have all contributed to what we know about the Fen flora and fauna, and many of these have also generously added to the land owned by the National Trust and the financial well-being of the reserve. To these should be added natural history enthusiasts from all over the country who make pilgrimages to Wicken Fen and, last, but by no means least, the Fen staff themselves. It seems invidious to attempt to catalogue the distinguished naturalists and benefactors who have been involved in the Fen. Instead, it is perhaps more appropriate to look at changing trends in natural history studies at Wicken Fen and, in particular, at the development of species recording on the Fen.

The earliest records that can confidently be located within the present reserve are to be found among the botanical notebooks and herbarium specimens of C. C. Babington, a Cambridge Professor of Botany (Chapter 7) and enthusiastic collector of Coleoptera. Most of his plant records are post-1850, although he began visiting the Fen in the 1820s, perhaps in pursuit of beetles. The Fen beetles appear to have exerted a particularly powerful magnetism, and the University Museum of Zoology contains many specimens from Wicken collected by such distinguished coleopterists as Charles

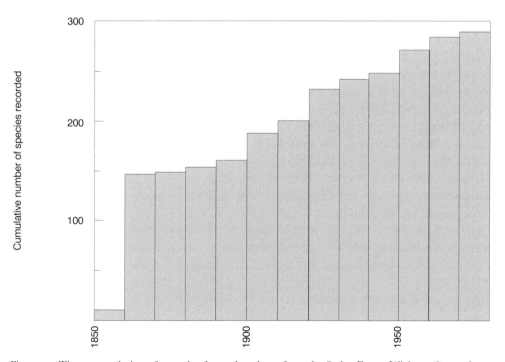

Figure 79   The accumulation of records of vascular plants from the Sedge Fen at Wicken, 1850–1980, as revealed by the Fen's botanical records[36]

Darwin (as an undergraduate, just prior to the Beagle voyage), F. Balfour-Browne, G. R. Crotch, H. Donisthorpe, J. Omer Cooper, J. A. Power, D. Sharp and the Revd C. E. Tottenham. Not only was the Fen itself well worked, but the boats taking the sedge crop to Cambridge were also searched for their Coleoptera.[36,38]

The richness and rarity value of the insect fauna provided the impetus for the preservation of the Fen (Chapter 10). G. H. Verrall and the Hon. N. C. Rothschild, both Presidents of the Royal Entomological Society of London, were among the Fen's chief benefactors (see Fig. 81, p. 278). The Lepidoptera were first recorded by Frederick Bond in the 1850s and subsequently formed a focus for much entomological activity (Chapter 7). Access and collecting were at first unlimited (although permission to use lights on the Fen at night was suspended by the Government during the First World War). However, in 1931, amid growing fears that many lepidopteran specimens were being sold commercially, and that the Fen was coming under heavy collecting pressure by individuals and natural history societies, a permit system was introduced. Permits were administered by an Entomological Sub-committee and included the pro-viso that no more than six swallowtails were allowed to be taken per visit.

Whilst enthusiastic recording of the Fen flora in the early years of the century had paved the way for quantitative ecological studies, the contemporary Professor of Zoology, J. Stanley Gardiner, recognized that similarly detailed work on the fauna would be 'most uncertain until a complete list of the fauna had been compiled'.[39] He set this achievement as one of his chief goals during the 1920s and '30s, and *The Natural History of Wicken Fen*, published between 1923 and 1932,[40,41] represents the fruits of this endeavour. Gardiner gathered together chapters on 32 different groups of animals, plants, fungi and protists, containing lists of species and accounts of their distribution and natural history. This remarkable book is a treasure-house of information about the state of the Fen between the Wars, providing a set of measures by which sub-sequent records and the consequences of management may be assessed.

Probably as a result of this exercise, the value of knowing the precise location of records of uncommon plants and animals on the Fen was driven home to the Committee. In 1932, the Entomological Sub-committee proposed that the Pieces of the Fen be labelled 'so that collectors may know precisely where their specimens have been caught'.[42] This was eventually achieved in 1936 by the placing of iron posts to mark various parts of the Fen.

When a new edition of the *Guide* to the Fen[43] was needed in 1946, it was proposed that this should have appended as complete lists of species as possible, to be 'a stimu-lus to collectors' to visit the Fen and send in their records. Another wave of enthusiatic recording activity, which included the founding of the Wicken Fen Ringing Group (Chapter 9.1) began with the appointment of Charles Mitchell in 1961. The first in the series of *Guides to Wicken Fen*, a topographical and botanical guide by F. J. Bingley and S. M. Walters, was first published in 1966.[44] This was followed in rapid succession by checklists to molluscs;[45] vascular plants;[46] birds;[47] bryophytes;[48] triclads;[49] spiders;[50] but-terflies and day-flying moths;[51] microlepidoptera;[52] lichens;[53] and mammals.[54] The guides to vascular plants, birds and butterflies have been revised at intervals, and a guide to dragonflies and damselflies, with details of the flight period at Wicken, has been produced.

From the earliest days, the Executive Committee has appointed Zoological and Botanical Secretaries to oversee management of the fauna and flora, to keep the records and to consider applications for permits for study. Today, permits are issued for specific studies or, exceptionally, for general collecting of 'token' specimens. Permits are issued annually and a number of rules apply. A strict protocol for running moth-traps is required and all permit-holders are asked to submit a species list or report on their findings. Between 1993 and 1995, an average of about 20 permits per annum were issued for zoological studies, about half of these involving Lepidoptera, and a slightly smaller number for botanical projects.

The botanical records are held on a card index and computer file, including dates of records, site details and other comments. The locations of botanical records within the Fen tend now to be given as compartment numbers, by grid reference or by refer-ence to named features such as droves (see map, Appendix A).

The number of invertebrate species to be dealt with is vastly greater than that of plants, so specialist recorders were appointed in the 1980s to co-ordinate the records of their particular group. The co-ordinators have generated a card index which includes site details marked on an accompanying map, and, where aquatic invertebrates are concerned, the water-bodies from which they are recorded are identified according to a system of reference numbers. The species lists are also kept up to date on a computer file by the Zoological Secretary. The card index can be consulted in the William Thorpe Building and copies of current checklists are made available to interested par-ties. Since 1980, permit holders have received an occasional Newsletter to keep them up to date on developments and notable sightings on the Fen.

The job of recording is never-ending. For some groups, such as the Diptera, scores of species have been added to the Fen list annually as individuals and field meetings report their finds, but only a few new species of vascular plants, birds or macrolepid-optera are now being reported. One of the great values of checklists, however, is to stimulate further recording activity, seeking out those species which 'should' be there, or have not been seen for half a century. The compilation of checklists as a compan-ion to this book has elicited a tremendous response from recorders of several groups, most notably the Diptera, and it is hoped that many more records will result from pub-lication of the fruits of their efforts.

MONITORING THE RESULTS OF MANAGEMENT

Monitoring should be an essential element in the management of any nature reserve. It provides the background information for the planning and inception of new manage-ment practices and is the means by which the effectiveness of any such operation may be assessed. However, monitoring takes a good deal of time if it is to be carried out accurately and at sufficiently frequent intervals for the results to be useful. A further problem arises when monitoring over long periods of time: where it is necessary to employ a succession of recorders, variation in expertise and enthusiasm and slight differences in technique can all but swamp the real changes taking place from year to year.

The active management programme pursued by the wardening staff at Wicken Fen leaves very little time for monitoring. Such monitoring as has been carried out in the past has largely been inadequate for assessing the results of all this activity. There are notable exceptions, of course, and these studies have moulded the present management plan. The Godwin Triangle (Chapter 6) and the five remaining Godwin Plots (Chapter 5) are small areas of the Fen in which the vegetation cover has been accurately mapped and monitored for over 50 years. The long-term academic studies of the Sedge Fen by Cambridge botanists, the regular activities of the bird ringers over two decades (Chapters 9.1 & 9.2), the wildfowl counts (Chapter 9.4), the butterfly census initiated in the 1980s by the Head Warden, Tim Bennett (Chapter 8), and recent studies of ditches (Chapter 3) have helped us to predict what ought to happen when we adopt a new variant on the management scheme for a particular habitat. But, in most cases, we have only casual observations to show what actually happened and over what time course.

The need for more monitoring on a systematic basis has become more acute in recent years. The call for a review of the subject has come partly from the wardening staff who, in implementing the practical management and in their daily contact with the Fen, are most aware of the changes their work brings about. The revision of the management plan in 1992 has also provided an added impetus. In 1989, a meeting of the Local Advisory Panel considered what should be the priorities for monitoring on the Fen and the best ways to achieve these aims. While all may be in favour of increased monitoring, it is more difficult to decide how the available expertise and time might be most profitably employed.

Five main approaches to monitoring on the Fen emerge as particularly tractable. First, selected species should be identified for annual counting or mapping. Secondly, where a new management regime is to be implemented with a specific aim, its progress should be monitored in a sequence of recordings, beginning in advance of the new regime. Thirdly, 'one-off' surveys of particular areas of the Fen or of specific groups of organisms should be carried out as and when the expertise becomes available. Fourthly, those counts which form part of wider surveys should continue. And fifthly, fixed-point photography of some areas of the Fen should be initiated and repeated at intervals of months to years, depending on the purpose of the records. A photographic archive might then be set up to include the vertical aerial photographs taken at intervals (the earliest dates from 1929) (see Fig. 60, Chapter 10) by the Royal Air Force and the Committee for Aerial Photography of Cambridge University.

Some of these proposals are already being implemented at the Fen. For example, the responses of the *Viola persicifolia* population to management have been studied since 1983 (Chapter 7) and will continue as part of English Nature's Species Recovery Programme. A list of additional plant species to be studied in detail has been drawn up by the Botanical Secretary and is based partly on those for which good records already exist, such as *Taraxacum palustre*. Other species to be included are those showing evident signs of changes in distribution and abundance: for example, *Ranunculus lingua* which appears to be spreading along the droves. Also of concern are alien and invading animal species, such as mink (*Mustela vison*), muntjac (*Muntiacus muntjak*) and Canada geese (*Branta canadensis*); Warden Ralph Sargeant began a survey of the breeding success of Canada geese in 1990 and of the numbers of mink in 1997.

A number of habitats or areas of the Fen where changes are already evident or are predicted have been identified for monitoring. The colonization of the Borrow Pit by freshwater invertebrates since its creation in 1989 has been studied by Dr G. D. Howells and the butterflies in the area of new tree-planting in compartment 68 are recorded on a regular basis. An issue of continuing concern is the effect of different cutting regimes on the sedge-fields, particularly on the abundance of *Peucedanum*; the areas containing the best *Peucedanum* are now managed differently from the main sedge areas (Chapter 11), and the effects of this are been monitored. The most dramatic changes are likely to take place on Adventurers' Fen during the conversion of former arable land to wet grazing meadow (Chapter 13). A monitoring system involving fixed-point photography was set up by Assistant Head Warden Grant Lohoar to document the transition, and botanists from the Institute of Terrestrial Ecology are monitoring the ecological changes.

Although the significance of hydrological conditions for the ecology of the Fen has been apparent from the earliest days of the reserve, systematic monitoring of water-levels seems not to have been among the Committee's priorities. Godwin and Bharucha's studies of the 1920s,[55] and studies carried out in the 1970s[56] and '80s[57] have told us a great deal about the behaviour of the water-table over fairly short periods and a little about changes between distant points in time. However, there are no long runs of continuous data that would allow the effect of long-term trends, or exceptional years, to be clearly recognized. It seems that the Sedge Fen and Verrall's Fen have become wetter since the water-proofing of Howe's and Spinney Banks (Chapter 11) and vegetational changes seem to be occurring as a consequence (Chapters 5 & 6), but no hydrological data exist for the crucial period. The present Committee has committed itself to the installation of a system of dip-wells covering the entire reserve, in which water-levels will be monitored at regular intervals. This project, which is organized by hydrologists from Cranfield University under Dr D. Gowing and Dr M. Hann, is intended to provide the base-line data needed to interpret any vegetational changes on the Fen and will also play a crucial role in the development of the 'marshland reserve' on Adventurers' Fen.

Perhaps the most cost-effective approach to monitoring is to carry out repeat surveys of groups of organisms, or areas of Fen, that have previously been thoroughly recorded. The Godwin Triangle and Plots are the most obvious examples, but other projects are being actively encouraged. For example, in 1991, Dr J. R. Laundon revisited the Fen after twenty years to record the lichens and compare the status of a number of species over the intervening period (Chapter 6). The flora of St Edmund's Fen was surveyed by Dr J. M. Lock in 1972 and another survey for comparative purposes is planned. Some new groups of organisms are also to be included: for example, surveys of the rotifer fauna of the brickpits and ditches have been carried out by Mrs R. Pontin in 1992 and 1994.[58]

The key to the success of this new effort lies in the involvement of people who have the expertise, enthusiasm and opportunity to carry out the work. Wicken Fen has a wide range of such people who can be called upon to help. Many of the Local Advisory Panel are distinguished naturalists and the collective expertise of the Panel covers a very wide range of organisms. Some members of the Panel who are teaching officers in the University and colleges are able to offer projects to their students at the Fen. It is possible to incorporate field projects with students into a programme of long-term monitoring, but it is vital that the procedures used are sufficiently robust to withstand the change of personnel from year to year. Most importantly, perhaps, the wardening staff have themselves taken a leading role in monitoring.

Some help in monitoring is available from outside the immediate circle of the Fen's local supporters. In recent years, the National Rivers Authority and the Institute of Freshwater Ecology have surveyed the fish populations of the Lodes and Mere as part of periodic wider surveys of East Anglian waterways (Chapter 3) and scientists from the Institute of Terrestrial Ecology, English Nature and Cranfield University are closely involved in several major studies and reintroductions on the Fen.

Most of these projects have been achieved without cost to the Fen, but, under some circumstances, gifts of time and goodwill must be acknowledged by financial commitment on the part of the Committee. Some studies require prolonged periods of study at the Fen, or considerable travel to and from the site, and in these circumstances it is appropriate that visiting workers' expenses should be defrayed. At Wicken Fen, as at many nature reserves, monitoring has tended to be regarded as 'desirable but not essential' and, as a corollary, has been supported by donations of time and money, rather than being part of the budget. However, the management plan of 1992[59] fully recognizes the integral importance of monitoring and seeks to incorporate it into the normal budget. The spur came in 1991, when a donation allowed a fund to be set up in memory of the Cambridge mycologist Dr S. Garrett. This gift has been matched by the National Trust, and the fund will be used to support small research projects associated with the Fen.

EDUCATION AT WICKEN FEN

The tradition of University of Cambridge field trips to Wicken, started in the early 1920s, has continued to the present day. The departments of Botany (now Plant Sciences), Zoology, Geography and Agriculture (later Applied Biology) have all brought student groups to see typical fenland animal and plant communities, to study soil factors and hydrology, and, most recently, to witness the implementation of management for conservation. Some of these undergraduates have undertaken individual experimental or survey work on the Fen as part of their degree course, or as volunteers after graduating.

Over the years, many undergraduates have taken part in long-term projects, adding their findings to a growing corpus of information which, by its very continuity, reveals trends that cannot be detected in one-off studies. One such project is the continued monitoring of the Godwin Plots by botany students under the direction originally of Godwin and subsequently of D. E. Coombe and P. J. Grubb (Chapter 5). The practical classes run in the Department of Zoology by Dr G. Salt from the 1940s–'60s, in which students dissected *Lipara* galls collected from the reed-beds (Chapter 4), yielded intriguing quantitative data on year-to-year fluctuations in the populations of the gall-formers, their parasites and inquilines.

The Department of Applied Biology made particular use of the Fen, encouraging students to carry out short practical projects at Wicken Fen as part of their second or third-year degree courses. Copies of the results of these brief initial forays into ecological research are kept in the Fen archives. The students might spend up to a week at the Fen, living in the Ganges Hut, or commuting daily from their colleges. During this period, the William Thorpe Building would be transformed into a bustling laboratory, with students coming and going with equipment and samples at all hours of the day and night. The Department closed in 1989 and summer field-courses in Ecology have, for the present at least, migrated to other sites.

Homerton College, Cambridge, an institution for the training of teachers, has used Wicken Fen for decades. Day and half-day trips are made to the Fen annually, and Homerton staff and students contributed to the making of the film about the Fen which promoted the Appeal in the 1960s (Chapter 9.1). Environmental education was introduced into the Education curriculum by the late William Palmer, the Head of Biology at Homerton (see Fig. 66, Chapter 11). As an enthusiastic naturalist and member of the Wicken Fen Committee, he recognized the value of the Fen as a place where the basic principles of ecology and conservation could be taught.

The Fen's involvement with schools began in earnest with the appointment of Charles Mitchell in 1961. The Secretary of the Committee, Max Walters, clearly appreciated the Fen's potential for education and that, conversely, an effective education programme would become a necessary element in the development of the reserve: in 1964, he noted that the future lay 'with school and school teacher parties' and asked 'Are we to lead this trend or have action forced upon us?'[42]

The Fen soon became a popular venue for school study visits. In 1968 alone, there were 156 visiting party groups, and concern was expressed about the pressure from such numbers on the fragile nature of the Fen. Throughout the 1970s, the educational function of Wicken Fen was much discussed by the Committee, particularly with regard to protecting the Fen and demands on staff time; it was felt that such activities should not interfere substantially with the day-to-day management of the Fen. The case for continuing to encourage the younger age groups was strongly defended by the Warden, who argued that they were unlikely to exert damaging pressure on the habitats. A wide variety of questions was raised during the course of the debate: do Nature Reserves have a specific role in education? Should access be limited to university and higher education groups? Is a site such as Wicken Fen ideally suited to all levels of education, including the youngest age groups?

As pressure on the Sedge Fen mounted due to an increasing number of school groups, it was decided to set aside part of the reserve for their exclusive use. In 1986, an Education Area was established adjacent to St Edmund's Fen. This area includes a litter field and a number of new ponds designed expressly for sampling the freshwater habitat. The boardwalk (Chapter 11) has also become a major focus for educational groups keen to explore on their own: the circuit leads them through the main sights and sounds of the Fen and they cannot get lost.

To alleviate the demands on the Fen management staff, an Education Team of three was employed in 1987, with funding from the Community Programme of the Manpower Services Commission. Their brief was to develop the educational facilities at Wicken Fen and to encourage, and to work with, local visiting schools. The scheme lasted for two years, after which the National Trust assumed responsibility for the education service, appointing a part-time Education Warden, Sylvie Ballard. With further funding from the Trust, the post became full-time in 1990. The appointment of an Education Warden also serves to safeguard the fen habitats, in that numbers of visiting groups are controlled and a strict code of behaviour is observed. By 1993, more than 6,000 students, in 180 groups, were visiting the Fen annually. The capacity of the Fen for school groups is largely determined by the availability of staff at peak periods. Here, as in other aspects of Fen management, volunteers play a very active part.

In 1991, a scheme began whereby students from the Cambridge University Department of Education and Homerton College may gain extended professional experience by working at Wicken Fen. Students undertake a project, perhaps developing teaching material, in geography, history, biology or environmental studies, according to their main subject interests.

For the younger groups, the topics covered are wide-ranging, covering many of the attainment targets of the National Curriculum, but they are primarily designed to be fun. Learning about the social history of the Fens, puzzling over the identities of fenland flowers and seeking out 'creepy crawlies' from litter piles are as popular as the more usual pond-dipping. Resource materials are available to teachers, to help them to develop a programme for their visit to suit their individual needs. Occasionally, a topic or a National Curriculum attainment target is found in a surprising area: one group of 7–9-year-olds studied symmetry by observing dragonflies.

Junior age groups make up the majority of visiting schools and require the most attention from the Education Warden. The catchment area for Junior Schools is within an approximate radius of 35 miles of the Fen, although some travel much further as they specifically want to visit Wicken Fen and nowhere else will do. The younger visitors seem to have a natural empathy with the social and historical links with the fen environment and soak up the emotive sense of place. Older students have a more strongly intellectual approach and teachers accompanying Middle School and GCSE groups tend to be more specific in their knowledge and requirements. A-level, Higher Education and University groups, who may be tackling concepts such as

Conservation Management, usually avail themselves of an illustrated introductory talk by the Property Manager or Education Warden, whose enthusiasm and special local knowledge act as a catalyst to the students' own enquiries.

Once the need for conservation is recognized, many young people want to participate actively. There is no better way to learn about conservation than to practise it, and older students are encouraged to join one of the established voluntary associations, such as BTCV, and the National Trust's own Acorn projects. Wicken Fen received one of the early Council for Nature Conservation Corps work parties in 1960 (Fig. 71, Chapter 11) and the Fen owes much to the hundreds of young people who have worked there over the past three decades. The Ganges Hut provides a useful base for the work of conservation volunteers and is now also used by residential education groups.

Wicken Fen has another, more indirect, link with environmental education in Britain. In the 1940s, the Council for Promotion of Field Studies (now the Field Studies Council) was founded by Francis Butler, with an advisory team of biologists including Tansley and Godwin. Their plan, to provide residential centres in the countryside through which environmental education would be available to all, but especially to school children, can be recognized today as truly visionary. The first Field Centre was set up in 1943 at Flatford Mill in Suffolk, familiar to many as the subject of some of John Constable's best-loved paintings. Eric Ennion became the first Warden, leaving the medical practice in Burwell and his close association with Wicken Fen to do so. As an accomplished artist himself (Fig. 12, Chapter 4), and surrounded by inspiring landscape, Ennion provided classes for artists as well as for natural historians. A mix of subjects, a wide range of ages, and a warm family atmosphere remain the hallmarks of Flatford's style into the 1990s. The connection between Flatford and Wicken Fen has been maintained since Ennion's time through visits to the Fen by Flatford's botany courses and through the Field Centre's third Warden, F. J. Bingley, a member of the Wicken Fen Executive Committee in the 1960s and '70s and subsequently a member of the Local Advisory Panel (see Plate 11, Fig. 1).

The recent development of educational resources at the Fen reflects a growing commitment by the National Trust to expanding the educational role of its properties and to raising its profile as a conservation body. The children of today are the citizens and voters of tomorrow. If they learn to appreciate their local environment with a sense of wonder and responsibility, the countryside might be viewed a valuable and irreplaceable asset which they have a duty to conserve, as well as a right to enjoy.

EDUCATING THE PUBLIC: INTERPRETING THE FEN

Wicken Fen has become a popular place to visit. The National Trust has honoured its commitment to making the property accessible to the public by making available a network of footpaths, erecting hides and providing exhibitions in the William Thorpe Building and the Fen Cottage. All these measures not only enable the 30,000 or more visitors who visit the Fen each year to enjoy the reserve more fully but they also provide an opportunity to explain the objectives and practicalities of reserve management.

Confronted with the loss of fenland habitats and their species, few question the need for fenland reserves. However, there is a paradox about their management: reserves like Wicken Fen have been selected for their 'wildness' and yet they have to be managed almost as intensively as farmland. Reasons for this are obvious to naturalists, biologists and farmers who experience the dynamic nature of plant and animal communities and who perceive that the present communities depend on the ways previous generations exploited reed, sedge and water. But for most people the countryside appears more stable and static than it is, and so the need for management is not obvious. As the environment and conservation become increasingly important on the nation's agenda, it is vital that everyone should understand that conservation involves much more than putting a fence round a threatened habitat.

Conservation management costs money, and the public has a right to know why money has to be spent on managing nature reserves as well as on acquiring them in the first place. An entrance fee has been charged since 1979; while such a charge has obvious justification in stately homes with buildings and contents in constant need of repair, it is not apparent to some visitors to Wicken Fen why it is necessary to charge for what is, essentially, a walk in the countryside. Income from visitors (Fig. 75, Chapter 11) has made possible many of the Fen's major projects, such as the boardwalk, the restoration of the cottage, and the development of the conservation reed-beds (Chapter 4). It has also supported the development of a strong and dedicated wardening team. Wicken Fen has an important role in putting over the facts.

The need for active management of reserves like Wicken Fen is sometimes not fully appreciated by conservationists themselves: a visit to Wicken often changes their perception. An increasing number of international visitors from conservation bodies around the world are coming to the Fen, often through the auspices of the RSPB but sometimes through entomological and botanical contacts. In 1986, the Chairman of the Management Committee, Dr Norman Moore, was asked to make suggestions about the management of the 'Dragonfly Kingdom' at Ikedadani, near Nakamura in the Japanese island of Shikoku. This reserve was established to conserve its outstandingly rich dragonfly fauna: it supports no fewer than 64 species. Like Wicken Fen, it contains vulnerable habitats and is visited by thousands of people. Our experience with paths, the boardwalk, and the dipping pools for children, was particularly useful to the managers of the Japanese reserve.

The social history of Wicken Fen has until recently received rather less attention than the natural history. A museum of local tools and artefacts was opened in a small cottage in Lode Lane in 1958, but this was seriously damaged by fire in 1965. Although the building was repaired, the contents were dispersed and the museum was not reopened. In the late 1950s, the old windpump belonging to Bill Norman was rescued from dilapidation by Lord Fairhaven, who saw to its dismantling and restoration on its present site on the Sedge Fen by the wheelwright/millwright C. J. Ison. The windpump was further restored to working order in 1988, and has become one of the most evocative images of the Fen (Fig. 80). During the closing years of the 19th century, Norman's Mill was only one of about six pumps that would have been operating to move water through the drainage systems on Adventurers' Fen.[60,61] The windpump may be seen working, in full sail, on some windy days in high summer, when it is used to move water into Gardiner's Ditch (see Chapter 11). It has proved to be both cleaner and more efficient than the diesel pump, and is infinitely more beautiful. The Committee cherishes the idea of discovering and reconstructing another pump to move water through the new ditch-systems on Adventurers' Fen (Chapter 13).

Turf-digging on the Sedge Fen ceased before the National Trust took possession of the land (Chapter 10). However, in 1989, an experiment in reviving the traditional method of extraction began on the site of old diggings. Drawing on local memories of the practices current at Wicken at the turn of the century, two members of the wardening staff, Grant Lohoar and Sylvie Ballard, were able to establish an authentic method of working, assemble the necessary tools and discover how to use them.[62] As a direct link with the past, the first turf was cut by Alfie Sennitt, the son of one of the last local turf-cutters, using some of his father's tools.

Although methods and tools have been reconstructed, it has not so far been possible to recreate the correct conditions for turf-digging. In the last century, wind-driven pumps kept the ground dry enough for digging, but, with the demise of working pumps, and the recent restoration of higher water-levels on the Sedge Fen (Chapter 11), the new diggings have flooded and further workings will be impossible unless the water-table can be controlled in their vicinity.

The largest historical project undertaken to date has been the restoration of the small cottage, known as the Fen Cottage, 5 Lode Lane, close to the entrance to the reserve. Research into the history of the property has shown that the cottage was once two dwellings, but the exact date of their construction is as yet unknown. With twelve other similar dwellings, the cottages formed a hamlet known as 'The Lode' in the 18th and 19th centuries.

The livelihood of the people who lived in the hamlet was largely dependent on the Fen, where they cut sedge and litter, dug turf and clay, and caught wildfowl and fish.[63] Many of these goods were transported away from the community by fen boats, small versions of the fenland lighter (see Fig. 63, Chapter 11),[61] on Wicken Lode, while other goods, such as deals and timber, iron and lead, corn and wine, came into the community by the same route.[64]

The fabric of the cottages reflects the interdependency of the people and the Fen. Locally-found materials are used throughout: the bricks of the chimney stacks are made of gault clay; the walls are constructed of simple timber frames, using sawn timber or cut willow, infilled with tied reed bundles, overlaid with layers of gault clay and lime daub mixed with chopped sedge, and finished with a coating of lime plaster; in some places, turf (peat) has been used as the infill material; lime rendering on the outside walls provides a waterproof layer; the original roof was thatched entirely with sedge. During the restoration of the cottage in 1989 (Plate 16, Figs 1–4), 'like for like' materials and methods were used throughout, to achieve an honest repair.

Figure 80   The windpump, 8 August 1991

The interior has been furnished as it was in the 1930s, when George Butcher lived there after retiring from farming at Field Farm, Upware. George Butcher was born in 1852 in the thatched part of the cottage, which he bought in 1896 from the estate of his deceased sister Ann Elizabeth. He had previously purchased the tiled part in 1886 from Sarah Howlett, a widow. In 1925 the two dwellings were converted into one. During the winter of 1993/94, the original open (or, as it is called in Wicken, 'low') hearth was exposed in the tiled part of the cottage by removing the cast-iron fireplace and surrounding brickwork. The low hearth is now displayed to reveal the lifestyle of the inhabitants of a single-room dwelling in the 19th century, when turf would have been burned to provide heat for the room and for cooking. The census return for 1841 shows that David Howlett, his wife Sarah and their two children were living in the cottage at that time.

The cottage was officially opened in October 1990 by Lord Hemingford. Research continues to unfold the fascinating history of this property, and the presentation of the interior is gradually developing as information is uncovered and artefacts are discovered. The cottage was at first open to the public only on Sunday afternoons and Bank Holidays but it has attracted its own band of dedicated volunteers who make it possible to show the cottage at other times.

Wicken Fen's achievements in conservation have been recognized in the Europa Nostra Awards 1990, which are given to promote 'the protection of Europe's architectural and natural heritage'. A Diploma of Merit was awarded for the maintenance of water-levels, the restoration of the cottage and the construction of the boardwalk. The National Trust, in welcoming the award, summed up the Fen's achievement as illustrating 'the wide range of responsibilities which the Trust shoulders. The challenges of nature conservation, historic building restoration and public access are considered not as separate issues, but rather as elements of an integrated management which is central to the Trust's philosophy'.[65]

References

1 Tansley (1914)
2 Tansley (1935)
3 Godwin (1970), unpublished notes for exhibit; in archive.
4 Godwin (1978)
5 Richards (1932)
6 Richards (1952)
7 Hutchinson (1926), p. 243
8 Hutchinson (1989), letter in archive.
9 Hutchinson (1957)
10 Hutchinson (1967)
11 Hutchinson (1975)
12 Hutchinson (1993)
13 Conway (1936a)
14 Meredith (1978)
15 Harvey (1986)
16 Rowell et al. (1985)
17 Walters (1951)
18 Luck (1965)
19 Pollard (1981)
20 Pollard & Briggs (1984a)
21 Lahav-Ginott (1994)
22 Hollingsworth et al. (1995)
23 Dawson (1957)
24 Flowerdew et al. (1977)
25 Prŷs-Jones (1982)
26 Convey (1987)
27 Eagle (1994)
28 Duckworth (1990)
29 Jenkin (1928)

30 Jenkin (1982)
31 Polunin (1979)
32 Lee (1988)
33 Friday (1992)
34 Painter (1995)
35 Aldridge (in prep.)
36 Rowell (1983a)
37 Rowell (1988b)
38 Omer Cooper *et al.* (1928)
39 Gardiner (1932b)
40 Gardiner & Tansley (1923)
41 Gardiner (1925–32)
42 Wicken Fen Executive Committee Minute Books
43 Gardiner (1932c)
44 Bingley & Walters (1966)
45 Paul (1967)
46 Walters (1967)
47 Easy & Kirkland (1967)
48 Lock (1968)
49 Ball (1968)
50 Duffey (1970)
51 Smart (1972)
52 Emmet (1972)
53 Laundon (1973)
54 Flowerdew (1980)
55 Godwin & Bharucha (1932)
56 Gowing (1977)
57 Gilman (1988)
58 Pontin (1995)
59 Wicken Fen Local Management Committee Management Plan (1992)
60 Royal Commission on Historic Monuments (1972)
61 Friday & Ballard (in press)
62 Lohoar & Ballard (1992)
63 Wentworth-Day (1973)
64 Great Britain Statutes (1767), p. 93
65 The National Trust. Press release PR/91/1, 31 January 1991

13

The Next 100 Years

L. E. FRIDAY AND M. P. CHATFIELD

A S THIS BOOK is going to press, the reclamation of 52ha of former arable land adjacent to the National Trust land on Adventurers' Fen is well under way. The purchase of seven fields on Priory Farm effectively completes the 'jigsaw' of lands acquired by the Trust since the entomologist J. C. Moberley sold it the first few acres of the Sedge Fen in 1899 (Fig. 81).

From the earliest days, the Trust's policy at Wicken Fen has been to secure as much of the original fen as possible.[1] Most of the existing reserve was acquired during the first decades of the twentieth century, the largest contributor being G. H. Verrall, who managed to amass many tiny holdings, 239 acres in all, which he bequeathed to the Trust on his death in 1911.[2] The Hon. N. C. Rothschild similarly bought up and gave land, including 30 acres of Lapwing Farm on Adventurers' Fen. The land at the west end of Priory Farm was always looked upon as a highly desirable addition to the holdings: in both 1945 and 1952, the land became available, but the Committee was 'unable to take any action, however theoretically desirable.'[3]

Even if enough money had been found to buy the land, it is not clear what could have been achieved with it. Until very recently, the Fen staff have been fully stretched in attempting to restore the Sedge Fen to a semblance of its former glory, and the Priory Farm lands increase by about 25 per cent the size of the National Trust's holdings. However, there is now a feeling that the management of the Sedge Fen is under control. This is because investment in specialized machinery has produced considerable improvements in working efficiency and also because the Committee now agrees that the existing area of sedge and litter-fields is approaching the limit to what can reasonably be mown on a regular cycle.

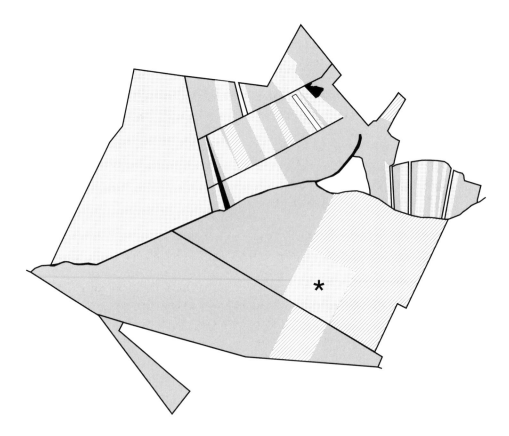

Figure 81   The sequence of land acquisition:

1899 (black): the original strip of land (2 acres) sold to the National Trust by Mr Moberley for £10

1900–1911 (light stipple): the '30 acres' bought in 1899 for £60 by The Hon. N. C. Rothschild and given to the Trust in 1901 is marked by an asterisk; virtually all of the remainder was bequeathed to the Trust by G. H. Verrall in 1911.

1912–1944 (heavy stipple): the majority of land on the Sedge Fen was acquired from the Aspland family, and on Adventurers' Fen from W. Norman.

1945–1994 (diagonal shading): the 52ha of Priory Farm land acquired in 1993 are distributed between the two large blocks in the south-east corner.

Commons and land still in private ownership are shown in white.

Thoughts have naturally turned to the land on the opposite bank of Wicken Lode. There were great plans for Adventurers' Fen when the lands was reclaimed from the Government in the 1950s, but after the first flush of ambitious activity, during which the Mere was excavated (Chapter 9.1), financial and physical constraints have prevented these ever coming to fruition. Dreams of creating a 'Marshland Reserve' have resurfaced from time to time, and it seems that these may now become reality.

When in 1992, Priory Farm again came on the market, the financial climate was somewhat different. Funds for the purchase were secured by generous grants from the Countryside Commission, East Cambridgeshire District Council, and Cambridgeshire County Council as well as from the National Trust. Furthermore, a ten-year Stewardship Scheme was entered into with the Countryside Commission which covers the entire National Trust land between Wicken Lode and Burwell Lode. The scheme allows for a payment per acre per annum, plus agreed sums for certain works throughout the ten years: the creation of ponds, scrapes and ditches and the conversion of the arable to wet grazing meadow.

The long-term nature of the Stewardship Agreement has provided the security essential to the Committee's decision to accept responsibility for the management of the Priory Farm land. At the same time, this very aspect of the scheme has posed problems: the details of the scheme had to be agreed at the outset, but since then many changes, some quite fundamental, have become necessary in order to achieve the original aims. This has required frequent negotiation with the Countryside Commission, and latterly with the Ministry of Agriculture, Fisheries & Food, which has assumed responsibility for the scheme.

The first steps towards restoring the arable land were taken in 1994. Land- and water-levels were surveyed and the potential for raising the water-table assessed. Scrapes and ponds were then excavated and the deep ditch network widened and the sides sculpted into shallow slopes (Fig. 82). The existing system of clay banks and waterproof membranes was extended to enclose the entire area and a system of internal dams installed in order to control the movement of water within the site.

It rapidly became evident, however, that the original plan for water management was hopelessly inadequate. In the wet winter of 1994–95, the internal controls failed to retain water in the areas intended and the fields awaiting seeding were flooded for many months. The ditches and scrapes were not behaving as anticipated and water was flowing freely between the fields because of previously unsuspected layers of sand and gravel in the peat. To make matters worse, the new ditches had been dug without regard for the sub-irrigation system installed by the previous landowner; indeed, no plans could be found to reveal the original pattern of the pipework so the influence that this system will have in draining or irrigating parts of Priory Farm must be deduced by trial and error.

The problem of water supply and control continues to exercise the Committee. The water-level in the original arable drainage system lay at almost two metres below the surface. To bring it close to the surface and maintain it at that level requires an additional one million cubic metres of water to be held within the boundary. Where will

Figure 82   New ditches and scrapes on Priory Farm land, January 1995

this water come from? Unlike the Sedge Fen, Adventurers' Fen is hydrologically isolated from the lode system and must rely on water abstraction to make good losses due
to evaporation, which may amount to the equivalent of one metre's depth in a hot
summer. Abstraction from the lodes is not possible during the summer, so it will be
necessary to draw off water during the winter and store it for release in summer. These
fundamental changes in the provision and management of water of the reserve are
incorporated in a water-level management plan designed for the Fen's immediate
hydrological area drawn up in 1996 by the Environment Agency (formerly the NRA).[4]

The task of creating grazing pasture has been undertaken by the Institute of
Terrestrial Ecology, Monks Wood, as part of a wider project on practical methods of
wetland restoration. After the vestiges of the crops and volunteer weed growth were
dealt with and the ground prepared, most of the area was sown, in April 1995, with a
mixture of 'British-grown' grass seeds (principally creeping bent (*Agrostis stolonifera*), red
fescue (*Festuca rubra*) and rough meadow-grass (*Poa trivialis*)). About 15ha were left to
develop a cover of vegetation, from the soil seed-bank and by natural colonization.

In the first summer, all the fields, but particularly the 'natural regeneration' area,
produced a magnificent growth of agricultural weeds. Several new species were added
to the Fen flora, including potato (*Solanum tuberosum*) and linseed (*Linum usitatissimum*).
This weed-growth posed a serious threat to the establishment of a grass sward and had
to be cut repeatedly. The grass seedlings suffered a second setback as one of the driest
summers on record took hold and it finally proved necessary to reseed the area in
October 1995.

Growth has subsequently been much better and the sward has been sufficiently robust to support grazing by sheep. In future, cattle will be used: our experience of grazing on the existing areas of Adventurers' Fen suggests that cattle produce the sort of rough surface that favours some of the Fen's more unusual vascular plants and invertebrates.[5] The effects of grazing on the composition of the sward will be carefully monitored and stocking levels adjusted in order to prevent rushes becoming dominant as they have on parts of Adventurers' Fen.

At the centre of the site lies the '30 acres' given to the Trust by the Hon. Charles Rothschild and the scene of Alan Bloom's titanic struggle with scrub and bog-oaks (Chapter 11). Bloom eventually succeeded in 'reclaiming' the '30 acres' in the 1940s and they have been under cultivation ever since. These three fields are being used for an experiment on the effect of different water-table heights on the establishment of fen herb species. A hydrological gradient exists across the fields, such that in some areas the water-table is at the same level as the surrounding land, while some areas are, on average, wetter, and others are drier. The experimental fields have been sown with grasses in the same way as the rest of the land, but experimental plots have been planted with herbs raised from Wicken material: devil's-bit scabious (*Succisa pratensis*), ragged-robin (*Lychnis flos-cuculi*), meadow thistle (*Cirsium dissectum*), meadowsweet (*Filipendula ulmaria*), common meadow-rue (*Thalictrum flavum*) and water mint (*Mentha aquatica*). The fields will then be grazed. These six species can be expected to show varying responses to the different water-tables, and possibly also to grazing – the fields will be grazed under the same regime as the rest of the site.

The acquisition of the Priory Farm land has given impetus to a review of the management of the entire area known as Adventurers' Fen. After wide consultation with the Local Advisory Panel, the RSPB, the Environment Agency and others, the Management Committee has decided to attempt to increase the area of reed along the southern boundary of the reserve by positive hydrological management. In this way, we hope to increase the chances of attracting birds dependent on this particular habitat; it is perhaps our only hope of again having bittern (*Botaurus stellaris*) breeding on the Fen.

The area immediately surrounding the Mere has received very little positive management since the 1950s. As part of the Stewardship scheme, the area of scrapes around the Mere has been greatly increased and a more rigorous regime of cattle-grazing initiated. We have already been rewarded by lapwing (*Vanellus vanellus*) breeding successfully for the first time for several years (Chapter 9.4) The spoil from the scrapes has been used to produce a bank which will not only screen the new water-bodies from the public, but it also accommodates hides from which waterfowl can be watched without undue disturbance. This development is very much in keeping with the ethos of the Stewardship scheme of making the land accessible to the public. There are, however, some wonderfully green and secret places in the centre of Adventurers' Fen that are best left to moorhen, coot and great-crested grebes.

* * *

We are sometimes asked what we are trying to achieve by all this activity at Wicken Fen. Perhaps the simplest answer is that we are trying to take the Fen backwards through time, to restore some of the biological diversity lost since the turn of the century. It is hard to read Alan Bloom's account of his struggle to drain and cultivate Adventurers' Fen[6] or to watch the film he made of his efforts[7] without admiration and heartfelt recognition of his excellent intentions. And yet we embark on undoing his work without regret: Britain is not at present in a state of food shortage and agricultural land all over the country is coming out of production. Now is an excellent time to attempt to restore lost wetland habitats and fenland species, and to recreate a landscape that has all but disappeared in 20th-century Britain.

References

1 Gardiner (1928), pp. 382–383
2 National Trust (1923)
3 Wicken Fen Executive Committee Minutes (17 September 1952)
4 Environment Agency (1996)
5 Perry (17 January 1993), letter in archive
6 Bloom (1944)
7 'Reclaimation 1941', archive film, East Anglian Film Archive

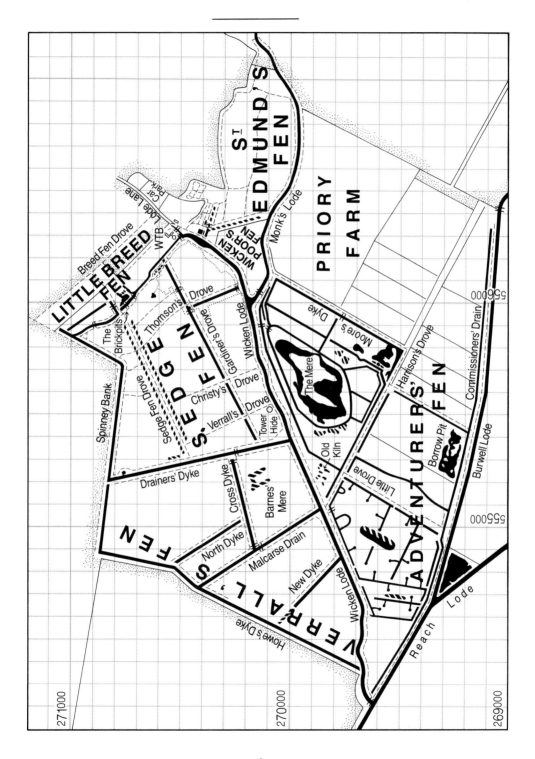

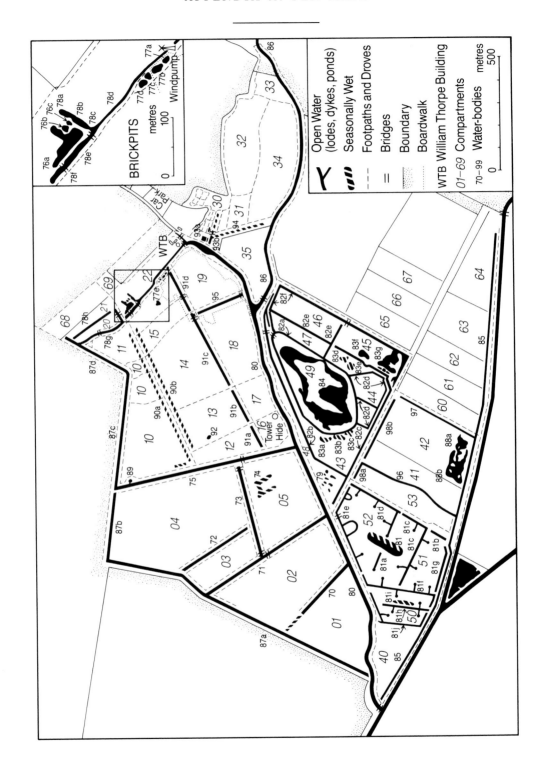

APPENDIX B: THE MANAGEMENT YEAR

G. LOHOAR

Table B1: Approximate allocation of time (man days) to different tasks in 1989. The time taken by different tasks varies considerably from year to year due to weather, changes in techniques and adoption of new projects. The 1989 figures illustrate the dominance of the reed harvest after the reed fields had been expanded and before the task was shared with the thatcher (see Chapter 4); the reed harvest accounted for only 74 man days in 1990.

	Wardens*	Volunteers	% Total
Reed harvest	126		11.0
Sedge harvest	76	31	9.4
Scrub	37	57	8.2
General work	94		8.2
Administration	93		8.2
Machinery	87		7.6
Maintenance	85		7.5
Visitors	82		7.2
Summer litter	32	33	5.7
Paths and droves	59		5.2
Wardening	46		4.0
Reed-bed conservation	45		3.9
Meetings/talks	25		2.2
Spring litter	20		1.7
Mere	12	6	1.6
Brinking	18		1.6
Autumn litter	17		1.5
Boardwalk	17		1.5
Adventurers' Fen	12		1.0
Amenity mowing	7		0.6
Biological monitoring	5		0.5
TOTAL MAN DAYS	1013	127	

TOTAL MAN DAYS INCLUDING VOLUNTEERS = 1140

* These figures do not include the Education Warden, who is engaged with education and interpretation on a full-time basis throughout the year.

Table B2: Seasonal work patterns (man days per month, including volunteers) in 1989

	J	F	M	A	M	J	J	A	S	O	N	D
Reed harvest	35	44	11	15	16							
Reed-bed conservation	24	11	11	1								
Mere	3					1	12	2				
Biological monitoring			1		1	1		1	1			
Spring litter				18	2							
Paths & droves				3	2		3	1	1	32	7	10
Brinking						7					12	
Boardwalk						1	4	3	1		8	
Summer litter							40	22				
Autumn litter									16	1	1	
Scrub	5	2	9	23			44	28	1		4	5
Maintenance	3	10	26	15	5	3	1	5	13	4		
Machinery	4	2	1	18	18	8	1	15	6	3	4	7
Visitors	7	6	9	6	12	6	6	8	6	6	5	5
Wardening	2	2	3	5	10	4	3	3	1	3	5	5
Administration	7	7	5	8	7	6	9	9	9	7	9	9
General work	1	3	2	4	3	7	7	5	15	15	16	16
	J	F	M	A	M	J	J	A	S	O	N	D

REFERENCES

Notes:

NHWF = *The Natural History of Wicken Fen*, 6 volumes: 1923, Gardiner, J. S. & Tansley, A. G. (eds); 1925, 1926, 1928, 1929, 1932, Gardiner, J. S. (ed.). Cambridge, Bowes & Bowes.
NT (WFLC) = National Trust, the Wicken Fen Local Committee.
Numbers in square brackets indicate chapters in which references occur; P indicates Preface.

Aldridge, D. C. (in prep.). PhD thesis, University of Cambridge. [3,11,12] *Reproductive ecology of bitterling (Rhodeus sericeus Pallas) and unionid mussels.*

Atkinson, R. (1996). The effect of reed cutting in Wicken Lode on the winter distribution and abundance of fish and macroinvertebrates. MS. in Fen archive. [11]

Babington, A. M. (ed.) (1897). *Memorials, Journal and Botanical Correspondence of Charles Cardale Babington.* Cambridge, Macmillan & Bowes. [7]

Babington, C. C. (1857). *Senecio paludosus. Phytologist* (New Series) **2**: 303. [7]

—— (1860). *Flora of Cambridgeshire.* London, van Voorst. [5,6,7,10]

Baillie, S. R. & Peach, W. J. (1992). Population limitation in Palaearctic African migrant passerines. *Ibis* supplement **1**: 120–132. [9]

Balfour-Browne, F. (1926). The aquatic Coleoptera of the Wicken Fen area, Cambridgeshire. *In* Gardiner J. S. (ed.), *NHWF*, pp. 201–216. [3]

Ball, I. (1968). *The freshwater triclads of Wicken Fen.* Guides to Wicken Fen, No. 6. Wicken, NT (WFLC). [12]

Barnett, S. F. & Green, R. E. (1972). Bird ticks. *Wicken Fen Group Report* **4**: 34–35. [9]

Bennett, T. J. (1988). Butterflies and butterfly-watching in Cambridgeshire. *Nature in Cambridgeshire* **30**: 31–35. [8]

Bibby, C. J. (1968). Report on ringing at Wicken Fen in summer 1968. [9]

—— (1970). Population estimates and mist netting: An Interim Report. *Wicken Fen Group Report* **2**: 26–29. [9]

—— (1971). Survival of Reed and Sedge Warblers. *Wicken Fen Group Report* **3**: 19–23. [9]

—— (1973a). The mass coverage weekends. *Wicken Fen Group Report* **5**: 18–21. [9]

—— (1973b). Bullfinch survival and populations. *Wicken Fen Group Report* **5**: 25–27. [9]

—— (1974). Bearded Tits in Cambridgeshire and Huntingdonshire, 1972–74. *Cambridge Bird Club Report for 1973* **47**: 56–58. [9]

—— (1977). Observations on the moult of the Tree Sparrow. *Ringing & Migration* **1**: 148–157. [9]

—— (1981). Wintering Bitterns in Britain. *British Birds* **74**: 1–10. [9]

—— & Lunn, J. (1982). Conservation of reed-beds and their avifauna in England and Wales. *Biological Conservation* **23**: 167–186. [4 9]

Bingley, F. J. & Walters, S. M. (1966). *Wicken Sedge Fen, a topographical and botanical guide.* Guides to Wicken Fen, No. 1. Wicken, NT (WFLC). [12]

Bircham, P. M. M. (1970). Weight changes in the Lesser Redpoll. *Wicken Fen Group Report* **2**: 32–33. [9]

—— (1972). Diurnal and seasonal weight changes of the Redpoll. *Wicken Fen Group Report* **4**: 30–31. [9]

—— (1974). Management work 1974. *Wicken Fen Group Report* **6**: 22–23. [9]

—— (1978). Migration and movements of birds ringed at Wicken Fen. The first ten years. *Wicken Fen Group Report* **10**: 22–28. [9]

—— (1983). Standardised mist netting results 1982. *Wicken Fen Group Report* **12**: 12–14. [9]

—— (1989) *The Birds of Cambridgeshire.* Cambridge, University Press. [9]

Bloom, A. H. V. (1944). *The Farm in the Fen.* London, Faber & Faber. [4,9,10,11,13]

Briggs, D., Block, M. & Jennings, S. (1989). The possibility of determining the age of colonies of clonally propagating herbaceous species from historic records: the case of *Aster novi-belgii* L. (first recorded as *A. salignus* Willd.) at Wicken Fen Nature Reserve, Cambridgeshire. *New Phytologist* **112**: 577–584. [7]

Brindley, H. H. (1904). The Mollusca of Cambridgeshire. *In* Marr, J. E. & Shipley, A. E. (eds), *Handbook to the Natural History of Cambridgeshire*, pp. 114–138. Cambridge, University Press. [3]

—— (1925). The Mollusca of Wicken Fen. *In* Gardiner, J. S. (ed.), *NHWF*, pp. 154–162. [3]

Brooke, M. de L. & Davies, N. B. (1987). Recent changes in host usage by Cuckoos *Cuculus canorus* in Britain. *Journal of Animal Ecology* **56**: 873–883. [9]

—— & —— (1988). Egg mimicry by Cuckoos *Cuculus canorus* in relation to discrimination by hosts. *Nature* **335**: 630–632. [9]

—— & —— (1989). Provisioning of nestling Cuckoos *Cuculus canorus* by Reed Warbler *Acrocephalus scirpaceus* hosts. *Ibis* **131**: 250–256. [9]

Buckland, S. T. & Baillie, S. R. (1987). Estimating bird survival rates from organised mist netting programmes. *Acta Ornithologica* **23**: 89–100. [9]

Burgess, N. D. & Evans, C. E. (1988). *The management of reed-beds for birds. Management Case Study*. Sandy, RSPB. [4]

Burrows, C. N. R. (1902). British Lepidoptera in 1902. *Entomologist's Record and Journal of Variation* **14**: 284. [11]

Cadbury, C. J. (1983). Survey of Breeding Wildfowl and Waders of Wet Grasslands in Cambridgeshire, 1980 and 1982. *Cambridge Bird Club Report for 1982* **56**: 28–34. [9]

——, Green, R. E. & Allport, G. (1987). Redshanks and Other Breeding Waders of British Saltmarshes. *RSPB Conservation Review* **1**: 37–40. [9]

Cantabrigia Depicta (1763) A concise and accurate description of the University and town of Cambridge, and its environs. Cambridge, J. Bentham, for W. Thurlbourn & J. Woodyer. [10]

Chalmers-Hunt, J. M. (1966). Early photograph taken at Wicken Fen, Cambridgeshire, with notes on its associations. *Entomologist's Record and Journal of Variation* **78**: 298. [10]

Chance, E. P. (1940). *The Truth About The Cuckoo*. London, Country Life. [9]

Clapham, A. R., Tutin, T. G. & Moore, D. M. (1987). *Flora of the British Isles* (edn 3). Cambridge, University Press. [7]

Clarke, R. (1986). Hen Harrier Winter Roost Survey in Cambridgeshire. *Cambridge Bird Club Report for 1985* **59**: 44–48. [9]

Convey, P. (1987). *Influences on mating behaviour and reproductive success in the Odonata*. PhD thesis, University of Cambridge. [12]

—— (1989). Influences on the choice between territorial and satellite behaviour in male *Libellula quadrimaculata* Linn. (Odonata: Libellulidae). *Behaviour* **109**: 125–141. [8]

Conway, V. M. (1936a). *Studies in the autecology of* Cladium mariscus *R.Br.* PhD thesis, University of Cambridge. [12]

—— (1936b). Studies in the autecology of *Cladium mariscus* R. Br. I. Structure and development. *New Phytologist* **35**: 177–204. [5]

—— (1936c). Studies in the autecology of *Cladium mariscus* R. Br. II. Environmental conditions at Wicken Fen, with special reference to soil temperatures and the soil atmosphere. *New Phytologist* **35**: 359–380. [5]

—— (1937). Studies in the autecology of *Cladium mariscus* R. Br. III. The aeration of the subterranean parts of the plant. *New Phytologist* **36**: 64–96. [5]

—— (1938a). Studies in the autecology of *Cladium mariscus* R. Br. IV. Growth rate of the leaves. *New Phytologist* **37**: 254–278. [5]

—— (1938b). Studies in the autecology of *Cladium mariscus* R. Br. V. The distribution of the species. *New Phytologist* **37**: 312–328. [5,11]

Corbet, S. A., Perrin, R. M. S., Hartley, D. R., Lancashire, P. D., Mace, H. A. F., McClay, A. S., Morton, J. R., Parfitt, R. E., Reid, D. G., Tomiak, R. H. H., Wheatley, K., Willmer, P. G. & Willows, R. I. (1980). Diel changes in plankton and water chemistry in Wicken brickpit. *Hydrobiologia* **74**: 249–271. [3]

Cowie, N. R., Sutherland, W. J., Ditlhogo, M. K. M. & James, R. (1992). The effect of conservation management of reed-beds. II. The flora and litter disappearance. *Journal of Applied Ecology* **29**: 277–284. [4]

Cripps, D. (1984). *Copper and arsenic pollution of Borth Bog*. BSc. thesis, Biology Department, University of Wales at Aberystwyth. [11]

Darby, H. C. (1983). *The Changing Fenland*. Cambridge, University Press. [1]

David, R. W. (1990). The distribution of *Carex appropinquata* Schumacher (*C. paradoxa* Willd.) in Great Britain and Ireland. *Watsonia* **18**: 201–4. [7]

Davies, N. B. & Brooke, M. de L. (1988). Cuckoos versus Reed Warblers: adaptations and counteradaptations. *Animal Behaviour* **36**: 262–284. [9]

—— & —— (1989a). An experimental study of co-evolution between the Cuckoo *Cuculus canorus* and its hosts. I. Host egg discrimination. *Journal of Animal Ecology* **58**: 207–224. [9]

—— & —— (1989b). An experimental study of co-evolution between the Cuckoo, *Cuculus canorus*, and its hosts. II. Host egg markings, chick discrimination and general discussion. *Journal of Animal Ecology* **58**: 225–236. [9]

—— & —— (1991). Co-evolution of the Cuckoo and its hosts. *Scientific American* **264**: 66–73. [9]

—— & Green, R. E. (1976). The development and ecological significance of feeding techniques in the Reed Warbler. *Animal Behaviour* **24**: 213–229. [9]

Dawson, N. (1957). *The ecology of Fenland Carabidae*. PhD thesis, University of Cambridge. [12]

—— (1965). A comparative study of the ecology of eight species of Fenland Carabidae (Coleoptera). *Journal of Animal Ecology* **34**: 299–314. [5]

Day, J. (1988). Marsh Harriers in Britain. *RSPB Conservation Review* **2**: 17–19 [9]

Day, J. C. U. (1981). Status of Bitterns in Europe since 1976. *British Birds* **74**: 10–16. [9]

Dempster, J. P. (1976). The swallowtail butterfly at Wicken Fen. *Nature in Cambridgeshire* **19**: 11–14. [8]

—— (1995). The ecology and conservation of the Swallowtail butterfly (*Papilio machaon* L.) in Britain. *In* Pullin, A. S. (ed.), *Ecology and Conservation of Butterflies*, pp. 137–149. London, Chapman & Hall. [5,11]

—— & Hall, M. L. (1980). An attempt at re-establishing the swallowtail butterfly at Wicken Fen. *Ecological Entomology* **5**: 327–334. [8]

——, King, M. L. & Lakhani, K. H. (1976). The status of the swallowtail butterfly in Britain. *Ecological Entomology* **1**: 71–84. [8]

Ditlhogo, M. K. M., James, R., Laurence, B. R. & Sutherland, W. J. (1992). The effect of conservation management of reed-beds. I. The invertebrates. *Journal of Applied Ecology* **29**: 265–276. [4]

Duckworth, J. W. (1990). *Parental care in the Reed Warbler*. PhD thesis, University of Cambridge. [12]

—— (1991). Responses of breeding Reed Warbler *Acrocephalus scirpaceus* to mounts of Sparrowhawk *Accipter nisus*, Cuckoo *Cuculus canorus* and Jay *Garrulus glandarius*. *Ibis* **133**: 68–74. [9]

Duffey, E. (1970). *The spiders of Wicken Fen*. Guides to Wicken Fen, No. 7. Wicken, NT (WFLC). [12]

Eagle, D. M. (1994). *Grouping behaviour as a defence against predation in whirligig beetles*. PhD thesis, University of Cambridge [12]

Eastham, L. E. S. (1932). Wicken Fen fauna: a review. *In* Gardiner, J. S. (ed.), *NHWF*, pp. 630–636. [3]

Easy, G. M. S. & Kirtland, C. A. E. (1967). *Birds of Wicken Fen*. Guides to Wicken Fen, No. 4. Wicken, NT (WFLC). [9,12]

Emmet, A. M. (1972). Microlepidoptera of Wicken Fen: an annotated check list. *Proceedings of the British Entomological and Natural History Society* **5**(2): 52–74. Reprinted as No. 9 of the Guides to Wicken Fen. [8,12]

Ennion, E. A. R. (1942). *Adventurers Fen* (edn 1). London, Methuen. [4,9]

—— (1949). *Adventurers Fen* (edn 2). London, Herbert Jenkins. [4,11]

Environment Agency (1996). Water Level Management Plan for Wicken Fen. [13]

Evans, A. H. (1904). The birds of Cambridgeshire. *In* Marr, J. E. & Shipley, A. E. (eds), *Handbook to the Natural History of Cambridgeshire*, pp. 75–99. Cambridge, University Press. [9]

—— (1911). A short flora of Cambridgeshire, chiefly from an ecological standpoint, with a history of its chief botanists. *Proceedings of the Cambridge Philosophical Society* **16**: 197–284. [6]

Evans, A. H. (1923a). The Fens of the Great Level, their drainage, and its effect on the flora and fauna. *In* Gardiner, J. S. & Tansley, A. G. (eds), *NHWF*, pp. 3–49. [3,7,9,10]

—— (1923b). Full list of plants growing in the Old Fen land at Wicken. *In* Gardiner, J. S. & Tansley, A. G. (eds), *NHWF*, pp. 50–51. [3,7]

—— (1925). Wicken and Burwell Fens fifty years ago & now. *In* Gardiner, J. S. (ed.), *NHWF*, pp. 87–91. [5,6,10,11]

—— (1939). *A Flora of Cambridgeshire*. London, Gurney & Jackson. [5,7]

Everett, M. J. (1989). Reedbeds – a scarce habitat. *RSPB Conservation Review* **3**: 14–19. [9]

Falk, S. J. (1991). *A review of the scarce and threatened flies of Great Britain*. Part 1. (Research and Survey in Nature Conservation No. 39). Peterborough, Nature Conservancy Council. [8]

Farren, W. S. (1926a). Memories of Wicken. *In* Gardiner J. S. (ed.), *NHWF*, pp. 173–189. [5,10,11]

—— (1926b) A note on the levels of the Fens around Wicken. *In* Gardiner, J. S. (ed.), *NHWF*, pp. 190–197. [2]

Flowerdew, J. R. (1980). *The mammals of Wicken Fen*. Guides to Wicken Fen, No. 11. Wicken, NT (WFLC). [12]

——, Hall, S. J. G. & Brown, J. C. (1977). Small rodents, their habitats, and the effects of flooding at Wicken Fen, Cambridgeshire. *Journal of Zoology* **182**: 323–342. [5,12]

Fojt, W. (1994). The conservation of British Fens. *British Wildlife* **5**: 355–366. [P]

Foster, J. E. (ed.) (1905). *Churchwardens' Accounts of St. Mary the Great, Cambridge from 1504 to 1635*. Cambridge. [10]

Fowler, G. (1933). Fenland waterways, past and present; South Level District, Part 1. *Cambridge Antiquarian Society Proceedings and Communications* **33**: 108–128. [10]

Fox, A. D. & Salmon, D. G. (1989) The winter status and distribution of gadwall in Britain and Ireland. *Bird Study* **36**: 37–44. [9]

Friday, L. E. (1988). *Utricularia vulgaris*, an aquatic carnivore at Wicken Fen. *Nature in Cambridgeshire* **30**: 50–54. [3]

—— (1992). Measuring investment in carnivory: seasonal and individual variation in trap number and biomass in *Utricularia vulgaris* L. *New Phytologist* **121**: 439–445. [12]

—— (1994). Wicken Fen: the management of a nature reserve. *In* Harrison R. (ed.), *Manual of Heritage Management*, pp. 135–139. Oxford, Butterworth Heinemann. [11]

—— & Ballard, S. M. (in press). Wicken Fen, June 13, 1923: an annotated extract from the Diary of Robert Gurney. *Nature in Cambridgshire*. [10,12]

——, Grubb, P. J. & Coombe, D. C. (in prep.) Studies in the ecology of Wicken Fen: the Godwin Plots revisited. [5]

Gardiner, J. S. (ed.) (1925–32). *The Natural History of Wicken Fen* **2–6**. Cambridge, Bowes & Bowes. [P,3,9,12]

—— (1928). Wicken Fen. *In* Gardiner, J. S. (ed.), *NHWF*, pp. 371–384. [P,3,5,13]

—— (1932a). Omissions and additions. *In* Gardiner, J. S. (ed.), *NHWF*, pp. 644–648. [3]

—— (1932b). Preface. *In* Gardiner, J. S. (ed.), *NHWF*, pp. iii–viii (bound at end of Vol. VI). [P,10,12]

—— (1932c). *A Guide to Wicken Fen*. London, National Trust. [11,12]

—— & Tansley, A. G. (eds) (1923). *The Natural History of Wicken Fen* **1**. Cambridge, Bowes & Bowes. [P,3,9,12]

Geltman, D. V. (1992). *Urtica galeopsifolia* Wierzb. ex Opiz (Urticaceae) in Wicken Fen (E. England). *Watsonia* **19**: 127–129. [7]

Gibbons, D. W., Reid, J. B. & Chapman, R. A. (1993). *The New Atlas of Breeding Birds in Britain and Ireland: 1988–1991*. London, T. & A.D. Poyser. [9]

Gilman, K. (1988). *The hydrology of Wicken Fen*. Final Report. Llanbrynmair, Institute of Hydrology. [2,12]

Godwin, H. (1929). The 'sedge' and 'litter' of Wicken Fen. *Journal of Ecology* **17**: 148–160. [5,6,11]

—— (1931). Studies in the ecology of Wicken Fen. I. The ground water level of the Fen. *Journal of Ecology* **19**: 449–473. [2]

—— (1932). The Fen Fire of 1929 and its effects on vegetation. *In* Gardiner, J. S. (ed.), *NHWF*, pp. 595–600. [5]

—— (1936). Studies in the ecology of Wicken Fen. III. The establishment and development of fen scrub (carr). *Journal of Ecology* **24**: 82–111. [6]

—— (1941a). Studies of the post-glacial history of British Vegetation. II. Fenland pollen diagrams. *Philosophical Transactions of the Royal Society, series B* **230**: 239–284. [10]

—— (1941b). Studies in the ecology of Wicken Fen. IV. Crop-taking experiments. *Journal of Ecology* **29**: 83–106. [5,11]

—— (1978). *Fenland: Its Ancient Past and Uncertain Future.* Cambridge, University Press. [10,11,12]

—— (1985). *Cambridge and Clare.* Cambridge, University Press. [8]

—— & Bharucha, F. R. (1932). Studies in the ecology of Wicken Fen. II. The fen water table and its control of plant communities. *Journal of Ecology* **20**: 157–191 [2,5,6,11,12]

—— & Tansley, A. G. (1929). The vegetation of Wicken Fen. *In* Gardiner, J. S. (ed.), *NHWF*, pp. 385–446. [5,7,10]

——, Clowes, D. R. & Huntley, B. (1974) Studies in the ecology of Wicken Fen. V. Development of fen carr. *Journal of Ecology* **62**: 197–214. [6]

Gooch, W. (1813) *General View of the Agriculture of Cambridgeshire.* London, Neely & Jones. [10]

Gowing, J. W. (1977). *The hydrology of Wicken Fen and its influence on the acidity of the soil.* MSc thesis, Cranfield Institute of Technology. [2,12]

Great Britain Statutes (1767). *An Act for draining part of the Bedford Level.* London. [12]

Green, R. E. (1971). Temperatures of Reed and Sedge Warblers. *Wicken Fen Group Report* **3**: 33–35. [9]

—— (1974). A new approach to moult studies. *Wicken Fen Group Report* **6**: 37–41. [9]

—— (1975). The survival rate of adult Reed Warblers. *Wicken Fen Group Report* **7**: 16–21. [9]

—— (1976). Adult survival rates for Reed and Sedge Warblers. *Wicken Fen Group Report* **8**: 23–26. [9]

—— (1985). Estimating the abundance of breeding snipe. *Bird Study* **32**: 141–149. [9]

—— & Cadbury, C. J. (1987). Breeding Waders of Lowland Wet Grasslands. *RSPB Conservation Review* **1**: 10–13. [9]

Griffiths, B. M. (1925). The phytoplankton of the Wicken Fen area. *In* Gardiner, J. S. (ed.), *NHWF*, pp. 116–121. [3]

Harris, T. W. (1926). Notes on the flora of the experimental pond. *In* Gardiner J. S. (ed.), *NHWF*, pp. 255–257. [3]

Harvey, H. J. (1969). Diurnal and seasonal changes in Reed Warbler and Sedge Warbler weights. *Wicken Fen Group Report* **1**: 17–22. [9]

—— (1974). Automatic data handling. II. The wing length of adult Reed Warblers. *Wicken Fen Group Report* **6**: 7–11. [9]

—— (1986). Monitoring the fen dandelion at Wicken Fen. *Nature in Cambridgeshire* **28**: 35–39. [7,12]

—— & Meredith, T. C. (1981). Ecological studies of *Peucedanum palustre* and their implications for conservation management at Wicken Fen, Cambridgeshire. *In* Synge, H. (ed.), *The Biological Aspects of Rare Plant Conservation*, pp. 365–377. London, John Wiley & Son. [5]

Haslam, S. M. (1972). *The Reed* (edn 2), 43pp. Norwich, Norfolk Reed Growers Association. [4]

Hollingsworth, P. M., Gornall, R. J. & Preston, C. D. (1995). Genetic variability in British populations of *Potamogeton coloratus* (Potamogetonaceae). *Plant Systematics & Evolution* **197**: 71–85. [11,12]

Hubbard, C. E. (1968). *Grasses* (edn 2). Harmondsworth, Penguin Books Ltd. [7]

Hughes, A. E (1983). A study of Blackbird weights through the year at Wicken Fen. *Wicken Fen Group Report* **12**: 19–22. [9]

Hutchinson, G. E. (1926). Hemiptera–Heteroptera. Part 1. Hydrobiotica and Sandalioryncha. *In* Gardiner, J. S. (ed.), *NHWF*, pp. 234–252. [3,12]

—— (1957). *A Treatise on Limnology. I. Geography, Physics and Chemistry.* New York, Wiley. [12]

—— (1967). *A Treatise on Limnology. II. Introduction to Lake Biology and the Limnoplankton.* New York, Wiley. [12]

—— (1975). *A Treatise on Limnology. III. Limnological Botany.* New York, Wiley-Interscience. [12]

Hutchinson, G. E. (1993). *A Treatise on Limnology. IV. The Zoobenthos* (Y. H. Edmondson (ed.)). New York, John Wiley & Son. [12]

Innes, J. L. (1977). Adult survival rates for Blue and Long-tailed Tits. *Wicken Fen Group Report* **9**: 14–16. [9]

—— (1978). Annual survival of Wrens and Dunnocks. *Wicken Fen Group Report* **10**: 16–19. [9]

Jenkin, P. M. (1928). The Cladocera of Wicken Fen. *In* Gardiner, J. S. (ed.), *NHWF*, pp. 356–365. [3,12]

—— (1982). Temperature, hydrochemistry and plankton in Wicken brickpits 1930–1. *Hydrobiologia* **97**: 37–61. [3,12]

Jenyns, L. (1845). On the turf of the Cambridgeshire Fens. *Transactions of the Sections of the British Association* 1845: 75–76. [6,11]

Johnson, R. (1985). *An investigation into the cyprinid hybrid community of Wicken Fen Mere.* Unpublished report, pp. 34–93. Huntingdon, Anglian Water Authority. [3]

Kemp, J. (1981). Breeding long-eared owls in West Norfolk. *Norfolk Bird and Mammal Report for 1980* **25**(5): 262–264. [9]

Kerrich, G. J. & Spooner, G. M. (attrib. G. J. Kerrich) (1938) Hymenoptera. *In* Imms, A. D. (ed.), *Victoria County History of Cambridgeshire and the Isle of Ely* **1**: 162–189. [8]

Lack, D. (1934). *Birds of Cambridgeshire.* Cambridge, Cambridge Bird Club. [9]

Lack, P. (1986). *The Atlas of Wintering Birds in Britain and Ireland.* Calton, T. & A. D. Poyser. [9]

Lahav-Ginott, S. (1994). *Characteristics of dioecy in nettles (Urticaceae).* PhD thesis, University of Cambridge. [7,12]

Langslow, D. R. (1971). Wing length and brood patches as a guide to sexing Willow Warblers and Chiffchaffs. *Wicken Fen Group Report* **3**: 30–32. [9]

Laundon, J. R. (1973). *Lichens of Wicken Fen.* Guides to Wicken Fen, No. 10. Wicken, NT (WFLC). [6,12]

Lee, D. G. (1988). *Environmental change and freshwater macroinvertebrates at Wicken Fen, Cambridgeshire.* PhD thesis, University of Cambridge. [3,12]

Lewis, D. J. (1932). The mosquitoes of Wicken Fen. *In* Gardiner, J. S. (ed.), *NHWF*, pp. 548–559. [3,8]

Lindley, K. (1982). *Fenland Riots and the English Revolution.* London, Heinemann Educational. [10]

Lock, J. M. (1963). Recent bryophyte records from Wicken Fen. *Nature in Cambridgeshire* **7**: 34–38. [6]

—— (1968). *List of the bryophytes of Wicken Fen.* Guides to Wicken Fen, No. 5. Wicken, NT (WFLC). [12]

—— (1972). *Survey of St Edmund's Fen.* Report to the Executive Committee. MS. in archive. [11]

Lohoar, G. & Ballard, S. (1992). *Turf-digging at Wicken Fen.* Wicken, NT (WFLC). [11,12]

Lousley, J. E. & Kent, D. (1981). *Docks and Knotweeds of the British Isles.* BSBI Handbook No. 3, pp. 160–163. London, BSBI. [7]

Luck, K. E. (1965). *Autecology of* Calamagrostis epigeios *(L.) Roth and* C. canescens *(Weber) Roth.* PhD thesis, University of Cambridge. [7,12]

Lunel, T. (1984). *Phosphate and nitrate in freshwater at Wicken Fen.* MS. in archive. [3]

McGarry, S. (1982). *Chromatium* in a brickpit at Wicken Fen. *Nature in Cambridgeshire* **25**: 21–22. [3]

Marchant, J. H., Hudson, R., Carter, S. P., & Whittington, P. (1990). *Population trends in British breeding birds.* BTO/NCC. [9]

Marr, J. E. (1928). Fossil vertebrates. *In* Gardiner J. S. (ed.), *NHWF*, pp. 296–299. [10]

Meredith, T. C. (1978). *The ecology and conservation of* Peucedanum palustre *at Wicken Fen.* PhD thesis, University of Cambridge. [5,12]

—— & Grubb, P. J. (1993). Peucedanum palustre (L.) Moench. Biological Flora of the British Isles. *Journal of Ecology* **81**: 813–826. [5]

Messent, P. R. (1969). Weight variations of certain finches, buntings and sparrows. *Wicken Fen Group Report* **1**: 23–28. [9]

Miller, S. H. (1889). *The Handbook to the Fenland.* London, Simpkin, Marshall. [10]

Milwright, R. D. P. (1976). Standardised mist netting and bird populations. *Wicken Fen Group Report* **8**: 10–15. [9]

Mitchell, A. T. (1894). Collecting at Wicken. *Entomologist* **27**: 28–29. [10]

Moore, J. (?1706). *A Mapp of the Great Levell of the Fens....as it is now drained.* [10]

Moore, J. A. (1986). *Charophytes of Great Britain and Ireland*. BSBI Handbook No. 5. London, BSBI. [7]

Moss, B. (1983). The Norfolk Broadland: experiments in the restoration of a complex wetland. *Biological Reviews* **58**: 521–61. [3]

—— (1988). *Ecology of Fresh Waters: man and medium* (edn 2). Oxford, Blackwell Scientific Publications. [2]

Mountford, J. O., Lock, J. M., Walters, S. M. & Bennett, T. J. (1995) *A Checklist of the vascular plants of Wicken Fen*. Wicken, NT (WFLC). [7]

Muir, R. C. (1951). A report on the birds at Wicken Fen 1951. *Cambridge Bird Club Report* **25**: 24–25. [9]

National Trust for Places of Historic Interest or Natural Beauty (1923) 'Terrier' of Wicken and Burwell Fen estates. *In* Gardiner, J. S. & Tansley, A. G. (eds.), *NHWF*, p. 52. [13]

—— (1996). *Wicken Fen Visitor Survey*. The Tourism Company, for the National Trust. [11]

Naylor A. K. (1974) Weight variation of Blackbirds and Song Thrushes at Wicken Fen. *Wicken Fen Group Report* **6**: 13–21. [9]

Nevinson E. B. (1916) Aculeate Hymenoptera and Chrysididae at Wicken. *Entomologist's Monthly Magazine* **52**: 90–91. [8]

—— (1926) Hymenoptera Aculeata. *In* Gardiner, J. S. (ed.), *NHWF*, pp. 253–254. [8]

O'Brien, M. & Smith, K. W. (1992). Changes in the status of waders breeding on wet lowland grasslands in England and Wales between 1982 and 1989. *Bird Study* **39**: 165–176. [9]

Oldham, C. (1926) Additions to the Mollusca of Wicken Fen. *In* Gardiner, J. S. (ed.), *NHWF*, pp. 198–200. [3]

Omer Cooper, J. (1925). The higher Crustacea. *In* Gardiner, J. S. (ed.), *NHWF*, pp. 140–153. [3]

——, Perkins, M. G. L. & Tottenham, C. E. (1928) The Coleoptera of Wicken Fen. *In* Gardiner, J. S. (ed.), *NHWF*, pp. 267–295. [5,8,12]

—— & Tottenham, C. E. (1932) The Coleoptera of Wicken Fen. *In* Gardiner, J. S. (ed.), *NHWF*, pp. 489–538. [3,8]

Owen, M., Atkinson-Willes, G. L. & Salmon, D. G. (1986). *Wildfowl in Great Britain* (edn 2). Cambridge, University Press. [9]

Painter, D. J. (1994). Some records of aquatic Coleoptera and Mollusca from Wicken Fen. *Nature in Cambridgeshire* **36**: 88–91. [3]

—— (1995). *Fen ditch excavation patterns: effects on aquatic communities*. PhD thesis, University of Cambridge. [3,8,12]

—— & Friday, L. E. (1995). Restoring fenland ditches: the case of Wicken Fen N.N.R. *In* Wheeler, B. D., Shaw, S. C, Fojt, W. J. & Robertson, R. A. (eds.), *Restoration of Temperate Wetlands*, pp. 241–250. Chichester, John Wiley & Sons Ltd. [3]

Paul, C. R. C. (1967). *Mollusca of the Wicken Sedge Fen*. Guides to Wicken Fen, No. 2. Wicken, NT (WFLC). [12]

Peach, W. J., Buckland, S. T. & Baillie, S. R. (1990) Estimating survival rates using mark-recapture data from multiple ringing sites. *The Ring* **13**: 87–102. [9]

——, Baillie, S. R. & Underhill, L. (1991) Survival of British Sedge Warblers in relation to West African rainfall. *Ibis* **133**: 300–305. [9]

Perrin, R. M. S. (1982) Chemistry of the waters of Wicken Fen. *Nature in Cambridgeshire* **25**: 22–29. [2]

Perring, F. H. (1968). Vascular plant records. *Nature in Cambridgeshire* **11**: 36–37. [3]

——, Sell P. D., Walters, S. M. & Whitehouse, H. L. K. (1964) *A Flora of Cambridgeshire*. Cambridge, University Press. [2]

Pollard, A. J. (1981). *Genecological studies of* Urtica dioica L. PhD thesis, University of Cambridge. [12]

—— & Briggs, D. (1982). Genecological studies of *Urtica dioica* L. I. The nature of intraspecific variation in *U. dioica*. *New Phytologist* **92**: 453–470. [7]

—— & —— (1984a). Genecological studies of Urtica dioica L. II. Patterns of variation at Wicken Fen, Cambridgeshire, England. *New Phytologist* **96**: 483–499. [7,12]

—— & —— (1984b). Genecological studies of *Urtica dioica* L. III. Stinging hairs and plant-herbivore interactions. *New Phytologist* **97**: 507–522. [7]

Pollard, E. (1977). A method for assessing changes in the abundance of butterflies. *Biological Conservation* **12**: 115–134. [8]

—— (1979). A national scheme for monitoring the abundance of butterflies. *Proceedings and Transactions of the British Entomological and Natural History Society* **12**: 77–90. [8]

—— & Hall, M. L. (1980). Possible movement of *Gonepteryx rhamni* (L.) (Lepidoptera: Pieridae) between hibernating and breeding areas. *Entomologist's Gazette* **31**: 217–220. [8]

Polunin, N. V. C. (1979). *Studies on the ecology of* Phragmites *litter in freshwater*. PhD thesis, University of Cambridge. [3,4,12]

—— (1982). Processes contributing to the decay of reed *Phragmites australis* litter in fresh water. *Archiv für Hydrobiologia* **94**: 182–209. [3]

Pond Action (1991). *Preliminary results from the National Pond Survey: single season analysis of macroinvertebrate samples from 111 NPS sites*. 16pp. Report 91/9. Oxford Brookes University, Pond Action. [3]

Pontin, R.M. (1995). Rotifers of Wicken Fen, Cambridgeshire: a preliminary survey. *Nature in Cambridgeshire* **37**: 20–24. [12]

Preston, C. D. (1991a). *Lemna minuscula* in Cambridge. *Nature in Cambridgeshire* **33**: 52–54. [3]

—— (1991b). Charophyte records. *Nature in Cambridgeshire* **33**: 70. [7]

—— (1993). Charophyte records. *Nature in Cambridgeshire* **35**: 86. [7]

—— & Croft, J. M. (1997). *Aquatic plants in Britain and Ireland*. Colchester, Harley Books.

Proctor, M. C. F. (1956). A bryophyte flora of Cambridgeshire. *Transactions of the British Bryological Society* **3**: 1–49. [6]

—— (1992). Regional and local variation in the chemical composition of ombrogenous mire waters in Britain and Ireland. *Journal of Ecology* **80**: 719–736. [2]

Prŷs-Jones, O. E. (1982). *Ecological studies of foraging and life history in bumblebees*. PhD thesis, University of Cambridge. [8,12]

Ratcliffe, D. E. (1977). *A Nature Conservation Review*, 2 vols. Cambridge, University Press. [1]

Ray, J. (1660). *Catalogus plantarum circa Cantabrigiam nascientium*. London, J. Martin. (in translation as *Ray's Flora of Cambridgeshire*, Ewen, A. H. & Prime, C. T. (1975) (eds and translators). Hitchin, Wheldon & Wesley). [7]

Redfern, C. P. F. (1978). Survival in relation to sex in Reed Warbler populations. *Wicken Fen Group Report* **10**: 34–38. [9]

Relhan, R. (1785). *Flora Cantabrigiensis*. Cambridge, Merrill; edn 2 (1802), Deighton; edn 3 (1820), Deighton. [7]

Richards, P. W. (1932). The Bryophyta of Wicken Fen. *In* Gardiner, J. S. (ed.), *NHWF*, pp. 539–543. [6,12]

—— (1952). *The Tropical Rainforest*. Cambridge, University Press. [12]

The Reporter (25.5.48). Cambridge, University Press. [11]

Rodwell, J. S. (ed.) (1991a). *British Vegetation Communities. I. Woodlands and scrub*. Cambridge, University Press. [5,11]

—— (ed.) (1991b). *British Vegetation Communities. II. Mires and heaths*. Cambridge, University Press. [5]

—— (ed.) (1992). *British Vegetation Communities. III. Grassland and montane communities*. Cambridge, University Press. [5]

—— (ed.) (1995). *British Vegetation Communities. IV. Swamps and tall-herb fens*. Cambridge, University Press. [5]

Ross-Craig, S. (1954). *Drawings of British Plants*. VII. Leguminosae, pl. 74. London, G. Bell & Sons. [7]

Rowell, T. A. (1982a). The origins of the Wicken Fen brickpits. *Nature in Cambridgeshire* **25**: 21–22. [3,10]

—— (1982b). Wicken Poor's Fen: origins and land use history. *Cambridgeshire Local History Society Council Bulletin* **37**: 7–10. [10]

—— (1983a). *History and management at Wicken Fen*. PhD thesis, University of Cambridge. [P,2,5,6,10,11,12]

—— (1983b). The fen violet at Wicken Fen. *Nature in Cambridgeshire* **26**: 62–65. [7]

—— (1986a). The history of drainage at Wicken Fen, Cambridgeshire, England: a guide to ecological development. *Biological Conservation* **35**: 111–142. [3,10]

—— (1986b). Sedge (*Cladium mariscus*) in Cambridgeshire: its use and production since the 17th century. *Agricultural History Review* **34**: 140–148. [10]

—— (ed.) (1988a). *Peatland handbook*. Peterborough, NCC. [4]

—— (1988b). *A bibliography of Wicken Fen* (edn 2). MS. in archive. [12]

—— & Harvey, H. J. (1988). The recent history of Wicken Fen, Cambridgeshire, England: a guide to ecological development. *Journal of Ecology* **76**: 73–90. [6,7,10]

——, Guarino, L. & Harvey, H. J. (1985). The experimental management of vegetation at Wicken Fen. *Journal of Applied Ecology* **22**: 217–227. [5,12]

Royal Commission on Historic Monuments (1972). *An Inventory of Historical Monuments in the County of Cambridge. Vol II. North-East Cambridgeshire*. London, HMSO. [10,12]

Rudd, J. A. (1982). *The mosquitoes of Wicken Fen – ecological studies*. MS. in archive. [8]

—— (1986). The mosquitoes of Wicken Fen. *Nature in Cambridgeshire* **28**: 13–19. [8]

Salt, G. (1947). Teaching fieldwork – II. An entomological example. *The School Science Review* **107**: 73–79. [4,8]

Saunders, J. T. (1925). The hydrogen ion concentration of the waters of Wicken Fen. *In* Gardiner, J. S. (ed.), *NHWF*, pp. 162–172. [3]

Saville, N. & Chapman, H. (1988) Buzz pollination of comfrey at Wicken Fen. *Nature in Cambridgeshire* **30**: 16–20. [8]

Sell, P. D. (1987). The dactylorchids of Wicken Fen. *Nature in Cambridgeshire* **29**: 69–72. [7]

Sharrock, J. T. R. (1976). *The Atlas of Breeding Birds in Britain and Ireland*. Berkhamsted, T. & A. D. Poyser. [9]

Sheail, J. (1987). *Seventy-five Years in Ecology: The British Ecological Society*. Oxford, Blackwell Scientific Publications. [P]

Sheldon, W. G. (1916). Wicken Fen: its past, its present condition and its future. *Entomologist* **49**: 1–4. [10]

Shirt, D. B. (ed.) (1987). *British Red Data Books. 2: Insects*. Peterborough, Nature Conservancy Council. [3,8]

Smart, J. (1972). *Butterflies and day-flying moths*. Guides to Wicken Fen. no. 8, Wicken, NT (WFLC). [12]

Smith, K. W. (1983). The status and distribution of waders breeding on wet lowland grassland in England and Wales. *Bird Study* **30**: 177–192. [9]

Spencer, R. & the Rare Breeding Bird Panel (1993). Rare breeding birds in the United Kingdom in 1990. *British Birds* **86**: 62–90. [9]

Spooner, G. M. (1929). *Lipara similis* Schn. at Wicken Fen. *Entomologist's Monthly Magazine* **65**: 42–43. [8]

—— (1930). The bees, wasps and ants of Cambridgeshire. *Cambridge Daily News*, Cambridge. [8]

Stace, C. (1991). *New Flora of the British Isles*. Cambridge, University Press. [1]

Swaffham Prior Naturalists' Society (1835) *Minutes*. Cambridge University Library: Add 6460. [7,10]

Tansley, A. G. (1914). Presidential address. *Journal of Ecology* **2**: 194–202. [12]

—— (1935), The use and abuse of vegetational concepts and terms. *Ecology* **16**: 284–307. [12]

Thomas, G. J., Allen, D. A. & Grose, M. P. B. (1981). The demography and flora of the Ouse Washes, England. *Biological Conservation* **21**: 197–229. [9]

Thorne, C. J. R. (1971). Grotty leg. *Wicken Fen Group Report* **3**: 17–18. [9]

—— (1973). Growth of Reed Warblers. *Wicken Fen Group Report* **5**: 33–35. [9]

—— (1974). Moult of 12 species at Wicken Fen. *Wicken Fen Group Report* **6**: 32–37. [9]

—— (1975). Wing length of Reed Warblers. *Wicken Fen Group Report* **7**: 10–13. [9]

—— (1976). Primary moult of finches in Cambridgeshire. *Wicken Fen Group Report* **8**: 26–29. [9]

—— (1977). Standardised mist netting, 1977 Results. *Wicken Fen Group Report* **9**: 11–12. [9]

—— (1978). Standardised mist netting, 1978 Results. *Wicken Fen Group Report* **10**: 10–11. [9]

—— (1980). Standardised mist netting, 1979 and 1980 Results. *Wicken Fen Group Report* **11**: 12–13. [9]

—— & Bennett, T. J. (1982). *The Birds of Wicken Fen*. Cambridge, The Wicken Fen Group. [9]

—— & —— (1989). *A summary checklist of the Birds of Wicken Fen*. Guides to Wicken Fen, No. 12. (Edn 2, 1995). Wicken, The Wicken Fen Group and The National Trust. [9]

Thorpe, W. H. (1938). Aves. *In* Imms, A. D. (ed.), The Zoology of Cambridgeshire. *In* Darby, H. C. (ed.), *A scientific survey of the Cambridge district*, pp. 61–63. London, British Association for the Advancement of Science. [9]

Tutt, J. W. (1891). Notes of the season – Wicken Fen. *Entomologist's Record and Journal of Variation* **2**: 176–179. [10]

Unwin, D. M. (1987). The effect of management on insect species richness at Wicken Fen. *Nature in Cambridgeshire* **29**: 37–40. [8]

Wallis, A. (1904). The flora of the Cambridge district. *In* Marr, J. E. & Shipley, A. E. (eds.), *Handbook to the Natural History of Cambridgeshire*, pp. 209–237. Cambridge, University Press. [4,5,6]

Walters, S. M. (1951). *Variations in* Eleocharis palustris *agg.* PhD thesis, University of Cambridge. [7,12]

—— (1958). *Nitella tenuissima*, a rare British charophyte. *Proceedings of the Botanical Society of the British Isles* **3**: 104. [7,11]

—— (1967). *List of the vascular plants of Wicken Fen.* Guides to Wicken Fen, No. 3. Wicken, NT (WFLC). [7,11,12]

—— (1974). The rediscovery of *Senecio paludosus* L. in Britain. *Watsonia* **10**: 49–54. [7]

—— (1976). *The aquatic flora of Wicken Fen: evidence for deterioration.* MS. in Wicken Fen archive. [3]

Way, J. M. & Davis, B. N. K. (1965). Use of chemicals on nature reserves a) Experiments on the use of chemicals as management tools in Nature Reserves and their indirect effects on the flora and fauna. *Monks Wood Experimental Station Report for 1960–1965*, pp. 67–69. London, The Nature Conservancy. [11]

Wells, S. (1828). *History of the Drainage of the Great Level of the Fens called Bedford Level.* 2 volumes. London. [10]

Wentworth-Day, J. (1973). *A History of the Fens.* Wakefield, EP Publishing. [12]

West, W. (1898). Notes on Cambridgeshire plants. *Journal of Botany* **36**: 259. [6,7]

Wheeler, B. D. (1980). Plant communities of rich-fen systems in England and Wales. III. Fen meadow, fen grassland and fen woodland communities, and contact communities. *Journal of Ecology* **68**: 761–788. [7]

Wicken Fen Executive Committee (1925–86). *Minute Books*, in archive. [4,9,11,12,13]

—— (1936). *Wicken Fen Management Scheme* (Thorpe, W. H.). *In* WFEC Minute Books. [11]

—— (1956). *Memorandum on Management of Wicken Fen* (Walters, S. M.). *In* WFEC Minute Books [11]

Wicken Fen Local Management Committee (1986–). *Minutes*, in archive. [3,11]

—— (1986). *Management Plan 1986–92* (Harvey, H. J. (ed.)). MS. in archive. [11]

—— (1992). *Management Plan 1992–1997* (Friday, L. E. (ed.)). MS. in archive. [11,12]

——. *Botanical records.* [6,7,11]

——. *Zoological records.* [8,11]

Williams, P. H. (1982). The distribution and decline of British bumble bees (*Bombus* Latr.). *Journal of Apicultural Research* **21**: 236–245. [8]

—— (1986). Environmental change and the distributions of British bumble bees (*Bombus* Latr.). *Bee World* **67**: 50–61. [8]

Wilmott, A. J. (ed.) (1922). *Babington's Manual of British Botany*, 1922 (edn 10). London, Gurney & Jackson. [7]

—— (1948). Plant notes. *Watsonia* **1**: 121. [7]

Wood, A. H. (1929). The Trichoptera of Wicken Fen. *In* Gardiner, J. S. (ed.), *NHWF*, pp. 479–487. [3]

Wyllie, I. (1981). *The Cuckoo.* London, Batsford. [9]

Yapp, R. H. (1908). Sketches of vegetation at home and abroad. IV. Wicken Fen. *New Phytologist* **7**: 61–81. [2,5,6,7,10]

—— (1909). Stratification in the vegetation of a marsh. *Annals of Botany* **23**: 275–319. [5]

Yau, A. S. K. (1994). *Effects of fish predation on the zooplankton of Wicken Fen, Cambridgeshire.* MS. in archive. [3]

Yeo, P. F. (1976). *Aster* (naturalised species). *In* Tutin, T. G., Heywood, V. H., Burges, W. A., Moore, D. M., Valentine, D. H., Walters, S. M. & Webb, D. A. (eds), *Flora Europaea* **4**: 112–116. Cambridge, University Press. [7]

INDEX